MW01092682

BÉCHAMP OR PASTEUR?

A LOST CHAPTER IN THE HISTORY OF BIOLOGY

PASTEUR: PLAGIARIST, IMPOSTOR

THE GERM THEORY EXPLODED

"If I could live my life over again, I would devote it to proving that germs seek their natural habitat, diseased tissue – rather than being the cause of the diseased tissue."

– *Rudolph Virchow*

"Nothing is lost, nothing is created ... all is transformed. Nothing is the prey of death. All is the prey of life."

– *Antoine Béchamp*

"The specific disease doctrine is the grand refuge of weak, uncultured, unstable minds, such as now rule in the medical profession. There are no specific diseases; there are specific disease conditions."

– *Florence Nightingale*

Béchamp or Pasteur?

A Lost Chapter in the History of Biology

ETHEL DOUGLAS HUME

prefaced by

Pasteur: Plagiarist, Impostor
The Germ Theory Exploded

R.B. PEARSON

bechamp.org

Béchamp or Pasteur?
A Lost Chapter in the History of Biology
by Ethel Douglas Hume
was first published in 1923.

Pasteur: Plagiarist, Impostor
The Germ Theory Exploded
by R.B. Pearson
was first published in 1942.

This edition copyright ©2006 Bechamp.org

ISBN-10 0-9802976-0-5
ISBN-13 978-0-9802976-0-7

Bechamp.org
P.O. Box 168
Castlemaine
VIC 3450
Australia

web
www.bechamp.org

A Note from the Publisher

This volume contains new editions of two books which have been available only sporadically in the decades since their publication.

R. Pearson's *Pasteur: Plagiarist, Imposter* was originally published in 1942, and is a succinct introduction to both Louis Pasteur and Antoine Béchamp, and the reasons behind the troubled relationship that they shared for their entire working lives.

Whereas Pearson's work is a valuable introduction to an often complex topic, it is Ethel Douglas Hume's expansive and well-documented *Béchamp or Pasteur? A Lost Chapter in the History of Biology* which provides the main body of evidence. It covers the main points of contention between Béchamp and Pasteur in depth sufficient to satisfy any degree of scientific or historical scrutiny, and it contains, wherever possible, detailed references to the source material and supporting evidence. Virtually no claim in Ms Hume's book is undocumented – to have access to more material, one would need to be able to read French, and go to the original source material.

The reader will soon discern that neither Mr Pearson nor Ms Hume could ever be called fans of Pasteur or his 'science'. They both declare their intentions openly; that they wish to contribute to the undoing of a massive medical and scientific fraud. The publication of this present edition of their work is undertaken with complete empathy for that intention.

The text of both books has been comprehensively re-edited – for style more than content – the intention being to make for easier reading than the style of language used in the first half of the twentieth century would otherwise allow. I hope that the end result is an improvement, and that the authors would approve. I think they would.

I intend to publish in due course a collection of modern writings on Béchamp and pleomorphism. Any researchers who wish to be involved in such a project by contributing material or otherwise can make contact via the web site at *www.bechamp.org*.

David Major
dminoz@bechamp.org
November 2006

BOOK ONE

Pasteur: Plagiarist, Imposter
The Germ Theory Exploded

R. B. Pearson

First published in 1942

Author's Preface

It is a serious matter to attack the reputation of a famous man, especially one who has posed – and been accepted – as one of the world's greatest scientists. For many years, Pasteur has been looked upon as a founder and leader in serology; but it is always pertinent to look into the beginnings of any subject on which there is a difference of opinion, with the hope of finding the truth in the matter.

The writer has made an effort in his prior books and pamphlets to show that the germ theory is false, and that illness is practically always due to *errors of diet or manner of living*, the germs being present solely as scavengers of dead and waste tissues and foods, and *not as the cause of the disease.*

However, the erroneous belief that germs cause disease and must be controlled or eliminated before it can be cured is so widespread as to close the minds of many people to any other ideas on this subject.

For this reason it seems that a thorough investigation of this idea, the grounds on which it is based – and even the bona fides of those who started it on its way – is necessary before any sane ideas as to the proper treatment of disease can be widely promulgated.

When Ethel Douglas Hume's *Béchamp or Pasteur?* appeared in 1923, it seemed to be just the thing that would fill this gap and end the use of serums and other biologicals forever. But it is now 19 years since that book, which should have marked an epoch in the healing arts, was published. It did not receive the attention it deserved in medical circles and, though it is now in its second edition,[1] the medical profession are pushing biologicals harder than ever.

Hence it seems appropriate to go over the subject in order to show the truth regarding the falsity of Pasteur's ideas and claims to fame, and the fraudulent basis on which the germ theory rests, as was so well shown by Ms Hume in *Béchamp or Pasteur?,* and to add other facts and statistics that support the idea that the germ theory is false, in the hopes that it may receive wider circulation and more general attention, and possibly lead to a complete overhauling of the question of the treatment of disease, especially regarding serology.

---

1. Published by the National Anti-Vaccination League, London, England.

The translations from the French, and other material in Chapters 2, 3, 4 and 5 not otherwise credited, are from *Béchamp or Pasteur?* by Ethel Douglas Hume.

In closing, I wish to acknowledge my indebtedness to the Reverend and Mrs Wilber Atchison of Chicago for many suggestions and valuable assistance in the preparation of the manuscript. Miss L. Loat, secretary of the National Anti-Vaccination League of London, has also been very kind, responding to every request for information with more than could be used, some of it being especially compiled at the cost of considerable effort.

R. B. Pearson
January 15th, 1942

1.

The Prior History of the 'Germ Theory'

If you explore the history of the medical profession and the various ideas regarding the cause of disease that were held by leading physicians before Pasteur first promulgated his notorious 'germ theory', you will find convincing evidence that Pasteur discovered nothing, and that he deliberately appropriated, falsified and perverted another man's work.

The 'germ theory', so-called, long antedated Pasteur – so long, in fact, that he was able to present it as new – and he got away with it!

F. Harrison, Principal Professor of Bacteriology at Macdonald College (Faculty of Agriculture, McGill University), Quebec, Canada, wrote an *Historical Review of Microbiology*, published in *Microbiology*, a text book, in which he says in part:

> "Geronimo Fracastorio (an Italian poet and physician, 1483 – 1553) of Verona, published a work (*De Contagionibus et Contagiosis Morbis, et eorum Curatione*) in Venice in 1546 which contained the first statement of the true nature of contagion, infection, or disease organisms, and of the modes of transmission of infectious disease. He divided diseases into those which infect by either immediate contact, through intermediate agents, or at a distance through the air. Organisms which cause disease, called *seminaria contagionum*, he supposed to be of the nature of viscous or glutinous matter, similar to the colloidal states of substances described by modern physical chemists. These particles, too small to be seen, were capable of reproduction in appropriate media, and became pathogenic through the action of animal heat. Thus Fracastorio, in the middle of the sixteenth century, gave us an outline of morbid processes in terms of microbiology."

For a book published more than three hundred years before Pasteur 'discovered' the germ theory, this seems to be a most astonishing anticipation of Pasteur's ideas, except that – not having a microscope – Fracastorio apparently did not realize that these substances might be individual living organisms.

According to Harrison, the first compound microscope was made by H. Jansen in 1590 in Holland, but it was not until about 1683 that anything was built of sufficient power to show up bacteria. He continues:

> "In the year 1683, Antonius van Leenwenhoek, a Dutch naturalist and a maker of lenses, communicated to the English Royal Society the results of observations which he had made with a simple microscope of his own construction, magnifying from 100 to 150 times. He found in water, saliva, dental tartar, etc., entities he named *animalcula*. He described what he saw, and in his drawings showed both rod-like and spiral forms, both of which he said had motility. In all probability, the two species he saw were those now recognized as *bacillus buccalis maximus* and *spirillum sputigenum*.
>
> Leenwenhoek's observations were purely objective and in striking contrast with the speculative views of M. A. Plenciz, a Viennese physician, who in 1762 published a germ theory of infectious diseases. Plenciz maintained that there was a special organism by which each infectious disease was produced, that micro-organisms were capable of reproduction outside of the body, and that they might be conveyed from place to place by the air."

Here is Pasteur's great thought *in toto* – his complete germ theory – and yet put in print over a century before Pasteur 'thought of it', and published it as his own!

Note how concisely it anticipates all Pasteur's ideas on germs. While there seems to be no proof that Plenciz had a microscope, or knew of Leenwenhoek's *animalcula*, both are possible, indeed likely, as he was quite prominent; and he, rather than Pasteur, should have any credit that might come from such a discovery – *if* the germ theory has any value. This idea, which, to the people of that time at least, must have accounted easily and completely for such strange occurrences as contagion, infection and epidemics, would have been widely discussed in the medical or scientific circles of that time, and in literature available to Pasteur.

That it was widely known is indicated by the fact that the world-famous English nurse, Florence Nightingale, published an attack on the idea in 1860, over 17 years before Pasteur adopted it and claimed it as his own.

She said of 'infection'[1]:

"Diseases are not individuals arranged in classes, like cats and dogs, but conditions, growing out of one another.

Is it not living in a continual mistake to look upon diseases as we do now, as separate entities, which must exist, like cats and dogs, instead of looking upon them as conditions, like a dirty and a clean condition, and just as much under our control; or rather as the reactions of kindly nature, against the conditions in which we have placed ourselves?

I was brought up to believe that smallpox, for instance, was a thing of which there was once a first specimen in the world, which went on propagating itself, in a perpetual chain of descent, just as there was a first dog, (or a first pair of dogs) and that smallpox would not begin itself, any more than a new dog would begin without there having been a parent dog.

Since then I have seen with my own eyes and smelled with my own nose smallpox growing up in first specimens, either in closed rooms or in overcrowded wards, where it could not by any possibility have been 'caught', but must have begun.

I have seen diseases begin, grow up, and turn into one another. Now, dogs do not turn into cats.

I have seen, for instance, with a little overcrowding, continued fever grow up; and with a little more, typhoid fever; and with a little more, typhus, and all in the same ward or hut.

Would it not be far better, truer, and more practical, if we looked upon disease in this light (for diseases, as all experience shows, are adjectives, not noun-substantives):

- True nursing ignores infection, except to prevent it. Cleanliness and fresh air from open windows, with unremitting attention to the patient, are the only defence a true nurse either asks or needs.

- Wise and humane management of the patient is the best safeguard against infection. The greater part of nursing consists of preserving cleanliness.

- The specific disease doctrine is the grand refuge of weak, uncultured, unstable minds, such as now rule in the medical profession. *There are no specific diseases; there are specific disease conditions.*"

---

1. *Notes on Nursing*, 1st ed., 1860, p.32

Here you have Florence Nightingale, the most famous nurse in history, after life-long experience with infection, contagion and epidemics, challenging the germ theory 17 years before Pasteur put it forward as his own discovery! (See *Chapter 8*, p.50).

She clearly understood it and its utter fallacy better before 1860 than Pasteur did, either in 1878 or later!

Now, to see what a parasite Pasteur was on men who did things, let us digress and go back a few years, to the time when the study of germs was an outgrowth of the study of fermentation.

2.

Béchamp, Pasteur, and Fermentation[1]

About 1854, Professor Pierre Jacques Antoine Béchamp, one of France's greatest scientists, then Professor at the School of Pharmacy in the Faculty of Science at Strasbourg, later (1857-75) Professor of Medical Chemistry and Pharmacy at the University of Montpelier, a member of many scientific societies, and a Chevalier of the Legion of Honor, took up the study of fermentation.

He had succeeded in 1852 in so reducing the cost of producing aniline as to make it a commercial success, and his formula became the basis of the German dye industry. This brought him some fame – and many more problems to solve.

Up to this time, the idea prevailed that cane sugar, when dissolved in water, was spontaneously transformed at an ordinary temperature into *invert sugar*, which is a mixture of equal parts of glucose and fructose, but an experiment with starch had caused him to doubt the truth of this idea.

Therefore in May, 1854, Béchamp undertook a series of observations on this change, which came to be referred to as his 'Beacon Experiment'. In this experiment, he dissolved perfectly pure cane sugar in water in a glass bottle containing air, but tightly stoppered. Several other bottles contained the same solution, but with a chemical added.

In the solution without any added chemical, moulds appeared in about thirty days, and inversion of the sugar in this bottle then went on rapidly, but moulds and inversion did not occur in the other bottles containing added chemicals. He measured the inversion frequently with a polariscope.

These observations were concluded on February 3, 1855, and his paper was published in the *Report of the French Academy of Science* for

---

1. All quotations in Chapters 2, 3, 4, and 5, unless otherwise credited, are taken from *Béchamp or Pasteur?* by Ethel Hume, originally published by the National Anti-Vaccination League, London, England, and included in this book.

   Miss Hume conducted a thorough investigation of the writings of both Béchamp and Pasteur, and makes some astounding disclosures of plagiarism on the part of the latter, many of which are quoted herein.

   Also, the translations from the French used in these four chapters are all taken from *Béchamp or Pasteur?*

the session of February 19, 1855.[1]

This left the moulds without an explanation, so he started a second series of observations on June 25, 1856 (at Strasbourg) in order to determine their origin, and on March 27, 1857, he started a third series of flasks to study the effects of creosote on the changes. Both series were ended at Montpelier on December 5, 1857.

In the second series he spilled a little liquid from flasks 1 and 2 during manipulation, so these two flasks contained a little air in contact with the liquid. In these two flasks, moulds soon appeared, and alteration in the medium ensued.

He also found that the changes were more rapid in the flask in which the mould grew more rapidly.

In the other nine flasks there was no air, no mould formed, and no inversion of the sugar occurred; plainly air was needed for the moulds and inversion to occur. This proved beyond any possibility of doubt that the moulds and inversion of the sugar could not be 'spontaneous' action, but must be due to something in the air admitted to the first two flasks.

Yet Pasteur later called fermentation

"life without air, or life without oxygen."[2]

At this time, it was quite generally believed that fermentation could not take place except in the presence of albuminoids, which were in general use by Pasteur and others as part of their solutions. Hence, their solutions could have contained these living organizations to start with.

Béchamp's solutions contained only pure cane sugar and water, and when heated with fresh-slaked lime did not disengage ammonia – ample proof that they contained no albumen. Yet moulds, obviously living organisms, and therefore containing albuminoid matter, had appeared in these two solutions.

Béchamp proved to his own satisfaction that these moulds were living organisms and that cane sugar was inverted, as he said

"...only in proportion to the development of moulds... these *elementary vegetations* then acting as ferments."[3]

Pasteur, apparently overlooking the air contact, challenged Béchamp's statements, saying:

---

1. *Comptes Rendus de l'Academie des Sciences*, 40, p.436
2. *Encyclopaedia Brittanica*, 11th ed. 10, p.275
3. *Comptus Rendus de l'Academie des Sciences*, 46, p.44

"... to be logical, Béchamp should say that he has proved that moulds arise in pure sugared water, without nitrogen, phosphates or other mineral elements, for that is an enormity that can be deduced from his work, in which there is not the expression of the least astonishment that moulds have been able to grow in pure water with pure sugar without any other mineral or organic principles."[1]

Béchamp's retort to this was:

"A chemist *au courant* with science ought not to be surprised that moulds are developed in sweetened water, contained in contact with air in glass flasks. It is the astonishment of Pasteur that is astonishing"[2]

As Béchamp started with no nitrogen whatever except what was in the air in the first two flasks, it is probably the first time any growth or any kind of organism was proved to have absorbed nitrogen from the air. Apparently Pasteur could not grasp this idea!

In the preface to his last book, *The Blood and its Third Anatomical Element*, Béchamp says that these facts impressed him in the same way that the swing of the cathedral lamp had impressed Galileo. He realized that some living organisms had been carried into these two flasks in the small amount of air admitted, and acting as ferments had produced the mould and the inversion in the sugar. He compared the transformation of cane sugar in the presence of moulds to that produced upon starch by *diastase*, the ferment that converts starch into sugar.

He sent his report on these findings to the Academy of Science in December 1857, and an extract was published in its reports of January 4, 1858, though the full paper was not published until September of that year.[3]

He says of these experiments:

"By its title the memoir was a work of pure chemistry, which had at first no other object than to determine whether or not pure cold water could invert cane sugar and if, further, the salts had any influence on the inversion. But soon the question, as I had foreseen, became complicated; it became at once physiological and dependent upon the phenomena of fermentation and the question of spontaneous generation. Thus from the study of a simple chemical fact, I was led to

1. *Etudes sur la Biere*, 1876, p.310
2. *Les Microzymas*, p.87
3. *Annales de Chimie et du Physique*, 3rd series, 54, p.28

Béchamp, Pasteur and Fermentation 17

investigate the causes of fermentation, and the nature and origin of ferments."[1]

Although Schwann had suggested airborne germs in about 1837, he had not proved his ideas; now Béchamp proved them to exist.

Yet Pasteur in his 1857 memoirs still clings to the idea that both the moulds and ferments 'take birth spontaneously', although his solutions all contained dead yeast or yeast broth which might have carried germs or ferments from the start.

He does conclude that the ferment is a living being, yet states that this 'cannot be irrefutably demonstrated'.[2]

But Béchamp had demonstrated it 'irrefutably' in his paper, and had also proved that water alone caused no alteration, there was no spontaneous alteration, and that moulds do not develop, nor inversion occur, without contact with the air; thus some airborne organism must cause the moulds and the inversion.

According to Miss Hume, Béchamp was also the first to distinguish between the 'organized' or living ferment and the soluble ferment which he obtained by crushing the moulds, and which he found to act directly on the sugar, causing rapid inversion.

He named this substance *zymase*, in a paper *Memoirs on Fermentation by Organized Ferments*, which he read before the Academy of Science on April 4, 1864.[3]

Strange to say, exactly the same word is used by others whom various encyclopaedias have credited with this discovery in 1897, over 30 years later!

In this paper he also gave a complete explanation of the phenomena of fermentation as being due to the nutrition of living organisms; i.e. a process of absorption, assimilation, and excretion.

In the preface to *The Blood and its Third Anatomical Element*, Béchamp says:

> "It resulted that the soluble ferment was allied to the insoluble by the relation of product to producer; the soluble ferment being unable to exist without the organized ferment, which is necessarily insoluble.
>
> Further, as the soluble ferment and the albuminoid matter, being nitrogenous, could only be formed by obtaining the

---

1. *Les Microzymas,* p.55
2. *Comptes Rendus,* 45, p.1032;
   see also *Annales de Chimie et du Physique,* 3rd series, 52, p.404
3. *Comptes Rendus,* 58, p.601

nitrogen from the limited volume of air left in the flasks, it was at the same time demonstrated that the free nitrogen of the air could help directly in the synthesis of the nitrogenous substance of plants – which up to that time had been a disputed question.

Thus it became evident that since the material forming the structure of moulds and yeast was elaborated within the organism, it must also be true that the soluble ferments and products of fermentation are also secreted there, as was the case with the soluble ferment that inverted the cane sugar. Hence I became assured that that which is called fermentation is in reality the phenomena of nutrition, assimilation and disassimilation, and the excretion of the products disassimilated."

He explained further:

"In these solutions there existed no albuminoid substance; they were made with pure cane sugar, which, heated with fresh-slaked lime, does not give off ammonia. It thus appears evident that airborne germs found the sugared solution to be a favourable medium for their development, and it must be admitted that the ferment is here produced by the generation of fungi.

The matter that develops in the sugared water sometimes presents itself in the form of little isolated bodies, and sometimes in the form of voluminous colourless membranes which come out in one mass from the flasks. These membranes, heated with caustic potash, give off ammonia in abundance."

This proved that albuminoids were present, hence the little bodies were living matter. It also proves that Professor Béchamp understood the formation and growth of moulds and ferments in 1857, years before Pasteur comprehended these physiological processes!

In 1859, over a year after Béchamp's paper covering his 1857 experiments was printed, Pasteur started another experiment more in line with Béchamp's ideas; in fact it was apparently inspired by them.

He omitted all yeast but used ammonia, which contains nitrogen, in his solutions, and then ascribed the origin of lactic yeast to the atmospheric air. He was surprised that animal and vegetable matter should appear and grow in such an environment.

He says:

> "As to the origin of the lactic yeast in these experiments, it is solely due to the atmospheric air; we fall back here upon facts of spontaneous generation."

After asserting that excluding atmospheric air or boiling the solution will prevent the formation of organisms, or fermentations, he says:

> "On this point, the question of spontaneous generation has made progress."

In a still later memoir[1] plainly inspired by Béchamp's Beacon Experiment, Pasteur again constantly refers to the spontaneous production of yeasts and fermentation.

There is no question but that he still believed in spontaneous generation of germs and ferments at this time, and his reasoning appears somewhat childish when compared to Béchamp's work.

However, in 1860, he started another experiment in which he prepared 73 phials of unfermented liquid to expose at various points on a much advertised-in-advance trip. He opened and resealed various phials at different places, the last twenty on the Mer de Glace above Chamonix.

He practically repeated Béchamp's experiments here, but of course he had to use a different and more spectacular method to get attention.

From this time on, he veered away from spontaneous generation, and began to explain the same occurrences (fermentation) as being caused by germs in the air.

Paul de Kruif in *Microbe Hunters* (a grandiose attempt to exalt some of the original experimenters in serumology), glosses over Pasteur's willingness to steal credit for the ideas of others, and after describing his use, without credit, of Ballard's suggestion of the swan neck bottle to admit dust-free and germ-free air into a flask, says of this 'high Alps' experiment:

> "Then Pasteur invented an experiment that was – so far as one can tell from a careful search through the records – really his own. It was a grand experiment, a semi-public experiment, an experiment that meant rushing across France in trains, it was a test in which he had to slither on glaciers." (p.83)

However, de Kruif doubted thoroughly that it *was* Pasteur's, and well he might! Yet little did he realize how few of Pasteur's foolhardy

---

1. *Annales de Chimie et du Physique*, April 1860

claims were either his own or, in fact, even true in any particular.

In a discussion of spontaneous generation at the Sorbonne during a meeting on November 22, 1861, Pasteur had the nerve to claim, in the presence of Professor Béchamp, all credit for the proof that living organisms appeared in a medium devoid of albuminoid matter! Béchamp asked him to admit knowledge of Béchamp's 1857 work, but did not charge him with plagiarism, and Pasteur evaded the question, merely admitting that Béchamp's work was 'rigidly exact'. This was not an accident, but deliberate, premeditated fraud; however, Béchamp was too much of a gentleman to make any unpleasant charges.

That it took several more years to get the spontaneous generation idea entirely out of Pasteur's head is indicated by the article on Pasteur in the 14th Edition of the *Encyclopaedia Britannica*, which says:

> "The recognition of the fact that both lactic and alcohol fermentation were hastened by exposure to air naturally led Pasteur to wonder whether his invisible organisms were always present in the atmosphere or whether they were spontaneously generated. By a series of intricate experiments, including the filtration of air and the famous exposure of unfermented liquids to the pure air of the high Alps, he was able to declare with certainty in 1864 that the minute organisms causing fermentation were not spontaneously generated but came from similar organisms with which ordinary air was impregnated."[1]

Here it is again – not until 1864 did he give up his idea of spontaneous generation – and the high Alps adventure was only high theatre, well advertised in advance, to enable him to grab Béchamp's discovery, and yet have some 'new stuff' to attract attention to himself. Of course, he could not follow exactly the same methods; some one might bring up Béchamp's memoirs, hence the 'high Alps' and 'slithering on glaciers'.

His experiments made in 1859 also indicated knowledge of Béchamp's work without albuminoids, and his evasion of Béchamp's question at the Sorbonne meeting in 1861 lends further support to such a belief, while his attacks on Béchamp suggest that he recognized a rival and was keenly jealous.

Note that this final acceptance of ideas that Béchamp had brought forward six years earlier did not come until *after* Béchamp had published his complete paper, with a full and most thoroughly proven explanation of the processes of fermentation.

---

1. *Encyclopaedia Britannica,* 14th ed., 17, p.357

However, Pasteur had, on completion of his 'high Alps' experiment in 1860, accepted, or had begun to accept, the idea that germs of the air caused fermentation; and soon he leaped way ahead to the conclusion that these germs also caused disease, as Plenciz had suggested about a hundred years before!

Of this idea, he had no more proof than Plenciz, except that it was now known there were germs in existence, which Plenciz, apparently, did not prove.

Although Béchamp had made clear the physiological nature of fermentation in his paper on his 1857 experiments (published in 1858), and had given more complete details in his 1864 paper, Pasteur apparently had not fully grasped its true nature as late as 1872, when he published a paper in which he stated:

> "That which separates the chemical phenomenon of fermentation from other acts and especially from the acts of ordinary life is the decomposition of a weight of fermentative matter much greater than the weight of the ferment."[1]

Could anyone make such a statement who really understood the true nature of fermentative action? Apparently Pasteur did not!

In collaboration with Professor Estor, Béchamp answered this with an effort to make the nature of fermentation clear, in a paper printed on p.1523 of the same volume of the *Comptes Rendus*, in which he said:

> "Suppose an adult man to have lived a century, and to weigh on average 60 kilograms. He will have consumed over that time, besides other foods, the equivalent of 20,000 kilograms of flesh, and produced about 800 kilograms of urea.
>
> Of course, there is no suggestion that this mass of flesh and urea could at any moment of his life form part of his being. Just as a man consumes all that food only by repeating the same act a great many times, the yeast cell consumes the great mass of sugar only by constantly assimilating and disassimilating it, bit by bit. Now, that which only one man will consume in a century, a sufficient number of men would absorb in a day.
>
> It is the same with the yeast; the sugar that a small number of cells would consume in a year, a greater number would destroy in a day. In both cases, the more numerous the individuals, the more rapid the consumption."[2]

---

1. *Comptes Rendus*, 75, p.785 (session of Sept. 30th, 1872)
2. *ibid.*, p.1523 (session of Dec. 2nd, 1872)

Is that not clear enough, even for a man whose diploma was marked 'mediocre in Chemistry' (i.e. Pasteur) to comprehend? It seems that a child should be able to understand it.

Yet Pasteur repeated his statement four years later in *Etudes sur la Bier* (1876), so Béchamp's clear explanation apparently failed to have any effect – at least on him.

Here is proof that from eight to fourteen years *after* Béchamp had completely disclosed the physiological nature of fermentation and described its action in minute detail, Pasteur had not yet grasped the facts regarding the process!

In its article on fermentation, the *Encyclopaedia Britannica* says:

> "Fermentation, according to Pasteur, was caused by the growth and multiplication of unicellular organisms out of contact with free oxygen, under which circumstances they acquire the power of taking oxygen from chemical compounds in the medium in which they are growing. In other words, 'fermentation is life without air, or life without oxygen'. This theory of fermentation was materially modified in 1892 and 1894 by A. J. Brown, who described experiments which were in disagreement with Pasteur's dictum."[1]

As did Béchamp over 35 years earlier – in 1855 and 1858 – and Pasteur appropriated and perverted his ideas.

Pasteur also jumped to the conclusion that each kind of fermentation had one specific germ, while Béchamp proved that each micro-organism might vary its fermentative effect in conformity with the medium in which it finds itself. He also showed that these micro-organisms, under varying conditions, might even change their shape, as has been recently proved so conclusively by F. Loehnis and N. R. Smith of the U.S. Dept. of Agriculture and others.[2]

Pasteur, however, proceeded to classify his germs and label each with a definite and unalterable function, wherein he was wrong again, as we shall soon see.

---

1. *Encyclopaedia Britannica*, 11th ed., 10, p.275
2. *Journal of Agricultural Research*, July 31, 1916, p.675.

3.
Vinous Fermentation

Another step that went along with the work on fermentation in general was the discovery of the causes of diseases in French grapes. Béchamp, hearing of the commotion over this trouble in the vineyards, quietly took up a study of it in 1862, the year before Pasteur turned his attention to the subject.

Béchamp exposed to contact with air:

1) grape-must as found on the vines;

2) grape-must filtered; and

3) grape-must decolorized by animal charcoal.

They all fermented, but not equally so, and the moulds or ferments developed were not identical in these three experiments, which of course caused him to seek a reason for this.

On further experiments, with the rigid exclusion of all air (the whole healthy grapes, with stalks attached, being introduced directly from the vine into boiled sweetened water, cooled with carbonic acid gas bubbling through it), fermentation took place, and was completed in this medium, proving that air was not required. Hence the ferment must have been carried on the grapes, and was not airborne.

Professor Béchamp concluded that the organism causing the must to ferment must be carried on the grape, its leaves, or the vines, and that it might also be an organism injurious to the plants.

He published a volume on vinous fermentation in 1863, entitled *Lecons sur la Fermentation Vineuse et sur la Fabrication du Vin*, in which he discussed the subject.

He also presented two papers on the making of wine to the Academy, entitled *Sur les Acids du Vin* and *Sur l'utilité et les Inconvienient du Cuvages Prolongés dans la Fabrication du Vin – Sur la Fermentation Alcoolique dans cette Fabrication.*[1]

In October 1864 he presented a communication to the Academy of Science on *The Origin of Vinous Fermentation*, an exhaustive account of the experiments described above.[2]

---

1. *Comptus Rendus*, 57, pp.496, 674
2. *ibid*, 59, p.626 (session of Oct. 10th, 1864)

This paper was a complete study of the subject, in which he proved that vinous fermentation was due to organisms found on the skins of grapes and also often found on the leaves and other parts of the vine. Hence at times, diseased vines might affect the quality of the fermentation and the resulting wine.

So by October 1864, Béchamp had several papers in print, but what was Pasteur up to?

In 1862 Pasteur was admitted to the French Academy through the influence of Biot and the Mineralogical Section, which based its nomination and support on Pasteur's past work on crystallography; yet many attacks were made on his treatment of that subject, and he soon took the advice of friends to drop this line of work.

In March 1863, he met the Emperor and was soon sent to the vineyards to study the grape disease, with the prestige of having the Emperor's backing.

He published several papers on the vines and their troubles in the latter part of 1863 and in 1864, but apparently was still promoting his spontaneous generation theory which Béchamp had so completely exploded in 1858, and he did not guess correctly as to the cause of the trouble with the vines.

In 1865 he offered five papers, and others came later, but he does not seem to have hit on the right answer to the problem until 1872, when he made the great discovery that Béchamp was right again! In this year, Pasteur presented a memoir entitled *New Experiments to Demonstrate that the Yeast Germ that Makes Wine comes from the Exterior of Grapes.*[1]

As Béchamp had made the same statement in his 1864 paper and it had not been disproven in the intervening eight years, it was a pretty safe bet for Pasteur to make!

---

1. *Comptes Rendus*, 74, p.781 (session of Oct. 7th, 1872)

4.
Béchamp's Microzymas or 'little bodies'

As shown in the second chapter, Béchamp was the first to prove that the moulds accompanying fermentation were, or contained, living organisms, and could not be spontaneously generated, but must be an outgrowth of some living organism carried in the air.

This much was in his 1858 memoir, six years before Pasteur came to the same conclusions.

Being the first to realize that these moulds or ferments were living organisms, he naturally was also the first to attempt to determine their true nature and functions, and their origins.

On putting some under the microscope, he noted a diversity in appearance of the moulds and was soon involved in a study of cell life.

In his earlier experiments, Béchamp had used several salts, including potassium carbonate, in the presence of which the inversion of cane sugar did not take place. But when he repeated this experiment using calcium carbonate (common chalk) instead of the potassium carbonate, he found that inversion of the cane sugar *did* take place, even when creosote was added. This observation was so unexpected that he omitted it from his earlier memoir in order to verify it before publication of the fact.

In carefully controlled experiments he found that when chemically pure calcium carbonate, $CaCO_3$, was added to his sugar solutions, no inversion took place, but when ordinary chalk, even that chipped from the native rock without access of air, was used, inversion always occurred.

On heating the common chalk to 300 degrees, he found that it lost its powers of fermentation, and on examining more of the unheated common chalk under the microscope, he found it contained some 'little bodies' similar to those found in prior observations, and which he found did not exist in the chemically pure $CaCO_3$, nor in the chalk that had been heated.

These 'little bodies' had the power of movement and were smaller than any of the microphytes seen in fermentation or moulds, but were more powerful ferments than any he had encountered previously.

Their power of movement and production of fermentation caused him to regard them as living organisms.

He advised Dumas of his discovery of living organisms in chalk in December 1864, and later, on September 26, 1865, he wrote a letter which Dumas published. He stated:

"Chalk and milk contain already developed living beings, which is proved by the fact that creosote, employed in a non-coagulating dose, does not prevent milk from finally turning, nor chalk, without extraneous help, from converting both sugar and starch into alcohol and then into acetic acid, tartaric acid, and butyric acid..."[1]

Which was ample proof that there was a ferment, a living organism, present in both milk and chalk. He said of these:

"The naturalist will not be able to distinguish them by a description; but the chemist and also the physiologist will characterize them by their function.[2]

Professor Béchamp found that the chalk seemed to be formed mostly of the mineral or fossil remains of a 'microscopic world' and contained organisms of infinitesimal size, which he believed to be alive.

He also believed they might be of immense antiquity, as he had traced the block of limestone he had used to the Tertiary Period in geology; yet he found that stone cut from the solid ledge, with all air excluded, had 'wonderful' fermentative powers, which he traced to the same 'little bodies' that he had found to cause fermentation in his earlier experiments. He concluded that they must have lived embedded in the stone of the ledge for many thousands of years.

In 1866, he sent to the Academy of Science a memoir called *On the Role of Chalk in Butyric and Lactic Fermentations, and the Living Organism Contained in it.*[3]

In this paper, he named his 'little bodies' *microzymas,* from the Greek words for *small ferment.*

He also studied the relations of his microzymas of chalk to the molecular granulations of animal and vegetable cells, with many more geological examinations, and wrote a paper entitled *On Geological Microzymas of Various Origins*, which was abstracted in *Comptes Rendus* of the session of April 25, 1870.[4]

---

1. *Annales de Chimie et du Physique*, 4th series, 6, p246
2. *Les Théorie du Microzyma*, p.124
3. *Comptes Rendus*, 63, p.451 (session of Sept. 10th, 1866)
4. *Comptes Rendus*, 70, p.914

He proved that the molecular granulation found in yeast and other animal and vegetable cells had individuality and life, and also had the power to cause fermentation, and so he called them *microzymas* also.

He called his geological microzymas 'morphologically identical' with the microzymas of living beings.

In innumerable laboratory experiments, assisted now by Professor Estor – another very able scientist – he found microzymas everywhere, in all organic matter, in both healthy tissues and in diseased, where he also found them associated with various kinds of bacteria.

After painstaking study they decided that the microzymas rather than the cell were the elementary units of life, and were in fact the builders of cell tissues. They also concluded that bacteria are an outgrowth, or an evolutionary form, of microzymas that occur when a quantity of diseased tissues is broken up into its constituent elements.

In other words, all living organisms, he believed, from the one-celled amoeba to mankind, are associations of these minute living entities, and their presence is necessary for cell life to grow and for cells to be repaired.

Bacteria, they proved, can develop from microzyma by passing through certain intermediate stages, which they described, and which have been regarded by other researchers as different species!

The germs of the air, they decided, were merely microzymas, or bacteria set free when their former habitat was broken up, and they concluded that the 'little bodies' in the limestone and chalk were the survivors of living beings of long past ages.

This brought them to the beginning of 1868, and to test these ideas they buried the body of a kitten[1] in pure carbonate of lime, specially prepared and creosoted to exclude any airborne or outside germs.

They placed it in a glass jar and covered the open top with several sheets of paper, placed so as to allow renewal of the air without allowing dust or organisms to enter. This was left on a shelf in Béchamp's laboratory until the end of 1874.

When opened, it was found that the kitten's body had been entirely consumed except for some small fragments of bone and dry matter. There was no smell, and the carbonate of lime was not discoloured.

Under the microscope, microzymas were not seen in the upper part of the carbonate of lime, but 'swarmed by thousands' in the part that had been below the kitten's body.

---

1. *Les Microzymas*, pp.626

As Béchamp thought that there might have been airborne germs in the kitten's fur, lungs or intestines, he repeated this experiment, using the whole carcass of a kitten in one case, the liver only in another, and the heart, lungs and kidneys in a third test. These viscera were plunged into carbolic acid the moment they had been detached from the slaughtered animal. This experiment began in June 1875 and continued to August 1882 – over seven years.

It completely satisfied him that his idea – that microzymas were the living remains of plant and animal life of which, in either a recent or distant past, they had been the constituent cellular elements, and that they were in fact the primary anatomical elements of all living beings – was correct.

He proved that on the death of an organ its cells disappear, but the microzymas remain, imperishable.

As the geologists estimated that the chalk rocks or ledges from which he took his 'geological microzymas' were 11 million years old, it was proof positive that these microzymas could live in a dormant state for practically unlimited lengths of time.

When he again found bacteria in the remains of the second experiment, as he had in the first, he concluded that he had proved, because of the care taken to exclude airborne organisms, that bacteria can and do develop from microzymas, and are in fact a scavenging form of the microzymas, developed when death, decay, or disease cause an extraordinary amount of cell life either to need repair or be broken up.

He wrote in 1869:

> "In typhoid fever, gangrene and anthrax, the existence has been found of bacteria in the tissues and blood, and one was very much disposed to take them for granted as cases of ordinary parasitism. It is evident, after what we have said, that instead of maintaining that the affection has had as its origin and cause the introduction into the organism of foreign germs with their consequent action, one should affirm that one only has to deal with an alteration of the function of microzymas, an alteration indicated by the change that has taken place in their form." [1]

This view coincides well with the modern view of all germs found in nature, except those in the body, which are still looked on as causing the conditions they are found with, rather than being the result of

---

1. *Comptes Rendus*, 75, p.1525 (session of Dec. 2nd, 1872)

these conditions, which is their true relation to them.

The *Encyclopedia Britannica* says in the entry on bacteriology:

> "The common idea of bacteria in the minds of most people is that of a hidden and sinister scourge lying in wait for mankind. This popular conception is born of the fact that attention was first focused upon bacteria through the discovery, some 70 years ago, of the relationship of bacteria to disease in man, and that in its infancy the study of bacteriology was a branch of medical science.
>
> Relatively few people assign to bacteria the important position in the world of living things that they rightly occupy, for it is only a few of the bacteria known today that have developed in such a way that they can live in the human body, and for every one of this kind, there are scores of others which are perfectly harmless, and, far from being regarded as the enemies of mankind, must be numbered among his best friends.
>
> It is in fact no exaggeration to say that upon the activities of bacteria the very existence of man depends; indeed, without bacteria there could be no other living thing in the world; for every animal and plant owes its existence to the fertility of the soil and this in turn depends upon the activity of the micro-organisms which inhabit the soil in almost inconceivable numbers. It is one of the main objects of this article to show how true is this statement; there will be found in it only passing reference to the organisms which produce disease in man and animals; for information on these see *Pathology* and *Immunity*." [1]

The writer of the above thoroughly understands germs or bacteria with only one exception; *the bacteria found in man and animals do not cause disease.* They have the same function as those found in the soil, or in sewage, or elsewhere in nature; they are there to rebuild dead or diseased tissues, or rework body wastes, and it is well known that they *will not or cannot* attack healthy tissues. They are as important and necessary to human life as those found elsewhere in nature, and are in reality just as harmless if we live correctly, as Béchamp clearly showed.

---

1. *Encyclopaedia Britannica,* 14th ed., 2, p.899

5.
Silkworm Disease: another steal!

Between 1855 and 1865, a widespread epidemic among silkworms called *pebrine* alarmed the south of France, so much so that finally, in 1865, it drew national attention. Professor Béchamp, early in 1865, took up the study of this epidemic entirely at his own expense, and without the aid of others. He quickly found that it was caused by a small parasite.

His long experience with small micro-organisms, and the way creosote had inhibited their growth in his Beacon Experiment of 1854 and 1855, at once suggested the way out.

Hence he was able to state before the Agricultural Society of Herault the same year that *pébrine* was a parasitic disease and that thin creosote vapour would prevent the attack of the parasite.

However, in the meantime, the Government had taken an interest in the subject, and in June 1865 sent Pasteur down to investigate the disease.

Pasteur, with the prestige of being an official representative of the government, was able to centre all attention on his own work, to the depreciation of the work of others, though he admitted having never touched a silkworm before he started on this mission.

Nevertheless, the fact that something 'official' was being done caused agricultural societies to await his verdict, instead of at once taking up Professor Béchamp's ideas.

Pasteur's first statement on his new subject was made in September 1865, when he published a very erroneous description, claiming:

> "The corpuscles are neither animal nor vegetable, but bodies more or less analogous to cancerous cells or those of pulmonary tuberculosis. From the point of view of a methodic classification, they should rather be ranged beside globules of pus, or globules of blood, or better still, granules of starch, than beside infusoria or moulds... It is the chrysalide rather than the worm, that one should try to submit to proper remedies." [1]

---

1. *Comptes Rendus*, 61, p.506

This description shows that he had no conception of the real nature of the problem.

Béchamp's comment was:

> "Thus this chemist, who is occupying himself with fermentation, has not begun to decide whether or not he is dealing with a ferment." [1]

Pasteur, about this time, dropped his work because of the deaths of his father and two of his daughters, and before going back, spent a week at the Palace of Compiegne as the guest of Napoleon III.

In February 1866, he again took up the case of the silkworms and had the assistance this time of several able French scientists, yet they made very little progress on the problem.

Meanwhile, Béchamp had made further studies on *pébrine*, and sent a paper entitled *On the Harmlessness of the Vapors of Creosote in the Rearing of Silkworms* to the Academy of Science. In this article he repeated the statements he had made before the Agricultural Society at Herault and added that:

> "The disease is parasitical. *Pébrine* attacks the worms at the start from the outside and the germ of the parasite comes from the air. The disease, in a word, is not primarily constitutional." [2]

He described developing the eggs or seeds of the silkworm in an enclosure permeated with a slight odour of creosote, in which he produced eggs entirely free of *pébrine*, and it took so little creosote that his methods were commercially practical.

However, Pasteur had not yet found the true cause of the trouble. He sent a paper entitled *New Studies on the Disease of Silkworms* to the Academy, in which he said:

> "I am very much inclined to believe that there is no actual disease of silkworms. I cannot better make clear my opinion of silkworm disease than by comparing it to the effects of pulmonary phthisis. My observations of this year have fortified me in the opinion that these little organisms are neither animalcules nor cryptogamic plants. It appears to me that it is chiefly the cellular tissue of all the organs that is transformed into corpuscles or produces them." [3]

---

1. *Les Grand Problémes Medicaux*, p.7
2. *Comptes Rendus*, 62, p.1341 (session of June 18 1866)
3. *ibid*, 63, pp.126-142 (session of July 23 1866)

But again he guessed wrong, and neither he nor all of his assistants could prove statements that were false.

He also took a slap at Béchamp's paper by saying:

> "One would be tempted to believe, especially from the resemblance of the corpuscles to the spores of *mucorina*, that a parasite had invaded the nurseries. That would be an error."

And yet Béchamp had already proved beyond question that it was nothing else but a parasite! Possibly, jealousy caused Pasteur to take a contrary view.

Pasteur, apparently, had not finally given up his 'spontaneous generation' ideas until 1862 or 1864, and since then, had ascribed all signs of fermentation, and all disease, to airborne germs, yet here he denies that this disease is parasitic! And *after* Béchamp's papers proved it!

Béchamp answered him in a paper entitled *Researches of the Nature of the Actual Disease of Silkworms* which contained more proofs of its parasitical nature.

He said that the vibrant corpuscle:

> "... is not a pathological production, something analogous to a globule of pus or a cancer cell, or to pulmonary tubercles, but is distinctly a cell of a vegetable nature." [1]

In another paper[2] Béchamp described experiments that proved the corpuscle to be an organized ferment that would invert sugar, and produce alcohol, acetic acid, etc.

This paper seemed to convince Pasteur that Béchamp was right, for in January 1867, in a letter written to Durny, the Minister of Public Instruction, he began to claim all credit for Béchamp's ideas on the silkworm diseases.

Béchamp provided a still more complete account of his discovery which the Academy printed on April 29, 1867,[3] and the same issue contained a letter from Pasteur to Dumas, dated April 24,[4] in which he expressed regrets over his 'mistakes' and promised a paper with a complete story of the disease soon.

On May 13, 1867, Béchamp sent a letter to the Academy of Science pointing out Pasteur's errors and asking for recognition of the priority

1. *Comptes Rendus*, 63, p.311 (session of August 13, 1866)
2. *ibid*, 63, p.391 (session of August 27, 1866)
3. *ibid*, 64, p.873 (session of April 29, 1867)
4. *ibid*, 64, p.835 (session of April 29, 1867)

of his own discoveries regarding silkworm diseases.[1] He also sent another paper entitled *New Facts to Help the History of the Actual Disease of Silkworms and the Nature of the Vibrant Corpuscles.*[2]

In this paper he described the corpuscles as airborne and to be found on mulberry leaves, and he also described a second silkworm disease different from *pébrine*, which he called *flacherie*, and on which he had published a pamphlet privately, on April 11, 1867.

In the meantime he had also submitted several papers on various microscopic organisms, more or less broadening the general knowledge on this subject;[3] one of these was a general study of bacterial development from his microzymas.[4]

In a paper entitled *On the Microzymian Disease of Silkworms*[5] Béchamp gave a full description of this second disease called *flacherie*. This was published in the paper dated June 8, 1868, and on June 24 Pasteur wrote to Dumas claiming to have been the first to discover this second silkworm disease and demanding that a note he claimed to have sent to the Agricultural Society of Alais on June 1 be printed[6] (as the records then contained no proof of Pasteur's claim to this).

Béchamp answered this claim in a note entitled *On the Microzymian Disease of Silkworms, in Regard to a Recent Communication of M. Pasteur*,[7] which was published under the date of July 13, 1867, in which he referred to his pamphlet of April 11, 1867, (revised and reprinted March 28, 1868) and his papers of May 13 and June 10, 1867, all of which were prior to any publication of Pasteur's.

However, Pasteur used his prestige as a Government representative to brow-beat others into supporting him, and he was finally widely recognized, and Béchamp's claims as to the discoveries on silkworm diseases were ignored. The majority of those who knew that his claims were false were afraid to oppose anyone who was so close to Napoleon, and who had so much official standing as Pasteur then had.

In his book on the diseases of silkworms,[8] Pasteur takes all the credit for these discoveries, and shows how ignorant of the subject he still is by ridiculing Béchamp's statements that creosote was a preventative –

---

1. *Comptes Rendus*, 64, p.1042 (session of April 29 1867)
2. *ibid*, 64, p.1043 (session of April 29 1867)
3. *ibid*, 64, p.696 and 66, pp.366 and 421
4. *ibid*, 66, p.859 (session of May 4 1868)
5. *ibid*, 66, p.1160 (session of June 8 1868)
6. *ibid*, 66, p.1289 (session of June 29 1868)
7. *ibid*, 67, p.102 (session of July 13 1868)
8. *Studies sur le Maladie des Vers-a-sois*, 1870

so he knew of them!

Ethel Hume says that members of the Academy actually asked Professor Béchamp to drop his use of the word *microzyma*, and even to drop his work!

In *Microbe Hunters*, Paul de Kruif gives a slightly different version of Pasteur's work on silkworms from that outlined above. He states that Dumas, his old professor, appealed to Pasteur to help the silkworm growers of southern France, and continues:

> "Anything but a respecter of persons, Pasteur, who loved and respected himself above all men, had always kept a touching reverence for Dumas. He must help his sad old professor! But how? It is doubtful at this time that Pasteur could have told a silkworm from an angle worm! Indeed, when he was first given a cocoon to examine, he held it up to his ear, shook it and cried: 'Why there is something inside it!'" (p.91.)

De Kruif also ascribes the belated discovery that *pébrine* was a parasitical disease to Gernez, one of his assistants:

> "Gernez hurried to Pasteur. 'It is solved,' he cried, 'the little globules are alive – they are parasites! They are what makes the worms sick!'
>
> It was six months before Pasteur was convinced that Gernez was right, but when at last he understood, he swooped back to his work, and once more called the committee together:
>> 'The little corpuscles are not only a sign of the disease, they are its cause. These globules are alive, they multiply, they force themselves into every part of the moth's body.'" (p.95.)

It is strange that with the dispute raging between Béchamp and Pasteur over who had discovered that *pébrine* was a parasitical disease, Gernez did not speak of his own claims in the matter – perhaps a job was more important.

De Kruif continues:

> "He was 45. He wallowed in this glory for a moment and then – having saved the silkworm industry with the help of God and Gernez – he raised his eyes toward one of those bright, impossible, but always partly true visions that it was his poet's gift to see. He raised his artist's eyes from the sickness of silkworms to the sorrows of mankind:
>> 'It is in the power of man to make parasitic maladies disappear from the face of the globe, if the doctrine of spontaneous generation is wrong as I am sure it is!'" (p.97.)

His 45th year must have been 1867, and Béchamp had proven spontaneous generation wrong in 1855 or '56, as described earlier – at least 10 years beforehand.

Clearly de Kruif did not look far enough; the name of Béchamp – the only 'microbe hunter' who really understood their true place in nature – does not appear in his book *Microbe Hunters* at all!

In spite of all his errors in the work on silkworms, and because of his high position and royal favouritism, Pasteur was put in charge of the practical measures of fighting this parasite, and of course did not adopt Béchamp's method of using creosote vapour.

Dr A. Lateud, at one time editor of the *Journal de Médecine de Paris*, charged that whereas in 1850 France had produced 30 million kilograms of cocoons, its output had sunk to 15 million kilograms in 1866-7 due to the epidemic. After Pasteur's methods of 'prevention' had been introduced, production shrank to 8 million kilograms in 1873 and as low as 2 million kilograms in subsequent years. He continued:

> "That is the way in which Pasteur saved sericulture! The reputation which he still preserves in this respect among ignoramuses and short-sighted savants has been brought into being:
>
> – by himself, by means of his inaccurate assertions;
> – by the sellers of microscopic seeds based on on the Pasteur system, who have realized big benefits at the expense of the cultivators;
> – by the complicity of the Academies and public bodies, which, without any investigation, reply to the complaints of the cultivators: 'But sericulture is saved! Make use of Pasteur's system!' However, not everybody is inclined to employ a system that consists in enriching oneself by the ruination of others." [1]

Plainly his sins found him out here – at least with those who were in closest touch with the silkworm cultivators!

It is astonishing, in view of such a failure – and after Béchamp had shown how to prevent these diseases – that Pasteur's reputation did not go down in a public scandal!

Apparently royal favour and the Academies and public bodies protected him from this.

---

1. *Etudes sur la Rage*, pp.427-8

6.
Pasteur also a Faker – Antisepsis

While many of Pasteur's contemporaries must have known of his plagiarisms of Béchamp's work, they were cowed into silence, or kept out of the press by Pasteur's bullying tactics, as well as by his prestige, not only in the public eye and with royalty, but also with the 'Academies and public bodies' Dr Lateud refers to.

Ethel Hume goes on to show that his treatment for rabies and his anthrax serum were the same colossal failure and fraud, as will be shown in Chapter 8, and she discusses other plagiarisms on Pasteur's part, but it hardly seems necessary to go into all of these matters here. We have seen enough evidence of incompetence and fraud to forever doubt any further statements that bear his signature – but there is one more piece of work that is worth looking into.

Some years after the events we have described, Dr M. L. Leverson, an American physician, discovered some of Professor Béchamp's writings in New York and immediately realized that they anticipated Pasteur in certain important points. He went to France, met Professor Béchamp, and heard the story of the plagiarism from him, after which he did a great deal to bring Béchamp's work to public attention.

He was one of the first in the United States to recognize Béchamp's priority in regard to most of the discoveries generally credited to Pasteur, and in a lecture entitled *Pasteur, the Plagiarist*, delivered at Claridges Hotel, London, on May 25, 1911, outlined briefly Béchamp's claim to priority, and added the charge that Pasteur had deliberately faked an important paper!

He said in part:

> "Pasteur's plagiarisms of the discoveries of Béchamp – and of Béchamp's collaborators – run through the whole of Pasteur's life and work, except as to crystallography, which may or may not have been his own. I have not investigated that part of his career, nor do I feel any interest in it.
>
> The tracings of some of these plagiarisms, though they can be clearly demonstrated, are yet somewhat intricate, too much so for this paper; but there is one involving the claim by Pasteur to have discovered the cause of one of the diseased conditions

which assail the silkworm, which can be verified by anyone able to read the French language. It is the following..."

After then describing some of the material we have covered in Chapter 5, he continues:

"But I have a still graver and more startling charge to bring against Pasteur as a supposed man of science.

Scientific Bluff

Finding how readily the 'men of science' of his day accepted his fairy tales, in a voluminous memoir of no value (published in the *Annales de Chimie et de Physique* 3rd series., Vol. LVIII), is to be found on page 381 a section entitled *Production of Yeast in a Medium Formed of Sugar, of a Salt of Ammonia and of Phosphates.*

The real, though not confessed, object of the paper was to cause it to be believed that he, and not Béchamp, was the first to produce a ferment in a fermentative medium without albuminoid matter.

However, the alleged experiment described in the memoir was a fake – purely and simply a fake. Yeast *cannot* be produced under the conditions of that section! If those of my hearers or any other physician having some knowledge of physiological chemistry will take the pains to read this section of Pasteur's memoir with attention, he will see for himself that *yeast cannot be so produced,* and he can prove it by reproducing the experiment as described.

Now mark what – supposing I am right in this – this memoir *does* prove. It proves that Pasteur was so ignorant of physiological chemistry that he believed yeast could be so produced, *or else he was so confident of the ignorant confidence of the medical profession in himself, that he believed he could bluff it through.* In this last belief, he was correct for a time. I can only hope that the exposure I am making of Pasteur's ignorance and dishonesty will lead to a serious overhauling of all his work.

It was Béchamp who discovered and expounded the theory of antisepsis which Pasteur permitted to be ascribed to himself. In his *Studies on Fermentation,* Pasteur published a letter from Lord Lister, then Mr. Surgeon Lister, in which he claims that he learned the principles of antisepsis from Pasteur. I do not doubt this statement of the noble Lord, for besides accepting Mr. Lister as a gentleman of veracity, I will give you an additional reason for accepting that statement.

When Mr Lister began his antiseptic operations, they were generally successful, but a few days later his patients succumbed to carbolic acid or mercuric poisoning, so that it became a gruesome medical joke to say that 'the operation was successful, but the patient died'.

Now Mr Lister, though a very skilled surgeon and, I believe, having great powers of observation, had established the technique of his operations upon the teachings of a man who had plagiarized the discovery without understanding the principle upon which it was based. Not unnaturally, Lister used doses of carbolic acid, which, when placed upon an open wound or respired by a patient, were lethal.

But, thanks to his careful observations, he gradually reduced the quantity of carbolic acid or sublimate of mercury employed, until at last 'his operations were successful and the patients lived', as they would have done from the beginning, had he obtained his knowledge of the principles of antisepsis from their discoverer, Béchamp – who had warned against the use of any but a very minute dose of carbolic acid – instead of from the plagiarist Pasteur, who did not know why the dose should be so limited.

From the outline I have now given you, you may form some idea of the ignorance of the man who, for more than thirty years, official medicine has been worshipping as a god. But this is only a small part of the mischief perpetrated. Instead of making progress in therapeutics during the past thirty or forty years, medicine – outside of surgery – has fearfully retrograded, and the medical profession today is, in my judgment, in a more degraded condition than ever before in its history.

I know that at first your minds will rebel against this statement, but some facts will prove to every mind possessed of common sense that it is true."

The Danger of Inoculating

After discussing the practice of medicine in the past and saying that since Jenner's and Pasteur's days the modern effort is to make the sick well, he says of inoculations:

> "When a drug is administered by the mouth, as was beautifully pointed out by Dr J. Garth Wilkinson, in proceeding along the alimentary canal it encounters along its whole line a series

of chemical laboratories, wherein it is analysed, synthesized, and deleterious matter prepared for excretion, and finally excreted, or it may be ejected from the stomach, or overcome by an antidote.

But when nature's coat of mail, the skin, is violated, and the drug inserted beneath the skin, nature's line of defence is outflanked, and rarely can anything be done to hinder or prevent the action of the drug, no matter how injurious – or even fatal – it may be. All the physicians of the world are incompetent either to foresee its action or to hinder it.

Even pure water has been known to act as a violent and foudroyant poison when injected into the blood stream. How much more dangerous is it, then, to inject poisons known to be such, whether modified in the fanciful manner at present fashionable among vivisectionists or in any other manner. These simple considerations show that inoculation should be regarded as malpractice to be tolerated only in case of extreme danger where the educated physician sees no other chance of saving life.

The Germ Theory Fetish

Now the forcing of these inoculations upon individuals by law is one of the worst tyrannies imaginable, and should be resisted, even to the death of the official who is enforcing it. English-speaking people need to have ideals of liberty refreshed by a study of the history of Wat Tyler, who headed one of the most justifiable rebellions in history, and although treacherously murdered by the then Lord Mayor of London, his example should be held up to all our children for imitation...

The entire fabric of the germ theory of disease rests upon assumptions which not only have not been proved, but which are *incapable of proof*, and many of them can be proved to be the reverse of truth. The basic one of these unproven assumptions, the credit for which in its present form is wholly due to Pasteur, is the hypothesis that all the so-called infectious and contagious disorders are caused by germs, each disease having its own specific germ, these germs having existed in the air from the beginning of things, and that though the body is closed to these pathogens' germs when in good health, when the vitality is lowered the body becomes susceptible to their inroads."

I agree most heartily with Dr Leverson's statement that

> "the forcing of these inoculations upon individuals by law is
> one of the worst tyrannies imaginable, and should be resisted
> even to the death of the official who is enforcing it."

Strong words, but absolutely right!

Professor F. W. Newman of Oxford University has said:

> "Against the body of a healthy man, Parliament has no right
> of assault whatever under pretence of the public health; nor
> any the more against the body of a healthy infant. To forbid
> perfect health is a tyrannical wickedness, just as much as to
> forbid chastity or sobriety. No lawgiver can have the right.
> The law is an unendurable usurpation, and creates the right
> of resistance."

And Blackstone says:

> "No laws are binding upon the human subject which assault
> the body or violate the conscience."

In the case of the Union Pacific Railway vs Botsford, the United
States Supreme Court said:

> "... no right is held more sacred or is more carefully guarded
> by the common law than the right of every individual to the
> possession and control of his own person, free from all
> restraint or interference of others, unless by clear and
> unquestioned authority of law.
>
> > As well said by Judge Cooley:
> >
> > 'The right of one's person may be said to be a right of complete
> > immunity; to be let alone.' (*Cooley on Torts 29*)
>
> The inviolability of the person is as much invaded by a
> compulsory stripping as by a blow. To compel anyone, and
> especially a woman, to lay bare the body or to submit it to
> the touch of a stranger, without lawful authority, is an
> indignity, an assault, and a trespass." (*141 U.S. 250*)

In 1903, Judge Woodward of the New York Appellate Court said in
the Viemeister case:

> "It may be conceded that the legislature has no constitutional
> right to compel any person to vaccination."
>
> (*84 N.Y. Supp. 712*)

In the Supreme Court, Columbia County, N.Y., in 1910, Judge Le Boeuf, in the second trial of the Bolinger case, instructed the jury as follows:

> "Now I have charged you that the assault which is claimed to have existed here due to the forcible vaccination, that is, if it was against this man's will, is one which you must consider. And the reason of that is: This man, in the eyes of the law, just as you and I and all of us in this courtroom, has the right to be let alone. We all have the right to the freedom of our persons and that freedom of our persons may not be unlawfully invaded. That is a great right. It is one of the most important rights we have."

I believe these quotations from court documents indicate clearly that anyone has a right to protect himself or his family from the pus-squirters of the A.M.A.

Over 60 years ago the famous English physician, Dr Charles Creighton, said in *Jenner and Vaccination* (1879):

> "The anti-vaccinationists have knocked the bottom out of a grotesque superstition."

However, it has been revived, and needs some more 'knocks'.

The doctors will not willingly give up such a lucrative practice as the use of biologicals, and so parents and the public must do something to stop this blood-poisoning. What, then, can be done?

I have seen a little girl, upon being vaccinated (or 'inoculated'), go to school, promptly develop 'leaky heart valves' and die of 'heart trouble' about two years later, hardly ten years old. I don't believe that either her parents, schoolmates, or teacher, or even the doctor concerned, saw any connection between the vaccination, or inoculation, and the leaky heart valves – but there was a connection – see my pamphlet *The So-called Biologicals have Created a New Form of Heart Disease*.

And thousands of such deaths are caused every year. What are we going to do to stop it?

In the whole history of mankind, the only adequate answer to tyranny that humanity has ever had has been the overthrow of the tyrant; and the A.M.A. and their cronies have certainly been tyrannical in their efforts to sell their decayed animal-pus biologicals for many years. I believe that if these efforts at compulsion, coercion or compulsory laws to force the use of any kind of biological or so-called 'tests' of any kind are pushed much further, they will lead to trouble.

As we show in this book, the underlying 'germ theory' is a fraud, and everything based on it is also fraudulent, and should be forbidden by law; and when the public fully realizes what a colossal fraud the use of these decayed animal-pus concoctions is, you won't even be able to jail a man for shooting a pus-doctor who tries to vaccinate, inoculate, or 'test' his children.

We will outline, further on, a safe method of controlling infections.

Dr Leverson goes on to describe disease as nature's attempt to eliminate waste, and diseased tissues as being due to improper living; and suggests plenty of fresh air, the best of sanitation, very scanty clothes such as gymnasium costumes for everyday use, and a scientific study of diet; he believes overeating causes 'an enormous number of diseased conditions'.

All of these ideas would undoubtedly lead to better health and longer life than can be obtained through serology.

It is now over 30 years since Dr Leverson expressed the hope that his exposure would lead to a serious overhauling of Pasteur's work, and it should be done by someone who understands physiological chemistry.

I feel as he seems to – that the allopathic mind is hardly to be trusted with such important work!

7.
Are Biologicals Injurious?

The 11th Report of the Medical Officer of the Privy Council of England (1868) contains a paper by Dr Burdon Sanderson entitled: *On the Inoculability and Development of Tubercles* (p.91). In this paper he describes experiments he made which proved to his satisfaction that tuberculosis often followed the inoculation of animals with various materials (mostly biological) from non-tubercular sources, and that even a wound might be followed by tuberculosis. He says in part (p.92):

> "The facts from which I had concluded that tuberculosis may originate traumatically, although very limited in number, were so positive in nature that I ventured to state that the results of tuberculosis inoculation could be no longer regarded as necessarily dependent on any property or action possessed by the inoculated material in virtue of its having been taken from a tuberculous individual.
>
> The truth of this inference has now been established by the experiments of two competent observers, Dr Wilson Fox, Professor of Clinical Medicine in University College[1] and Dr Cohnheim of Berlin. The following paragraph contains a summary of their results, which are the more valuable as they were arrived at altogether independently and without knowledge either of each other's inquiries or mine.
>
> From the tabular summary of Dr Fox's experiments (117 in number) it appears that of 70 animals inoculated with various products derived from the bodies of non-tuberculous patients, about half (34) became tuberculous. In addition, five animals were inoculated with putrid but originally healthy muscle, and four of them became tuberculous, as was found when they were killed at various periods from 84 to 122 days after inoculation. Of seven animals in which setons or other mechanical irritants were introduced under the skin, two became tuberculous.[2]

---

1. *On the Artificial Production of Tubercle in the Lower Animals*, pub. McMillan, 1868
2. It is important to note that all these experiments were completed before the appearance of my last report.

This research, no less remarkable for the accuracy and completeness of the anatomical details, than for the conclusiveness of the experiments, was followed only the other day by another in Berlin, which although of similar nature, appears by internal evidence to have been conducted in entire ignorance of the fact that several of the questions investigated had already been completely settled in England.

Drs Cohnheim and Frankel, to establish whether artificial tubercle owe its origin to a specific virus,[1] introduced into the peritonaeal cavities of guinea pigs portions of various tumours (carcinoma, sarcoma, condyloma, etc.) as well as portions of healthy but partly decomposed tissue. Subsequently they employed in the same way a variety of insoluble inert substances such as blotting paper, charpie, gutta percha, caoutchouc, vulcanite, etc. In those animals that survived the immediate effects of the injury, emaciation supervened sooner or later and the animal eventually died with tuberculosis of the peritoneum, liver, spleen, lungs, and other organs, the morbid appearances corresponding in every respect with those described in my last report.

As regards the bearing of these facts on the general question of the nature and origin of tuberculosis; I concluded from my own observations that there is no structural distinction between the artificial disease and human tubercle, so long as the term is confined, as all accurate writers are now accustomed to confine it, to miliary tuberculosis; but I considered it necessary to maintain a reserve as to its relation with the many pathological processes which are spoken of as tuberculosis in the common language of practical medicine and surgery. In going so far the two pathologists already quoted have fully agreed with me.

Dr Fox says:

'I must confess that sceptical as everyone must naturally at first feel on this subject, the cumulative force of the evidence in favour of the tubercular nature of these growths appears to me irresistible. We are either dealing with tubercle, or we have before us a new and hitherto unknown constitutional disease of the rodentia, consisting of growths which, to the naked eye and in their histology, correspond with all the essential features of tubercle in man; which occur not only in the organs which are the chosen seats of tubercle in man, but also in the same parts of those organs; which have the same vital characters, and the same early

1. Cohnheim and Frankel, *Untersuchungen uber die ebertrayberkit der Tuberculose aut Thiere*, Virch. Archiv. Bd. xlv, 1868, p.216

degenerative cheesy changes, not suppuration nor acute softening, and with no marked characters sufficient to distinguish them from tubercle.[1]

Cohnheim says:

'All the marks by which tubercle is characterized are present; the agreement of the product of inoculation with human miliary tubercle could not be more complete than it is, whether regard be had to its extended distribution and to the great variety of organs affected, (peritoneum, pleura, lungs, liver, spleen, lymphatic glands, and even the choroid), or to its macroscopic and microscopic characters.' "

Gould, in his *Pocket Cyclopædia of Medicine and Surgery* describes 'acute miliary tuberculosis' as:

"An acute and rapid form of tuberculosis, which generally occurs in persons under 15 years of age, and in which the tubercle bacilli are rapidly disseminated through the body by the breaking down of some localized form of the disease ... the duration is from 2 to 4 weeks and the termination is fatal."

Or, could not this 'localized form' be introduced by a needle, in the way Dr Sanderson describes? Are not 'persons under 15' the school doctor's best customers for their so-called biologicals? And does not this 'rapid dissemination through the body' sound remarkably like de Kruif's description of the way in which Koch's tuberculous germs spread through his guinea pigs?

Ethel Hume says in *Béchamp or Pasteur?*:

"It is noteworthy that neither Pasteur nor any of his successors have ever induced a complaint by the inoculation of air-carried bacteria, but only by injections from bodily sources."

I believe this would account for a very large part of our 'miliary tuberculosis' in persons under 15; undoubtedly it followed the injection of some biological! And Ethel Hume's description would include *all* biologicals of every type!

Dr Sanderson continues:

"My further inquiries lead me to believe, in the first place that these characters belong much more generally to tuberculous growths than I had at first supposed; and secondly, that those normal tissues which possess them are much more liable to become the seat of the tuberculous process than others."

---

1. Fox *loc. cit.*, p.20, Cohnheim l.c.p. 219

This is probably the most striking evidence in print that almost any sort of inoculation can cause tuberculosis in the animal inoculated, and of course it is reasonable to deduce from this that the same non-tuberculous inoculations would cause tuberculosis in man, any man, and in all probability, from any biological product whatsoever! Yet the serum doctors will tell us that these products are perfectly harmless!

Tuberculin a fraud

The above article, which from the day it was first printed should have forever stopped the use of all biologicals on humans, was published over 20 years before Robert Koch of Berlin brought out his Tuberculin (in 1890), which proved such a terrible failure!

The Zoophilist for May 1st 1891 reported deaths in 123 'selected' cases in Berlin from November 1890 to February 1891 which caused Koch to fall 'under a cloud', but he did not give up until the government finally closed him down because of the terrible death rate!

Dr Paul de Kruif describes this work of Koch's on the tuberculosis germ in rather lurid language[1], yet recent efforts to produce a serum for tuberculosis seem to justify his words. He says of Koch's search for the microbe:

> "'I have it!' he whispered, and called the busy Loeffler and the faithful Gaffhy from their own spyings on other microbes.
>
> 'Look,' Koch cried, 'one little speck of tubercle I put into this beast six weeks ago – there could not have been more than a few hundred of those bacilli in that small bit – now they've grown into billions! What devils they are, those germs – from that one place in the guinea pig's groin they have sneaked everywhere into his body, they have gnawed, they have gone through the walls of his arteries ... the blood has carried them into his bones... into the farthest corner of his brain...'"

Read that over when your child brings home a card from school requesting permission to put *the same sort of stuff into his blood,* and tear up the card! He says that Koch found and grew 43 different families or varieties of these deadly germs. I believe that by the doctors' standards at least, this would necessitate 43 different serums to immunize one against all 43 families, and this is probably not all the varieties there are of tuberculosis germs alone.

However, de Kruif passes over tuberculin with astonishing brevity,

---

1. *Microbe Hunters*, p.131

considering the space given to other matters that were of less importance. He says apologetically:

> "...he was enormously respected, and against his own judgement he was trying to convince himself he had discovered a cure for tuberculosis. The authorities (scientists have reason occasionally to curse all authorities, no matter how benevolent) were putting pressure on him. At least so it is whispered now by veteran microbe hunters who were there and remember those brave times.
>
>> 'We have showered you with medals and microscopes and guinea pigs – take a chance now and give us a big cure, for the glory of the fatherland, as Pasteur has done for the glory of France!'
>
> It was ominous stuff like this that Koch was always hearing. He listened at last, and who can blame him, for what man can remain at his proper business of finding out the ways of microbes with governments bawling for a place in the sun – or with mothers calling? So Koch listened and prepared his own disaster by telling the world about his Tuberculin."[1]

And here de Kruif changes the subject very abruptly! On page 299 he refers to it again, in discussing malaria, as follows:

> "Dean of the microbe hunters of the world, Tsar of Science (his crown was only a little battered) Koch had come to Italy to prove that mosquitoes carry malaria from man to man.
>
> Koch was an extremely grumpy, quiet, and restless man now; sad because of the affair of his consumption cure (which had killed a considerable number of people) ... so Koch went from one end of the world to the other, offering to conquer plagues but not quite succeeding."

Neither are his successes in the use of serums, nor is there any likelihood of success in that direction, as we hope to show.

J.W. Browne, Medical Superindent of the Kalyra Sanatorium, South Australia, quotes Koch at length to the effect that, while an injection of tuberculin into a healthy person will probably start a tubercular sore, an injection into anyone already infected will counteract or 'kill' the first infection, without doing anything more!

Note that he *admits* that it causes tubercular sores in a healthy individual! Hence you'd better know whether you have tuberculosis or

---

1. *Microbe Hunters*, p.193

not before you take it!

However, this reversible characteristic of making the well sick, and the sick well, existed only in Koch's imagination, as is indicated in his own work. Anyone with such a belief must be credited with care in giving such stuff only to tubercular people, and those who received it died so fast the government had to shut him down! Incidentally, cattlemen have contended for many years that it made healthy cattle tubercular.

Dr Browne says:

> "To date, upwards of two hundred different forms of tuberculin have been prepared and described.
>
> The simple fact of the matter is that no one has yet been able to repeat Koch's experiment successfully. There is *no evidence but Koch's* in favour of tuberculin as a therapeutic cure for tuberculosis in guinea pigs, in calves, or in man. *No one but Koch* has been able to cure an infected guinea pig by the use of tuberculin of any sort.
>
> Koch, as Shera says, was an optimist. There is no question that tuberculin can do infinite harm. Scores of people have died prematurely at its hands. Never was there such a commercial vaccine as this one, and never has there been such a gigantic hoax. Tuberculin, Shera says, should not come within the range of vaccine therapy. Whatever good results are imputed to tuberculin must have occurred in spite of it, for its virtues are founded on experiments which cannot be repeated.
>
> The disbeliever too, can point to many cases where the administration of tuberculin in pulmonary disease has been undoubtedly followed by disaster and, while he freely admits the undoubted powers of the tuberculin therapist to stir up the embers and kindle the fire, he has hitherto asked him in vain for any evidence of power to extinguish the fire."

He (rightly, I believe) considers pulmonary tuberculosis to be at least in part 'and to a greater or less extent' a septicemia, and adds:

> "The failure of vaccines to affect the disease in any but an adverse manner is thus explained. As we all know, vaccines have invariably been found useless or worse than useless in septicemias."[1]

Such statements, coming from a physician of Dr Browne's

---

1. *Medical Journal of Australia*, Sydney, Oct. 22, 1921

experience, should write *finis* on the use of tuberculin as a cure forever; and it is no better as a 'test'.

Drs Petroff and Branch, in a discussion of the B.C.G. vaccine used on children, finds that tuberculin seems to spread tuberculosis in those who have the latent or 'benign' form which vaccination is supposed to give.

Note also that the tuberculin seemed to spread tuberculosis in these cattle 'tests' as it did in Koch's experiments on humans. They say:

> "Tzekhnovitzer claims that guinea pigs become hypersensitive to tuberculin after treatment with B.C.G ... 70% of those infected orally and 45% of those infected by the subcutaneous route react.

> *Immunity in animals vaccinated with B.C.G.*

> "Guerin, Richart and Bossiera studied a large number of cattle on a farm. On this farm in 1915 in a herd of 67 head, 47% reacted positively to the tuberculin test. Year after year, the positive animals were slaughtered. In 1918, 38% were still positive to the tuberculin test. In 1920, the number of reactors was 41.7%.
>
> Vaccination in the newborn cattle started on Jan. 1, 1921. In 1922, one year after the vaccination, 20 cattle gave a definitely positive and nine a very suspicious tuberculin reaction, or a total of 45% of 64 head. Many of these animals were vaccinated and revaccinated. In 1923 there remained 26 of the 1919-1920 year animals, all giving a positive tuberculin reaction."

Note that after 47% were slaughtered in 1915, as were all animals testing positive in the following years, 38% were tubercular in 1918, and a full 100% of those animals which remained from the 1919–20 vaccinated group *all* gave a positive 'test'. This was undoubtedly due either to the vaccines used or the 'tests' themselves, which confirms the opinions of the authorities quoted above! Could any dairyman survive such a loss?

They continue:

> "In the meantime, the second generation of these vaccinated animals were revaccinated, and the vaccination repeated each following year. There is no record of how many of the vaccinated cattle became infected, as the tuberculin test was omitted on Calmettes' suggestion, as he believes it to be of doubtful value, giving no information as far as exogenous (outside) infection is concerned.

> *Furthermore if in the vaccinated cattle an implantation of virulent organisms has taken place, setting up only a benign tuberculosis, tuberculin administered may bring about a violent allergic reaction disseminating the virulent organisms. In such an event, progressive disease may follow ...*
>
> Gradually the animal becomes resistant to this particular organism. *However, as soon as a new organism is introduced into the herd, the occurrence of the disease is much more marked than before."* [1]

They do not mention the fact that these 'implantations' may also occur in your child; nor do they realise that they can come through a change of the germ in the vaccine, as I showed in *Germ Mutation* (now out of print).

As occurred with 'flu' in the war, which was merely a mutation of the typhoid germ in the vaccines used against typhoid and paratyphoid, every vaccine may produce a 'new' form of germ which, as noted above, may 'make the occurrence of the disease much more marked than previously'.

This is why we had the 1918 flu epidemic, with the highest death rate on record. It is the reason Koch had so many deaths, and also the reason for the large increases in the death rates of other diseases as noted in Chapter 9.

Koch found 43 varieties or strains of tuberculosis and there are probably as many strains of any other disease. The very multiplicity of these strains, and the ease with which modification can occur on the shelf or in the tissues, is the fundamental reason why biologicals can *never* be used successfully.

F. Loehnis, soil biologist, and N. R. Smith of the U.S. Department of Agriculture have discussed this variability of germs at considerable length and conclude that any germ can break down into a filterable fluid and then develop into new forms that may be radically different from the original germ, their new characteristics depending mostly upon their environment. They believe this change is constantly going on in all groups of germs. [2]

Hence new strains are *always* being formed and are often *more virulent* than the old.

---

1. *American Journal of Public Health*, July, 1928
2. *Journal of Agricultural Research*, July 31, 1916, p.675

Doctors Petroff and Branch add:

> "It seems that in spite of the vaccinations with B.C.G., and the sociological measures, the implantation with violent tubercle has taken place...
>
> Lakhms of Lithuania, studying 472 vaccinated infants, reports that he obtained *10 times* more positive reactions in the vaccinated children than in the unvaccinated."

The real fact is that tuberculin never had any diagnostic value. It was not offered as a test on animals until its failure as a cure on humans caused the German government to forbid such use; in other words, the manufacturers 'discovered' or invented this new use for it to preserve a market. The 'test' on cattle circumvented both the prohibition and its ill-repute as a cure, thus continuing the profits, which is all it is good for.

Read the account of the United States Agricultural Department's 'tests' on animals infected with the hoof-and-mouth disease *from vaccines*, in Chapter 8.

In *Fasting and Man's Correct Diet*, *The Tuberculin Test a Fraud* (out of print), *Immunity* (also out of print), and *Drugless Cures*, I give additional evidence that the use of tuberculin was a fraud, utterly useless, and that more recent serums are no better.

Biologicals may dissolve the red blood corpuscles

It has also been found that the soluble ferments of many animal serums will, in some humans at least, dissolve the red blood corpuscles.

Elie Metchnikoff, the famous Russian scientist, says:

> "It has long been known, however, that the serum of the blood of many animals will destroy the red corpuscles of a different species. This demonstration was afforded during the period when attempts were being made to transfuse the defibrinated blood of mammals, especially of the sheep, into man. This practice had to be abandoned in consequence of the difficulties resulting from the solution of the human red corpuscles.[1]
>
> Later, Buchner[2] compared the action of *alexine* (the name given to the substance found to cause this action) to that of soluble ferments and referred it to the category of the digestive diastases."

---

1. *Immunity in Infectious Diseases*, p.87
2. *Munchen. med. Wchnscher*, 1900, s.1193

This *alexine* is probably the same thing described by Béchamp as the liquid ferment mentioned in Chapter 2, and it should not destroy or even injure perfectly healthy blood or tissues, but who is *perfectly* healthy?

Dr Leverson says in the preface to his translation of *The Blood and its Third Anatomical Element* that Béchamp isolated a series of soluble ferments which he called *zymases*, but which plagiarists renamed *diastases* to obscure his discoveries. Likewise, Béchamp discovered the reason for the coagulation of the blood.

Metchnikoff continues:

> "According to him the same *alexine* is capable of dissolving the red blood corpuscles of several species of vertebrates. Bordet,[1] in a series of researches made in the Pasteur Institute, confirmed this view. He came to the conclusion that the *alexines* of the various species of animals differ from one another. Thus the *alexine* of the blood serum of the rabbit is not the same as that found in the serum of the guinea-pig or dog. Nevertheless each of these *alexines* is capable of exerting a solvent action on the red blood corpuscles of several species."

He continues, on page 95:

> "It may, however, be admitted that the action of *alexine* (complement) comes under the category of phenomena that are produced by soluble ferments. The substance which dissolves the red blood corpuscles of mammals or a portion only of those of birds, undoubtedly presents great analogies to the digestive ferments. As has been mentioned repeatedly, it is very sensitive to the action of heat and is completely destroyed by heating for one hour at 55°C. In this respect, it closely resembles the macrocytase of macrophagic organs which also dissolves red corpuscles. As it is the macrophages which ingest and digest the red blood corpuscles in the organism, it is evident that *alexine* is nothing but the macrocytase which has escaped from the phagocytes during the preparation of the serums."

On page 401 of the same book, discussing artificial immunity against toxins rather than microbes, he says:

> "When micro-organisms, living or dead, are introduced into an animal, it is found that anti-toxins do not as a rule, appear

---

1. *Ann. de l'Inst Pasteur Paris*, 1899, vol. 13, p.273; *ibid*, 1901, vol. 15, p.312

in the fluids; in these cases, the reaction is set up mainly by the microphages. The microphages represent the principal source of anti-toxins."

Is this point clear? All animal blood serums can dissolve the red blood corpuscles of several other species of animals, and many of them, for example that of the sheep, can dissolve the red blood corpuscles of man!

It is also possible that due to the wide variations in the character of the blood and blood serum, etc., both in the animals used and in the patients treated, due to both individual and possibly also racial differences, the serum from any particular animal might have a very injurious effect on the blood or other body fluids of a percentage of human patients treated, as indicated by the many deaths that follow the use of anti-toxin, even though it might not be injurious to all.

Note that they compare this stuff to a soluble ferment, which can go through a china filter, and eat red blood corpuscles, pink dynamite and other things; and this is 'the principal source of anti-toxins'.

It may be true that most horses' blood serum will not dissolve human red blood corpuscles, but how can we know, with all the variations possible, both in the horse, and in man, that some particular horse serum will not dissolve the red blood corpuscles of one or more children in any school which the serum squirters choose to 'protect', as they call it?

This might be the direct cause of the tuberculosis discussed above, and many other troubles that often follow the vaccination of thousands of children, and others.

We quoted Professor Béchamp as to the amount of material a solvent ferment can digest in Chapter 2, and Béchamp and other authorities say that a solvent ferment will survive much higher temperatures than 55°C. This danger, therefore, exists in almost every biological on the market!

There is also the danger that some serum might contain the *alexine* of some animal other than a horse, which could be even more dangerous.

Furthermore, even though a serum cannot dissolve the red blood corpuscles, it might dissolve the leucocytes, the so-called white corpuscles, and this tendency seems to be much more common; in fact, it seems to be the basis of the process of artificial immunity!

For instance, Metchnikoff says:

"When into the peritonaeal cavity of vaccinated guinea-pigs a certain quantity of cholera culture containing virulent and very motile vibrios is injected, we find that in the peritonaeal fluid drawn off by means of a fine pipette, the vibrios have undergone profound changes in the refractory organism. Even a few minutes after the injection of the vibrios, the leucocytes disappear almost completely from the peritonaeal fluid; and only a few small lymphocytes and a large number of vibrios, the majority of which are already transformed into granules, are found; and there is presented a most typical case of Pfeiffer's phenomenon.

Alongside the round granules may be seen swollen vibrios, and others which have kept their normal form, but all are absolutely motionless. Some of these granules are gathered into small clumps, others remain isolated in the fluid. When to the hanging drop containing these transformed vibrios a small quantity of a dilute aqueous solution of methylene blue is added, we observe that certain granules stain very deeply, while others take on merely a very pale tint, scarcely visible. Many of these granules are still alive, because it is easy to watch them develop outside the animal and elongate into new vibrios. A large number of the granules, however, no longer exhibit any signs of life and are evidently dead.

R. Pfeiffer and certain other observers affirm that the granules may be completely dissolved in the peritonaeal fluid just as a piece of sugar dissolves in water. We have repeatedly sought for this disappearance of the granules in hanging drops of the peritonaeal fluid, without being able to find any diminution in the number of these transformed vibrios, even after several days. Nor have we been able to observe the phenomenon of the solution of the granules. It is, at any rate, indisputable that this granular transformation is a manifestation of very profound lesions undergone by the cholera vibrios under the influence of the peritonaeal fluid of the immunized animal.

On the other hand, one is compelled to the conclusion that the granular transformation is due, as we shall see later, to a fermentative action of the peritonaeal exudation." [1]

Some authorities have considered the leucocytes to be an essential part of the blood, in which case their dissolution should be a dangerous loss to the person concerned. In my opinion, however, the leucocytes

---

1. *Immunity in Infectious Diseases*, p.212

are nothing more than body waste or refuse in the process of elimination, and their dissolution immediately places a liquid toxic poison in the blood with no means of preventing it being absorbed, wherever the blood goes, into any and all tissues. Hence the possibility that the brain, the heart, or other organs not intended to handle these toxic poisons might absorb some of them.

Have you ever seen two leucocytes that were the same size or shape? They appear to vary widely in both characteristics – looking, in fact, more like crumbled cheese than living tissues.

Germs in serums may attack the heart valves

Other authorities have described other dangers in the use of serums, for instance Dr E. C. Rosenow, then of the Mayo Clinic, said over 25 years ago that certain varieties of germs in serums used in his experiments had 'an affinity for the heart valves'! [1]

He describes experiments in which he found that the green-producing variety of germs in the serums attacked the valves of the heart, while a certain hemolyzing variety attacked the body joints, thus causing rheumatism!

In November 1925, the Chicago Health Department stated that:

> "more children of the ages of 10 to 14 die of heart disease in
> Chicago than of all other children's diseases put together!"

If Dr Rosenow's statements are true, do you wonder that Chicago children are dropping dead on the street, with all the serumization that is practised in our schools? In the olden days, it was very rare for a child of 10 to 14 years of age to die of heart disease.

Dr Frederick Hoffman, Consulting Statistician of the Prudential Insurance Company of America, said:

> "Heart diseases in all civilized countries are the leading cause
> of death and of a vast amount of physical impairment. As far
> as it is possible to judge, the relative frequency of heart disease
> in proportion to population has everywhere been increasing
> during the last two decades, although evidence to this effect
> is more or less conflicting." [2]

While most diseases that kill mankind off have gone down at an almost wonderful pace since sanitation was first introduced to the world, this particular one is increasing, and for some reason the

---

1. *Journal of Infectious Diseases*, 14, pp.1-32, 1914
2. *The Problem of Heart Disease*, The Spectator, Aug. 29, 1929

authorities profess not to understand.

I would like to ask the reader to refer to some of the charts accompanying this text, for instance *Figure 4* (p.81).

Note that those immigrants from countries having compulsory vaccination die off at a rate *three to four times higher* than immigrants from countries not having compulsory vaccination.

There is no doubt that there are other causes to be considered, such as sanitation, living conditions, diet, and that the relative vitality of the different races may vary, so why should these death rates seem to divide simply on their vaccination status? And granting this, why does heart disease lead all other diseases in the difference between the high rates and the low?

It seems to me that this chart alone is very conclusive evidence that the statements we have quoted in this chapter, as to biologicals causing both tuberculosis and heart disease, are correct.

In regard to Italy, which passed a law requiring the compulsory vaccination of infants in 1888, we still class it in the 'without' column, because in 1910, the time of this census, probably not over 25% of the immigrants in New York State would be under 22 years of age and thus affected by the law, and it is very likely that the law was inefficiently enforced for the earlier years, thus allowing many to escape. Furthermore, all of those vaccinated would still be too young for the full effects of any injurious biologicals to become fully developed by 1910; hence Italy's inclusion in the unvaccinated column.

Statistics of later years seem to indicate that Italy now has death rates comparable with other countries having compulsory vaccination, which can only serve to strengthen the idea that the fad for serums is the cause! See *Figure 3* (p.80).

Dr Rosenow also speaks of yet other troubles that may follow the use of biologicals. In a series of articles dealing with the influenza epidemic of 1918 and published in *The Journal of Infectious Diseases*, and also in the *Collected Papers of the Mayo Clinic*, Vols 10, 11, and 12, he describes many changes in serums or in patients which rendered the serum useless.

In Vol. 10, p.919, he observes of the pneumococcus-streptococcus group, of which he thought mutation forms were responsible for the 1918 pandemic:

> "... marked changes in morphology, growth characteristics, infective powers, and immunological reactions. Many of these changes appear to be true mutations."

On page 949 of the same volume, he ascribed deaths following the use of certain serums to some change or mutation in either the serum or patient.

While, I believe, a serum is supposed to cure by 'agglutinating' all germs of that exact kind which it finds in the body, when there is a slight difference in germs, or changes occur, either in the patient's germs or in those in the serum, no 'agglutination' takes place, and the patient is apt to die, unless sanitary or other measures are taken to save him.

Most regular physicians will say in such a condition that there is no hope, but if drugless physicians are called in, or if enemas are given, there is more than hope. In fact I believe two or three enemas a day and an exclusive fruit juice diet for a while would save the great majority of these cases. However, this is not meant to be a discussion of the treatment of disease, which is covered in other books.

That this change or mutation of germs is a very serious handicap in treating diseases by means of serums or vaccines is indicated all through the series of ten papers that Dr Rosenow published in Vol. 12 of the Mayo Clinic papers.

He says in Vol. 12, page 920, that the serum used on some guinea pigs 'tended to localize in the lungs'.

In Vol. 12, page 1001, he says:

> "Moreover, marked changes in the immunological condition as measured by agglutination tests have occurred in a number of strains following successive (intratracheal) animal passages."

He added that when the changes occurred, 'no good effects were noted'.

If passage through animal tissue will cause 'marked changes in the immunological condition', how can anyone know that passage through human tissues, for example from the arm into the body, will not do the same?

And where can you find a serum or vaccine that has not had an animal passage at some previous time? They are nearly all propagated in animals at present and a substantial percentage of all 'passages' seem to cause a change. In table 4 he shows 35 changes in 44 cases, and one of the other nine had changed in a previous experiment; that makes changes in over 81% of the tests!

This change is no accident; in fact, it occurs with great frequency, as Béchamp proved many years ago.

And these changes in the germs mentioned are of vital importance, as they often merely substitute a new disease for the one vaccinated against. Pasteur seemed to recognize the importance of this point as he vehemently denied its possibility to the very last, and made bitter personal attacks on Béchamp and other colleagues who opposed his ideas for this reason.

Now that this has been proven so overwhelmingly, we can see how a vaccine for any one disease could start some other disease through these mutated forms. We shall then need more serums for the new diseases, and so on, *ad infinitum*.

In the pamphlets *Germ Mutation* and *Immunity, Artificial vs Natural*, I give some important evidence indicating that the 1918 influenza epidemic was caused by mutation in vaccines used to 'prevent' typhoid in the armies in Europe.

When they inoculated against typhoid, they soon found that they had a *para*-typhoid on their hands, and the percentage of paratyphoid in those inoculated was *identical to the second decimal place* with the percentage of typhoid in those *not* inoculated.[1] And when they gave two 'shots', one for each of these, they discovered a second paratyphoid, so to be scientific they called them 'A' and 'B'.

And, as scientists must always be 'scientific', they then gave the boys three shots, one for each of the above diseases, whereupon they found a fourth 'disease' – *influenza* – and the world's highest recorded death rate at that! The Surgeon General of the A.E.F. said of this 'influenza':

> "The ordinary clinical picture of typhoid paratyphoid is frequently profoundly modified in vaccinated individuals ... intestinal types of supposed influenza should always be considered as possible typhoid until proven otherwise. Vaccination is a partial protection only, and must be reinforced by sanitary measures."[2]

Furthermore, supposing that there is no change and that a serum or vaccine 'agglutinates' perfectly, what proof have we that it will either prevent or cure any disease?

Elie Metchnikoff, says:[3]

> "The most carefully studied case of the relations between natural immunity and agglutination is of that encountered

---

1. *Journal of the A.M.A.*, p.267, July 28, 1917
2. Army Circular quoted in *U.S.P.H. Report*, March 28, 1919, pp. 611, 614, 619
3. *Immunity in Infectious Diseases*, p.203

in the anthrax bacillus. We owe it to Gengou,[1] who at the Liege Bacteriological Institute carried out a very detailed investigation of this question.

He showed that the bacillus of Pasteur's first anthrax vaccine is agglutinated by the blood serum of a great number of animals. But he also showed that the serums which have the greatest agglutinative action on this bacillus do not come from the most refractory species. Human serum agglutinates most strongly the bacillus of the first vaccine (in the proportion of one part of serum to 500 parts of culture) but man is far from being exempt from anthrax.

Pigeons' serum, on the other hand, is completely without any agglutinative power, although this species resists not only the first vaccine but very often virulent anthrax. The serum of the ox, a species susceptible to anthrax, is more agglutinative (1:120) than that of the refractory dog (1:100).

All these facts fully justify the conclusion formulated by Gengou that *we cannot establish any relation between the agglutinating power and the refractory state of the animals to anthrax ... this conclusion may be extended to the phenomena of the agglutination of micro-organisms and to those of natural immunity in general.*"

It is quite likely that most physicians will acknowledge that when the changes in a germ as described above occur, there is practically no possibility of it preventing or curing any disease, and while these changes may not run as high as 80% with all biologicals, nevertheless we have shown that it can and does occur with sufficient frequency to render all such methods utterly unworthy of confidence, and unfit to rely on to any degree.

And Professor Metchnikoff's statement that agglutination is of no value as an indication of immunity or curing power seems to wipe out any small remaining chance that serums can be beneficial, under any conditions.

In other words, it seems that when we get vaccinated and fail to catch any disease afterwards, it is either only an accident, or is due more to our natural immunity than to the serum.

---

1. *Arch internat de Pharmocodyn*, Gand et Paris, 1899, Vol.6, 299;
   Ann. de L'Inst. Pasteur, Paris 1899, Vol. 13, p.642

8.
Animal Serology: Anthrax

Ethel Hume says[1] that a Frenchman named Delafond in 1838 announced that small rod-like objects were to be found in the blood of animals having splenic fever or *charbon* (now called anthrax), and when Pasteur brought out his one specific germ for each kind of fermentation, Devaine suggested that these little 'rods', which he named *bacteridia*, might be parasites and the cause of the splenic fever. However, his experiments were contradictory and it was not proven. Later, in 1878, Koch made some studies in which he discovered a formation of spores among his 'bacteridia'.

When Pasteur heard of this, he declared:

> "Anthrax is, therefore, the disease of the bacteridium, as trichinosis is the disease of the trichina, as itch is the disease of its special acarus."[2]

He claimed that the blood of an animal vaccinated with anthrax serum contained no other organisms but the bacteridia. As he considered these exclusively aerobic, the blood must be imputressible, because putrescence, he believed, was due solely to an anaerobic germ. (Later, when the Professors of the Turin Commission drew contrary conclusions from similar experiments, he charged that they had used sheep whose blood was 'septic' as well as tainted with anthrax!)

He claimed that a mixture of aerobic germs (the bacteridia), and anaerobic germs (of putrefaction) would 'neutralize the virulence' of the bacillus anthracis and, if injected into animals, would protect them from infection.

In reality these two germs are only different developments or outgrowths of Béchamp's microzymas, and should have much the same effect anywhere, namely that of scavengers of dead tissues or waste. Their action should be similar, and not counteractant to each other, as is indicated in *Chapter 2*.

Dr Colin, another member of the Academy, promptly challenged Pasteur's statement on the grounds that anthrax was sometimes found

---

1. *Béchamp or Pasteur?*
2. *The Life of Pasteur*, Rene Vallery Radot, p.260

in a virulent stage, yet devoid of the 'bacteridia'.

In the next session (March 12, 1878) Dr Colin charged that Pasteur had suppressed two statements in the printed record that he had made on the floor during the prior session, i.e. that 'the bacteridia of anthrax do not develop in the blood of healthy animals' and that 'the bacteridia will not supply germs to the organisms,' which left Dr Colin's criticism of these statements 'in the air', and, in addition, he charged that Pasteur had *deliberately* falsified the records of other criticisms Dr Colin had made.[1]

On April 30, 1878, Pasteur read before the Academy of Science a paper entitled *The Theory of Germs and their Application to Medicine and Surgery*[2], which also bore the names of Messrs Joubert and Chamberlain as co-authors. This was his first attempt to sell the 'germ theory'.

In this, among many false claims, was the statement that he had discovered 'the fact that ferments are living beings' – giving no credit to Béchamp whatever.

This paper also claimed that an infinitesimal quantity of their last produced culture was capable of producing anthrax with all its symptoms; yet their first experiments with it were failures; as the cultures, when sowed, produced a small spherical germ that was not even virulent, instead of the typical anthrax rods that were expected!

This was probably a true mutation but was not so recognized, the authors apparently believing it to be the result of an impurity getting into their cultures.

The *London Times* of August 8, 1881, about three years later, quotes Pasteur as saying before a sectional meeting of an international medical congress in session there:

> "... in the study of micro-organisms there was an ever present source of error in the introduction of foreign germs, in spite of the precautions that might be taken against them. When the observer saw first one organism and afterwards a different one, he was prone to conclude that the first organism had undergone a change. Yet this might be a pure illusion ... the transformation of a *bacillus anthracis* into a *micrococcus* did not exist."[3]

Note that he said this *21 years after* Miss Nightingale made her

---

1. *Béchamp or Pasteur?*, p.198 (original edition)
2. *Comptes Rendus*, 86, p.1037
3. *The Life of Pasteur*, by Rene Vallery Radot, p.329

famous statement that any germ could turn into another, as previously quoted on page 13.

And when their own experiments failed to bear out their claims that their culture would produce anthrax or any of its symptoms, and the germs that were produced had no resemblance to the anthrax germ, either in appearance or virulence, why should others believe that they could prevent anthrax through the use of this 'culture'?

But Paul de Kruif, in *Microbe Hunters*, a glorification of many famous pioneer serum faddists, paints a most astonishing picture of Pasteur's work on anthrax, and gives many startling details regarding the facts of the matter.

After describing the silkworm failure, he says:

> "But one of Pasteur's most charming traits was his characteristic of a scientific Phoenix, who rose triumphantly from the ashes of his own mistakes ... so it is not surprising to find him, with Reux and Chamberlain, in 1881 discovering a very pretty way of taming vicious anthrax microbes and turning them into a vaccine."[1]

He describes Pasteur's demonstration of his anthrax vaccine at Pouilly-le-Fort in May and June of that year in great detail, including the elaborate preparations, and he dwells on the fact that this experiment was framed by his enemies to destroy him, and that Pasteur realized that he was cornered, that he *must* succeed, or else abandon his work on germs.

It seems to me that we have now seen too many cases of deceitfulness, prevarication and deliberate fraud on Pasteur's part to place much confidence in his good faith under such conditions, and in fact one is justified in looking with suspicion on this experiment. Here were 48 sheep – 24 supposed to be vaccinated, lived, while 24 not vaccinated, died. In such a number the treatment might be differentiated quite easily. He could easily have injected the unvaccinated sheep with a slow poison and he might have used pure sterile water, or a syringe with a perforated piston, in a pretended injection of the vaccinated sheep!

This 'miracle', as de Kruif describes it, seems to be the only success in a long series of failures; the single result that gives the only real support to Pasteur's claims. After all the double-dealing and fraud that we have proven elsewhere, are we not entitled to be sceptical of

---

1. *Microbe Hunters*, by Dr Paul de Kruif, p.157

this? Does not his past conduct suggest that he could have been loading the dice? And he does not seem to have been able to repeat the success elsewhere!

De Kruif says of this fact (p.165):

> "Gradually, hardly a year after the miracle of Pouilly-le-Fort, it began to be evident that Pasteur, though a most original microbe hunter, was not an infallible god. Disturbing letters began to pile up on his desk; complaints from Montpotheir and a dozen towns of France, and from Packisch and Kapuvar in Hungary. Sheep were dying from anthrax – not natural anthrax they had picked up in dangerous fields, but anthrax they had got from those vaccines that were meant to save them! From other places came sinister stories of how the vaccines had failed to work – the vaccine had been paid for, whole flocks of sheep had been injected, the farmers had gone to bed breathing 'Thank God for our great man Pasteur', only to wake up in the morning to find their fields littered with the carcasses of dead sheep, and these sheep – which ought to have been immune – had died from the lurking anthrax spores that lay in their fields.*
>
> Pasteur began to hate opening his letters, he wanted to stop his ears against snickers that sounded from around corners, and then – the worst thing that could possibly happen – came a cold, terribly exact, scientific report from the laboratory of that nasty little German Koch in Berlin, and this report ripped the practicalness of the anthrax vaccine to tatters. Pasteur knew that Koch was the most accurate microbe hunter in the world!
>
> There is no doubt that Pasteur lost some sleep from this aftermath of his glorious discovery, but God rest him, he was a gallant man. It was not in him to admit, either to the public or to himself, that his sweeping claims were wrong...
>
> What a searcher this Pasteur was, and yet how little of that fine selfless candour of Socrates or Rabelais is to be found in him. But he is not in any way to be blamed for that, for while Socrates and Rabelais were only looking for truth, Pasteur's work carried him more and more into the frantic business of saving lives, and in this matter, truth is not of the first importance.
>
> In 1882, while his desk was loaded with reports of disasters, Pasteur went to Geneva, and there before the cream

---

* Or was it from the vaccines? – R. Pearson.

of disease-fighters of the world, he gave a thrilling speech, with the subject: *How to guard living creatures from virulent maladies by injecting them with weakened microbes.*"

And according to de Kruif, Koch made a devastating attack upon Pasteur's statements in a paper published shortly after this, in which he charged that practically all of Pasteur's claims for his anthrax vaccine were false, that his vaccines were not pure, and that he had concealed the bad results that had followed the wholesale use of the vaccines. He closed with:

> "Such goings-on are perhaps suitable for the advertising of a business house, but science should reject them vigorously."
> (p.168)

De Kruif adds:

> "Then Pasteur went through the roof and answered Koch's cool facts in an amazing paper with arguments that would not have fooled the jury of a country debating society."

How can de Kruif so praise a man, and describe the 'miracle of Pouilly-le-Fort' as 'amazing as any of the marvels wrought by the Man of Galilee', after giving such devastating evidence that his work was a failure, his ideas false, and the man himself deliberately dishonest, making false claims and concealing the extent of his failures?

In 1881, the Sanitary Commission of the Hungarian Government said of the vaccine viruses used in the anti-anthrax inoculation:

> "The worst diseases, pneumonia, catarrhal fever, etc., have exclusively struck down the animals subjected to injection. It follows from this that the Pasteur inoculation tends to accelerate the action of certain latent diseases and to hasten the mortal issue of other grave affections."[1]

Plainly it failed in their tests also, and the Hungarian Government forbade its use in that country.

It was not long before his vaccine was proven a failure elsewhere as well. In March 1882, a commission composed of members of the faculty of the University of Turin, Italy, conducted tests regarding the value of this anthrax prophylactic. A sheep having died of anthrax, after they had vaccinated some other sheep with Pasteur's cultures, they inoculated both these vaccinated sheep and also some unvaccinated sheep with the blood of the dead sheep. All of the sheep,

---

1. *Béchamp or Pasteur?*, Ethel Douglas Hume, p.346 of this volume.

both vaccinated and unvaccinated, subsequently died, proving the vaccine utterly worthless.

After about a year of dispute and passing the buck by correspondence, the Turin professors published a pamphlet in June 1883, containing some of Pasteur's contradictory statements together with their cutting criticisms thereof, under the title *Of the Scientific Dogmatism of the Illustrious Professor Pasteur*, which was signed by six professors of high standing. This, by citing contradictory statements Pasteur had made in different papers, along with their comments, just about destroyed his theories on anthrax.

This paper was translated into French, but Pasteur, with some adroit dissimulation, managed to survive the blow, and went on pushing his anthrax vaccine.

He soon had bacteriological institutes for experiments and the production and sale of his various serums and vaccines established in many parts of the world, the one in Paris being probably the first.

In 1888 an institute in Odessa, Russia, sent some anti-anthrax vaccines to Kachowka in southern Russia, where 4,564 sheep were soon vaccinated, and 3,696 of them promptly turned up their toes and died; a death rate of 81 percent, and from a supposed 'preventative' vaccine at that!

Dr Lutaud says in *Etudes sur la Rage* (p.419) that Pasteur was compelled to compensate many owners in France for animals killed by his vaccines, but his work went on.

Foot and Mouth Disease

Mr C. M. Higgins, of drawing ink fame, of Brooklyn, N.Y., some years ago wrote a book entitled *Horrors of Vaccination* in which he drew attention to the fact that official publications of the United States Government ascribed several epidemics of foot and mouth disease in this country *directly* to the use of vaccines or serums; especially those of 1902, 1908, and 1915.

The Chief of the Bureau of Animal Industry of the US. Department of Agriculture says in his report for 1902:

> "Most veterinary text books state that foot and mouth disease is a mild infection and that only 1 or 2 percent of the animals attacked die from it, the reader being left to infer that the losses do not exceed 2 or 3 percent of the value of the animals. Such a conclusion would be a grave mistake."

However, it seems to have been mild before its cause was traced to vaccines. The Secretary of Agriculture says in the department *1914 Year Book*, page 20:

> "There were outbreaks of foot and mouth disease in this country in 1870, 1880, 1884, 1902, and 1908. Since the close of the fiscal year 1914, the sixth outbreak has occurred. The first three, those of 1870, 1880 and 1884 were comparatively trifling. Those in 1902 and 1908 were more grave. The present one is the most serious and extensive of all.
>
> In 1902, the outbreak occurred in the New England States. In 1908 it originated in Detroit. The origin of each of these new outbreaks was traced to the importation of vaccine virus for the propagation of vaccine for use in vaccinating people against smallpox. The vaccine was imported from Japan where the foot and mouth disease exists. Each of these outbreaks was stamped out by methods which have proved most effective in preventing the disease from gaining a footing. These methods involved the killing of all infected and exposed animals, the burying of the carcasses, and the thorough disinfection of all premises with which the animals may have come in contact."

The first part of the 1914 outbreak was ascribed to 'an imported article used in tanning' (hides?) but when this was stamped out, a recurrence occurred near Chicago, in August 1915, that was traced to a Chicago laboratory making hog-cholera vaccines. Foot and mouth disease was found in 8 of 11 herds that had used this vaccine.

The Secretary of Agriculture says of this in the *1915 Year Book* (p.27):

> "It seems certain that this infection was produced by contaminated hog-cholera serum prepared in Chicago, in October 1914, at an establishment where the disease had not been known to exist at any time.
>
> ...pending investigation, all shipments of serum from Chicago were prohibited. It was found that some of the product of the establishment had been used on 11 herds of hogs.
>
> ...infected hogs were found in eight of the herds and all 11 herds were slaughtered at once."

Although they had found the disease in 8 herds on which the vaccine had been used, they decided to 'test' the serum, and *what* a test!

They knew, or were very sure, that the vaccine *had* given the hogs the foot and mouth disease, yet the first four tests on a total of 52 animals were all negative, but they had plenty of perseverance, and in the fifth 'test' and on the 62nd animal tested, they found foot and mouth disease!

If it took 'tests' on 62 animals to obtain proof that a vaccine that had already caused the disease could do so again, how can anyone know that it would not take two or three or more times 62 'tests' any other time, assuming, of course, that these *are* tests, which, again, I don't believe!

And after such a failure, how can any doctor or veterinarian consider any tests, such as the Schick, Dick, Tuberculin, Wasserman, etc., to be of any value whatsoever?

With all the evidence we have given that germs can change their characteristics, from Miss Nightingale and Professor Béchamp, to Lohnis, Rosenow and others, how can anyone expect a germ to remain constant through any 'test' or remain true to its original characteristics *after* being 'tested'?

The Secretary of Agriculture says of these so-called 'tests' – on the same page:

> "This is regarded as proof that the suspected serum actually was infected. Why the standard test used on 61 of the animals failed to reveal this fact is a matter for scientific investigation, and the bacteriologists of the department are at work on the problem. At the time of manufacture 0.5% of carbolic acid was mixed with the serum as a preservative. It is now believed that the acid, acting as a germicide, may have attenuated or partially destroyed the virus, so that tests previously considered safe failed to establish the presence of the infection."

If they had no better luck than Pasteur had with his anthrax tests, it will be a long time before they find out very much!

As the average serum is only some toxic decomposing proteins, and some germs that are really reworkers of dead tissues or waste, but which the doctors believe to be the *cause* of the dead tissues they are found with, the germs are very apt to change their characteristics as the toxins break up, just as they have repeatedly been shown to do elsewhere in nature.

Consequently, many serums would not remain constant through 61 tests, nor would anyone who sells serums to the public be likely to make 62 tests before telling their customers that it was pure serum!

Even after it is 'tested' it may change in storage, and how do they know when they have the right germ in the serum anyway, as the best authorities admit that some germs, such as the smallpox germ, have not been isolated?

The Secretary of Agriculture says (of hoof and mouth disease) on page 29 of the same volume:

> "Up to the present time, the germ has not been identified, although the scientists of Europe have studied the disease exhaustively for years."

They killed 168,158 animals valued at about $5,676,000 to suppress the 1914-15 epidemic.

Circular No. 325 of the Agricultural Department says:

> "Immunization in the 1914 outbreak was out of the question, as the only serum thus far produced gives but a passing immunity of only a few weeks duration, unstable at best."

Mr Higgins pointed out that the disease is more prevalent in countries that have compulsory vaccination than in others.

The U.S. Dept. of Agriculture quotes Dr Loeffler, head of the department handling the trouble in Germany, as saying before the 7th International Congress of Veterinary Surgeons at Baden Baden in 1899:

> "Foot and mouth disease is spreading more and more every year, and every year it costs the German Empire enormous sums. Necessary measures have been taken with the greatest care; suspected grounds have been closely quarantined; this measure had been extended to whole communities and even to entire districts; disinfection had been carefully carried out; and notwithstanding all this, the disease kept spreading."[1]

The Foot and Mouth Disease Commission of the U.S. Department of Agriculture published a chart[2] showing the trend of foot and mouth disease in Germany from 1886 to 1924, which is reproduced on the following page.

Note the tremendous increase in deaths that accompanied the first general use of serums in 1920.

The U.S. Department's *Farmers' Bulletin* No. 666 says:

> "Foot and mouth disease has prevailed in Europe for a great many years and has occasioned tremendous economic losses there.

---

1. *1920 Year Book*, U.S. Dept of Agriculture, p.651
2. *Report of the Foot and Mouth Disease Commission*, Dept of Agric. Bul. No 76, p.18

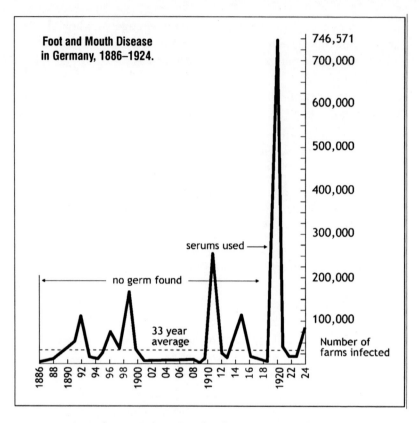

Foot and Mouth Disease in Germany, 1886–1924.

serums used →

← no germ found →

33 year average

746,571
700,000
600,000
500,000
400,000
300,000
200,000
100,000

Number of farms infected

1886 88 1890 92 94 96 98 1900 02 04 06 08 1910 12 14 16 18 1920 22 24

In Italy, France, Switzerland, Germany and Russia the plague has existed so long and has gained such a foothold that it is economically impossible to fight it with the American methods of slaughter and disinfection."

In Germany in 1911, 3,366,369 cattle, 1,602,927 sheep, 2,555,371 hogs and 53,674 goats were affected, or 7,578,371 animals of a total number of about 51,319,000 farm animals in the country at that time. As the chart indicates that about 247,000 farms were affected that year, this would give about 30.6 animals per farm. If the 1920 figures of 746,571 farms affected averaged the same, it would run to nearly 23,000,000 animals, close to half the number of animals in Germany! They used serums this year also, which probably helped spread it.

The same bulletin quotes one scientist as saying:

"...unless all the affected farms were absolutely isolated and the movement not only of livestock but of persons absolutely prohibited, the disease could not be stamped out. Such a quarantine is of course utterly impossible to enforce."

Italy, France, Germany and Switzerland have compulsory vaccination, hence large vaccine plants that can spread the disease, as occurred in the cases cited in the United States.

And of course neighbouring states with or without compulsory vaccination would be overrun by importation from these countries, though some, such as England, kept it out pretty well.

Other places where vaccination is pushed, such as Brazil, also have the disease, while Canada, the United States, Mexico, Australia and New Zealand, all of which are comparatively free from intensive vaccination drives, also seem to have only sporadic attacks of foot and mouth disease, which are generally easily stamped out.

How can the 'scientists' account for this?

Rabies or Hydrophobia

According to *Farmers' Bulletin No. 449* of the U.S. Agricultural Department, no one can catch rabies from an animal that bites them unless the animal has the disease. Furthermore, less than 15% of those bitten by a rabid dog and *not* treated will generally contract the disease. This is very different from the hullaballoo generally raised by the self-styled 'regular' doctors, and especially by health officers, over every dog bite they hear of. In an official publication such as the *Farmers' Bulletin*, this is quite an admission; unofficial and anti-vivisection sources of information generally place the percentage much closer to zero.

Bulletin No. 65 of the U.S. Hygienic Laboratory at Washington also admits that those who die after treatment die *earlier* than untreated cases! It says:

> "Nitsch has pointed out that in a large series of cases the deaths in spite of the Pasteur treatment occurred on average *earlier* than in untreated persons (64.5 to 90 days).
>
> There is some reason to believe that the rabies virus as it occurs in nature varies much in virulence, and that this is in some way related to the geographic distribution." (p.21)

To anyone who read *Chapter 7* it will be evident that (assuming it has value), one should not use a serum from a distant location if this is true, as the possibility of 'agglutination' would be very small where there were such variations. And to this they add:

> "Inoculation with spinal fluid obtained during life is wholly unreliable as it usually fails even in true cases of rabies." (p.36)

The New York Anti-Vivisection Society has published several pamphlets from which the following information is taken. They state that rabies is a very rare disease except where dogs have been injected with rabies serum, in which case it very often develops.

According to their views, a dog unable to find green grass to eat in winter is very apt to develop worms or maggots, or both, in the intestines, often perforating them, and driving the dog frantic. In this condition the dog will bite at everything blindly, foam at the mouth, and run amuck generally, refusing water and seeking solitude. Hay, grass, hide or bones fed to the dogs will cause the irritable conditions to disappear.

There are no real grounds for supposing that madness, as found in humans, occurs in dogs, nor can it be proved that the bite from a distracted animal can produce madness in anyone bitten. Further, so-called rabies can be shown to be the direct result of serum injections.

Competent authorities claim that in so-called 'real' rabies, a dog never foams at the mouth, but has a small amount of brownish stringy discharge hanging from the lips, and the eyes have a fiery glare.

In epilepsy, the dog trembles, his jaws champ violently and his voluntary muscles are powerfully convulsed; there is a copious discharge of white frothy saliva; he utters sharp cries and when recovering from the fit, the eyes are dull and stupid. This might be due to fright, or heat in summer.

They quote doctors of unquestionable authority as saying that no rabic germ has been found; and that finding so-called Negri bodies is no proof that the dog has rabies; as

> "they are found when all symptoms are absent and when all are present, so the diagnosis of rabies is pure guesswork,"

according to J.A. McLaughlin.

Even by A.M.A. standards, no successful serum can be made without the right germ, so this might account for the large number of deaths that follow the Pasteur treatment.

Some doctors say the bite of a rabid dog is absolutely harmless to man. C. W. Dulles, M.D., a famous authority on dog diseases and hydrophobia who looked up the records in many cities, says over a million dogs and cats were handled by dog catchers in 14 years, with many thousands of bites, but no treatment – and not a single case of hydrophobia appeared in these cases.

He and other doctors had posted for years standing offers of $100 to $1,000 for a genuine case of dog hydrophobia and had no claimants, though thousands of dogs were being killed yearly because of scares; one place claiming that 92% of those killed in one year had hydrophobia!

These doctors say chaining or muzzling a dog that has always been free is apt to cause the very irritability we want to avoid.

Pasteur's treatment causes rabies

In man, they say the death rate in France in cases of so-called rabies is 19 per 100 – the highest in the civilized world, and the same as before the Pasteur Institute was established; and cases of hydrophobia have enormously increased, while just across the Rhine in Germany, hydrophobia is almost unknown.

The year before Pasteur started his treatments, there were four deaths from hydrophobia in Paris; the year after there were 22! Not only France as a whole, but each department of France, and in fact every country that has allowed the Pasteur 'treatment' to be introduced, have all shown a sharp increase in the number of deaths from hydrophobia after such introduction!

In England there were several Pasteur Institutes doing a thriving business prior to 1902, when a commission was appointed to investigate rabies and the serum treatment, and the Institutes were abolished. They have had no hydrophobia since.

They claim that over 3,000 people died in England before 1902 after being bitten by dogs and then taking the Pasteur treatment, while more recently the London Hospital treated 2,668 persons bitten by dogs *without* using the Pasteur treatment, and *none* of them developed hydrophobia!

While these are not complete figures for England, there are nearly 6,000 cases of dog bite treated in institutions; and of these only those who had taken the Pasteur treatment died. Why not try something different?

And there has *never* been a case of hydrophobia in Norway, Sweden, Iceland, Denmark, Holland, Belgium, New Zealand and Australia, because those countries will not tolerate a Pasteur Institute within their borders.

They say the Pasteur treatment is very often the cause of rabies, is always dangerous, sometimes even murderous, and is never beneficial.

J. W. Dodson, M.D., of Brockport, N.Y., wrote years ago:

> "If people would only think for themselves and not blindly follow the agitator or grafter, we would soon be relieved of this pest, rabies."

For a safe, sane and logical treatment that has saved patients with rabies for over 100 years, we would recommend the *Buisson Bath*, a hot vapor or steam bath that is fully described in *Drugless Cures* by this author.

The tuberculin test

As the so-called tuberculin test has been rather fully discussed in the pamphlet *The Tuberculin Test a Fraud*, and in Chapter 7 of this volume, it seems hardly necessary to say more on this subject here.

Needless to say, it is as big a fraud as a 'test' on animals as it was as a 'cure' for humans, and there is a great deal of substantial evidence that the testing vaccine (or its needle) causes tuberculosis in cows and other animals, as it did in the human subjects used in Koch's experiments.

It should be absolutely forbidden, and those who use it should be barred from practice.

9.
Statistics

In any discussion of the value of a remedy or preventative for any disease, actual statistics of the results that have followed the use of such remedy or preventative in the past should be of great value in judging it, especially when the trend over a long period of years can be charted graphically.

Hence it seems proper to consider what a chart showing the death rates both before and after the introduction of some of these biological treatments, might indicate; especially when the results can be compared with the general trend following other methods of treatment of more or less similar diseases.

For this reason, this chapter contains several charts showing the death rates of several diseases both before and after the use of biologicals, as well as some of the death-rates of similar diseases with and *without* the use of biologicals.

These give an astounding confirmation of our contention that all biologicals are not only utterly useless, but are actually very harmful, and we urge a careful study of the charts.

These charts, together with the information that follows, should convince even the most faithful followers of Pasteur that the so-called 'germ theory' and the use of any and all biologicals is, as Dr Hudson says, *wrong*, and should be completely abandoned immediately.

FIGURE 1
Smallpox And Vaccination In Leicester, England

Note that in this chart during all the years that vaccination was actively pushed, through compulsory laws, etc., smallpox returned again and again, and usually after an increase in vaccination; culminating in the great epidemic of 1872. This came after a most intensive four year effort to completely vaccinate the population under a law (of 1867) that made refusal to submit to it a penal offense. And it came just after the supreme Medical Officer of England had announced that 97.5% of the population had either had smallpox or been vaccinated.

The worst epidemic came just when they had obtained the utmost in 'protection'! Also note that since this time, while vaccination has dropped off in Leicester, smallpox deaths have also dropped off, and in this case to none!

While the public has so lost confidence in vaccination that less than 6% of all newborn children in Leicester for the past 20 years were vaccinated, there has not been one single death from smallpox in the last 33 years of the records, from 1905 to 1938 inclusive.

There is probably no city or country having compulsory vaccination in the world that can show a record like this.

This chart indicates that vaccination is not only *not* a preventative, but that is probably an active and important instigator of smallpox.

We might mention here that Dr R. Garrow, Medical Officer of Health for Chesterfield, England, asks why it is that the case mortality rate from smallpox in all persons over the age of 15 in England and Wales for the years 1923-6 was *five* times as high in the vaccinated (0.3%), as in those who were unvaccinated (0.06%)![1] (He used official figures, and calculated only to one and two decimals; when figured to four decimals the rates become 0.324% and .0578%, nearer six times, the ratio between them being 5.6055 to 1. Other years seem to lean the same way, but to a lower ratio.)

If serums and vaccines have any value, as the pus-doctors have promised for so many years, why is not the ratio the other way around?

The *Vaccination Inquirer* of London, England,[2] says that in Brazil, where they have rigid compulsory vaccination laws, and most energetic compulsion, the death rate from smallpox per 100,000 population in Rio de Janeiro for 1913–1922, a 10 year period, was over *600 times as*

---

1. *British Medical Journal*, Jan. 14, 1928
2. *Vaccination Inquirer*, Jan. 2, 1928

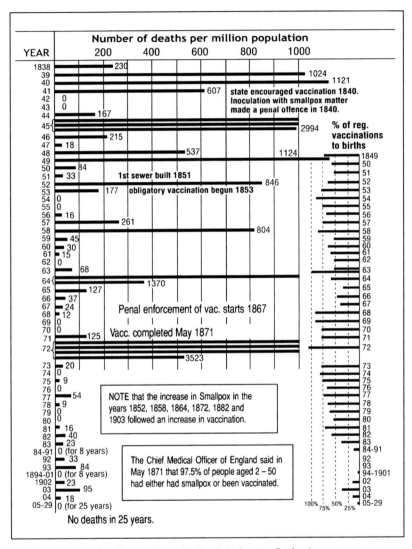

Smallpox and vaccination in Leicester, England

Note how every increase in vaccination as indicated in the lines in the right hand column was followed by an increase in the smallpox death rate.

high as that of London, where opposition is strong and the exemption laws are widely used!

If these are only 'accidents' as the doctors undoubtedly will claim, they at least prove that vaccines are useless; but my contention is that the use of animal pus injections is the *cause* of the higher figures.

FIGURE 2
Smallpox And Vaccination In Japan

As Japan has had the most intensive and thorough vaccination practice of any country, probably for the last 60 or 80 years, any bad effects that might be due to serum or other biologicals ought to be registered here more fully and plainly than in less serumized countries.

To get an idea as to what the effects of biologicals have been here, I have charted the death rates of several diseases in Japan for the period since 1885, from figures in the Annual Reports of the Statistical Bureau, filling in one or two gaps from the Japan *Year Book*, and have also charted the total number of vaccinations in each year.

Vaccination was introduced into Japan in 1849, and it is said that 'the people eagerly adopted it'. The first vaccination law was passed in 1874 and compulsory laws were passed in 1876, 1885, and 1909, each being more stringent than the previous one.

Now, I understand, a baby must be vaccinated within 90 days of birth, and again during the second and tenth years. As there have been over 187,679,000 vaccinations in Japan between 1885 and 1928 inclusive, any injurious effects of vaccination should be fully apparent here.

In 1890 animal lymph was introduced, at which time the death rate from tuberculosis and other lung troubles began to climb, and increased almost continuously for 28 years. Note that the peak years of vaccination are *all* followed by a rising death rate in these troubles, and that these tend to drop off when the number of vaccinations has been reduced for some years.

One recent yearbook stated that the race was 'degenerating' because the mothers had become negligent(!) but I believe the use of serums is more likely to be the cause of any 'degeneration', as well as the present high death rates from tuberculosis, etc.

Note also that in recent years, with no smallpox scares and no extraordinary vaccinations, the death rates of all diseases charted have turned definitely downward as the total number of yearly vaccinations has come down. This lends additional support to our argument.

The editor of the *Year Book* died in the early 1930s, and later figures are not uniformly compiled, nor all available, hence the chart – made in 1931 – has not been brought up to date.

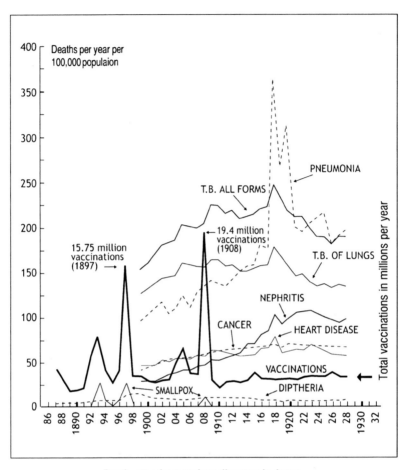

Death rates from various diseases in Japan.

Note how the increases in vaccinations in 1897 and 1908 were followed
by increases in tuberculosis, heart disease, pneumonia, etc.

FIGURE 3
Vaccines and Tuberculosis at School Ages

This chart bears out the view that biologicals can do the young no good. Note that the countries without any compulsory use of biologicals have the lowest death rates from tuberculosis among the young, while Japan stands at the opposite end, combining the most intensive compulsion known with the highest death rate.

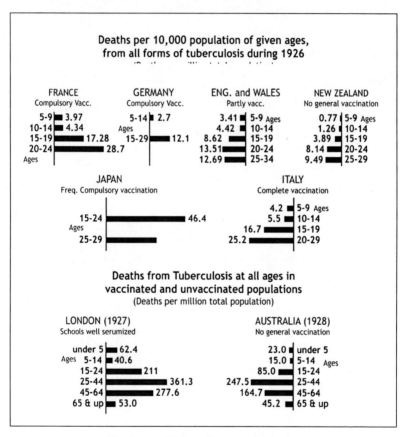

Vaccines and Tuberculosis at school ages

Note how much higher the death rate is in countries having compulsory vaccination, such as Japan and Italy, than in countries without compulsion, such as England, Wales and New Zealand.

FIGURE 4
Vaccines and other diseases

In the first three charts we showed that biologicals not only did not prevent smallpox, but on the contrary actually seemed to increase it, and furthermore, also increased tuberculosis in a substantial manner.

In *Figure 4* we show that *any* kind of biological given for any one disease can have a most astonishing effect in increasing other diseases

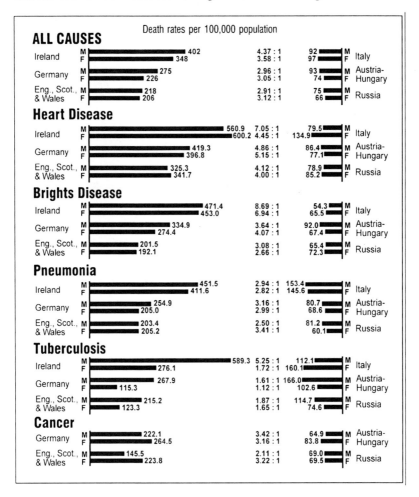

Death rates per 100,000 population

ALL CAUSES

Ireland	M 402 / F 348	4.37 : 1 / 3.58 : 1	92 / 97 M/F Italy
Germany	M 275 / F 226	2.96 : 1 / 3.05 : 1	93 / 74 M/F Austria-Hungary
Eng., Scot., & Wales	M 218 / F 206	2.91 : 1 / 3.12 : 1	75 / 66 M/F Russia

Heart Disease

Ireland	M 560.9 / F 600.2	7.05 : 1 / 4.45 : 1	79.5 / 134.9 M/F Italy
Germany	M 419.3 / F 396.8	4.86 : 1 / 5.15 : 1	86.4 / 77.1 M/F Austria-Hungary
Eng., Scot., & Wales	M 325.3 / F 341.7	4.12 : 1 / 4.00 : 1	78.9 / 85.2 M/F Russia

Brights Disease

Ireland	M 471.4 / F 453.0	8.69 : 1 / 6.94 : 1	54.3 / 65.5 M/F Italy
Germany	M 334.9 / F 274.4	3.64 : 1 / 4.07 : 1	92.0 / 67.4 M/F Austria-Hungary
Eng., Scot., & Wales	M 201.5 / F 192.1	3.08 : 1 / 2.66 : 1	65.4 / 72.3 M/F Russia

Pneumonia

Ireland	M 451.5 / F 411.6	2.94 : 1 / 2.82 : 1	153.4 / 145.6 M/F Italy
Germany	M 254.9 / F 205.0	3.16 : 1 / 2.99 : 1	80.7 / 68.6 M/F Austria-Hungary
Eng., Scot., & Wales	M 203.4 / F 205.2	2.50 : 1 / 3.41 : 1	81.2 / 60.1 M/F Russia

Tuberculosis

Ireland	M 589.3 / F 276.1	5.25 : 1 / 1.72 : 1	112.1 / 160.1 M/F Italy
Germany	M 267.9 / F 115.3	1.61 : 1 / 1.12 : 1	166.0 / 102.6 M/F Austria-Hungary
Eng., Scot., & Wales	M 215.2 / F 123.3	1.87 : 1 / 1.65 : 1	114.7 / 74.6 M/F Russia

Cancer

Germany	M 222.1 / F 264.5	3.42 : 1 / 3.16 : 1	64.9 / 83.8 M/F Austria-Hungary
Eng., Scot., & Wales	M 145.5 / F 223.8	2.11 : 1 / 3.22 : 1	69.0 / 69.5 M/F Russia

Mortality from highly fatal diseases among various groups of immigrants in New York State in 1910

Note that much higher death rates prevail among migrants from countries having compulsory vaccination (on left side of the diagram) than among immigrants from countries without compulsion (on the right side).

with which – if we believe the pus-doctors' theories – it should have absolutely no connection.

The reader should read *Chapter 7* and study *Figures 2, 3* and *4* together to appreciate how true are the statements made in that chapter.

The statistics in *Figure 4* are for all the foreign-born immigrants from the countries noted who were living in New York State in 1910. There were from 340,000 to 560,000 persons included in each national group, hence they should give a very reliable picture of the resistance to disease of the various groups.

Italy, as previously noted, had a compulsory vaccination law passed in 1888, but is included in the unvaccinated column because only a small percentage of these immigrants were subject to the law because of their age, and all of those were too young and too recently vaccinated for the bad effects to be fully developed by 1910, as explained on that page. Note, however, that all death rates in the Italian group average above those of the other two countries in the same column, with the single exception of Bright's disease.

Note also that in tuberculosis, all groups except Italy have a much higher death rate among the men, large numbers of whom are probably vaccinated with considerable frequency in the armies, than among women, very few of whom (except nurses), were likely to be vaccinated so often. Is there a plausible explanation for all the differences that are shown in these figures, apart from vaccination?

FIGURE 5

Death rates from important diseases in the registration area of the United States

As we saw in *Figure 4* that serums seemed to increase other diseases, this chart was drawn to find the general trend in the United States.

Note the increase in heart disease and compare this with what we say in *Chapter 7* (pp. 53–54) and with *Figures 4* and *6*. Cancer and nephritis seem to have a similar trend, though less marked.

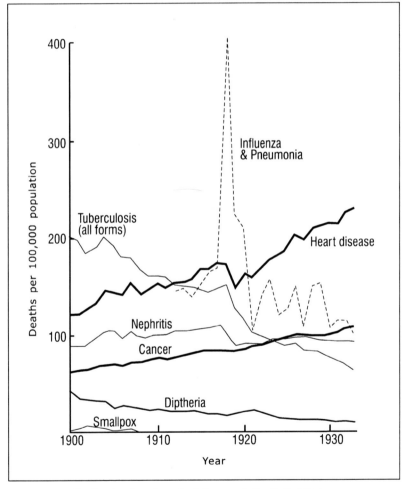

Death rates from important diseases in the United States

Note how the death rates from cancer and heart disease, which are aggravated by biologicals, have increased while others have gone down.

FIGURE 6
Diptheria, Scarlet Fever and Croup in England and Wales

Note that while scarlet fever and croup have had an enormous drop in death rate since 1871 without any serums being employed, diphtheria had a large increase. In fact, there was a real epidemic running from 1893 for about seven years, the period when anti-toxin was pushed the hardest! And the death rate for 1921–29 still averages above that of fifty years earlier!

In other words, with the 'help' of the anti-toxin to fight diphtheria, there is an increase in the death rate over 1871–89, while scarlet fever and croup have both had astonishing drops in mortality, over 96% and 99.8% respectively, *without* any anti-toxins to help.

There are official statements that anti-toxin was introduced into England in 1894, but it hardly seems possible that such a poisonous biological as this would be introduced and made compulsory on a national scale without any prior knowledge or experience with it whatever. For this reason, I believe that it was tried out experimentally in parts of England at least in 1893, or even earlier, and in this way the epidemic that started that year could have been started and kept going until the exemption laws reduced the number of customers.

The report of the Health Officer for Birmingham, England, for 1901 contains the following figure:

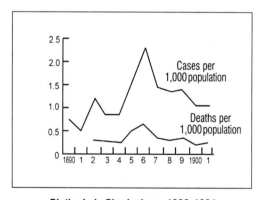

Diptheria in Birmingham, 1890-1901
From the report of the Health Officer for Birmingham, 1901.

There is no statement made as to when anti-toxin was introduced, but the rise in the death rate in 1895 would make me believe that it was in that year, and the Health Officer probably thought that this sudden increase at the time of the introduction of anti-toxin was merely

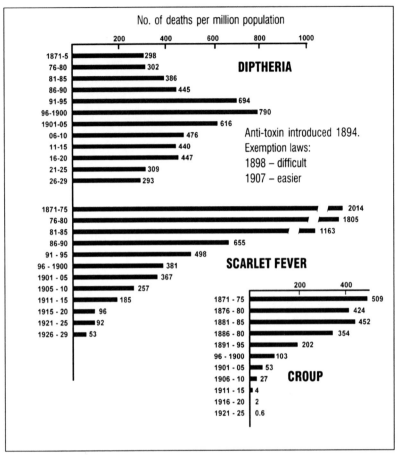

No. of deaths per million population

DIPTHERIA

Period	Value
1871-5	298
76-80	302
81-85	386
86-90	445
91-95	694
96-1900	790
1901-05	616
06-10	476
11-15	440
16-20	447
21-25	309
26-29	293

Anti-toxin introduced 1894.
Exemption laws:
1898 – difficult
1907 – easier

SCARLET FEVER

Period	Value
1871-75	2014
76-80	1805
81-85	1163
86-90	655
91 - 95	498
96 - 1900	381
1901 - 05	367
1905 - 10	257
1911 - 15	185
1915 - 20	96
1921 - 25	92
1926 - 29	53

CROUP

Period	Value
1871 - 75	509
1876 - 80	424
1881 - 85	452
1886 - 80	354
1891 - 95	202
96 - 1900	103
1901 - 05	53
1906 - 10	27
1911 - 15	4
1916 - 20	2
1921 - 25	0.6

Diphtheria, Scarlet Fever and Croup in England and Wales

Note how the diphtheria death rate was held up well above the 1871-80 rate ever since antitoxin was introduced in 1893, while the death rates from scarlet fever and croup have consistently gone down at a rapid rate without the use of any biological.

a coincidence that was 'just too bad', and it might be best not to call attention to it.

Clearly, he believed in anti-toxin; when the drive to vaccinate every one passed its peak in 1897, he very quickly notes that the case mortality rate in diphtheria averaged 25% from January to June (when school let out) and only 20% from July to December. This 20% drop he ascribes to the fact that 'the gratuitous distribution of anti-toxin was commenced in June, 1897'. He does concede that the school children were on vacation, with school vaccination programs suspended, might have had anything to do with it.

FIGURE 7
Diptheria and Anti-toxin in Leicester, England

While the diphtheria epidemic started in England in 1893, it did not reach Birmingham or Leicester until 1895, and the records show that anti-toxin was introduced into Leicester in 1895.

As the five-year periods did not bring out the great increase in diphtheria that followed the introduction of anti-toxin, and the corresponding reduction that occurred when the Exemption Laws were invoked for protection, I have charted these ten years individually. The group figures are in all cases yearly averages, hence comparable with the epidemic figures.

Note that here also diphtheria still has a higher death rate than that which prevailed for the 60 years before anti-toxin was introduced. Also, note how the curve of this epidemic follows the activities of the pus-squirters. Its rise and fall probably indicates fairly well the true effect of anti-toxin in many places where the figures are not published by the 'physicians' who know them. And it is still going on.

In 1935 Dr C. Millard, the Medical Officer of Health for Leicester, made a report on *Inoculation Against Diphtheria* to the Health Committee of the City Council[1] in which he advised against 'any action ... encouraging inoculation of the general public'.

He notes rises in the death rate in Birmingham and other towns after a large number of inoculations, and expresses the belief that 'much diphtheria is spread by carriers' and that inoculation is 'definitely increasing the numbers of carriers'.

He also quoted from a report[2] of the Medical Research Council to the effect that inoculation seems to increase the death rate in many cases.

This report indicates that statistics gave no evidence of improvement from inoculation in large scale diphtheria rates for total populations up to 1929. It says:

> "In France, the most inoculated country in Europe, the incidence of diphtheria continued to rise steadily from 1924 to 1930... Craster (1931) relates that in 1921 an anti-diphtheria campaign was started in Newark, but was confined to the schools. At first, the result appeared promising, but in 1926

---

1. *The Medical Officer*, 2nd and 9th March, 1935.
2. Special Report Series No. 195, *Active Immunization against Diphtheria*, S. Dudley *et al.*

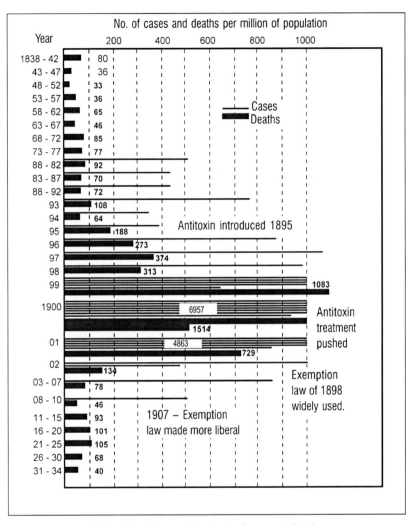

Diptheria in Leicester, England – Cases and Deaths.

Note how sharply the death rate rose after antitoxin was introduced in 1895, from
an average of 62 per year for the previous 57 years to a high of 1514 deaths in 1900.

morbidity and fatality started to rise, and in 1929 Newark
reported the highest diphtheria mortality in the United States
for that year. It was noticed that the brunt of the disease was
borne by the uninoculated children. Craster remarks:

> 'I am confident that this occurred as the result of a general
> carrier condition among the immunized group in the
> home.'" (p.105)

This 'confidence' that pre-school age children died at such a high rate while the inoculated school children go entirely free sounds fishy to me. I think it is a case of misplaced confidence. It seems impossible for some doctors to doubt the germ theory.

Dr Millard mentions a reference to an increase in case fatality in Kansas from 4.9% in 1920 to 7.3% in 1929 and says

> "Kinnaman (the State epidemiologist) believes that active immunization may actually increase the virulence of diphtheria bacilli"

and quotes the report as follows:

> "Immunized carriers pass organisms of the more virulent type to non-immunized children, with the result that the fatality rate is increasing each year among non-immunized children who contract diphtheria."

He also quotes the report to the effect that Detroit started a campaign in 1921, inoculating 3,000 a year for four years. In 1925 the yearly number was increased to 18,000 and in 1926 to 100,000. In this year there was:

> "... a sudden rise in the attack and death rates of diphtheria. During the five years ending with 1930, the mean diphtheria death rate in much-inoculated Detroit was higher than that recorded in any other city in the United States."

Dr Millard noted also that mortality from diphtheria for 1929 was 16.0 per 100,000 population, nearly four times the average of 4.1 for the last five years (1930–34) in Leicester, with no inoculations.

This sounds very much like what Dr J. W. Browne called 'stirring up the embers and kindling the fire' of tuberculosis.

Can you account for these increases with any other reasoning?

Dr W. Kellogg, director of the Bureau of Communicable Diseases, California State Board of Health, says the Schick Test should be abandoned completely. He adds:

> "The percentage of errors in reading reactions in those who are protein-sensitive is frequently as high as 50%, even in the hands of the most experienced."

What use is a test that is 50% wrong?

Dr J. Kilpatrick said before the Chicago Homeopathic Medical Society, December 4, 1928:

> "I have never seen a person with a clean tongue and pure breath, who would take diptheria on exposure to it."

FIGURE 8
Diptheria and Anti-toxin in certain U.S. Cities

On January 1, 1926, the A.M.A-ites started a drive to abolish diphtheria by 1930 by injecting Toxin Anti-toxin (T.A.T.) into all school children in the country, and, of course, they started on the large cities where they had large health departments and many school doctors and nurses to push the sale of the pus. The figures when charted do not indicate that diphtheria has been abolished, nor does it seem likely to be! On the contrary, most of the larger cities had an increase for the years following 1925 that probably will average more that 100% above the

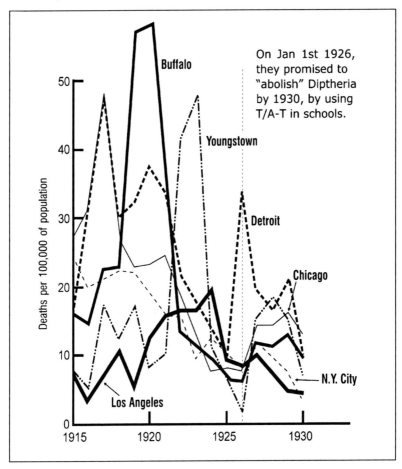

Deaths and use of toxin/anti-toxin in city schools in the U.S.

Note that the death rate declined until 1925, followed by a sharp rise in 1926/1927 in all cases, *after* the drive to sell anti-toxin started!

1925 figures.

This chart only includes a few cities in which the drive was particularly noticeable, and in which, if T.A.T. had any beneficial effects, a marked reduction in diphtheria should have occurred.

Yet 1930 is past, and diphtheria, instead of being abolished, is worst where T.A.T. was pushed the hardest!

The figures for 1915 to 1924 are taken from the 1924 volume of *Mortality Statistics* of the United States Census Bureau, while those for 1925 to 1928 are based upon the total deaths in the later volumes. The populations were estimated from the 1920 and 1930 figures by subtracting one-tenth of their difference from the latter figures, for each year prior to 1930. And as this would not be strictly accurate, no attempt was made to adjust the figures to July 1st populations, as is usual in figuring death rates. The 1923 figure for Detroit is estimated in the same way as it is omitted from the table.

The figures for 1929 and 1930 are deduced from a table in the 1925–30 report of the Chicago Health Department in the same way. These years are therefore not exact but should still be reasonably close to the true figures. The Youngstown figures for 1929 and 1930 were furnished by Mr J. Flood of Pittsburgh, Pa.

Note that this chart shows a very substantial trend downwards from 1915 to 1925 or 1926, when this big drive started, but following these two years there was a sharp increase which covered the years 1927–29 when the T.A.T. was most widely used.

I don't know whether the drop in 1930 was due to a let-up in the drive, or to hard times reducing the amount of food eaten by the public, which might improve the average health as it did in Holland during the war, or to a drop in the use of serums. However, I do not believe this drop was due to anti-toxin, nor do I believe that anti-toxin or any other biological will ever be of any assistance whatever.

This chart was made in 1931, and in trying to add to it recently I failed to find later figures for these cities; possibly the allopaths would like to keep them out of circulation.

A Real Cure

In 1879, before anti-toxin was discovered, Dr J. Kellogg of Battle Creek wrote a book on diphtheria in which he deplored death rates of 40% to 75%, which he said had occurred in many places at that time, and recommended an eliminative treatment with which he claimed to have had *no deaths* in treating over 400 cases.

As the case mortality rates in Chicago and many other cities have been between 8% and 10% in recent years, it seems to me that Dr Kellogg's methods would be a great improvement over any biologicals.

The evidence offered here should satisfy anyone that the use of animal pus to heal the sick is one of the greatest debacles in the history of mankind.

10.
Real Immunity

Many years ago the famous English physician Alexander Haig proved in *Uric Acid in the Causation of Disease* that the breakdown of human cell tissues was due primarily to uric acid formed in the breakdown of protein, and that all animal flesh contained some uric acid when eaten, hence was much more potent in starting this break-down than plant foods, which were all free of uric acid when fresh. He contended that germs were merely of secondary importance, and never the cause of the various conditions of ill-health with which they were frequently found.

Surprising confirmation of his ideas seems to come from some experiments conducted by F. Pottenger and D. Simonsen on cats.[1]

They put two groups of cats on diets of meat and vegetables, identical except that in one group the meat was given raw, and this group seemed to maintain normal good health throughout the experiments. In the other group the meat was all cooked, and this group showed an astonishing breakdown of health in all the animals.

They found every sign of lack of minerals, such as incomplete development of the skull or other bones, bowed legs, rickets, curvature of the spine, paralysis of the legs, convulsive seizure, thyroid abscesses, cyanosis of liver and kidneys, enlarged colon, and degeneration of the motor nerve ganglion cells throughout the spinal cord and brain stem, with some cells affected in the cerebellum and cerebral cortex.

Strange to say, *none* of the cats on raw meat had any of these troubles at all, yet millions of humans are afflicted with one or more of them, and have no conception of the cause, and neither have their doctors in most of the cases.

They add, of these cats:

> "The deficiency renders the experimental animals so deplete in important vitalizing factors that the third generation is unable to live beyond the period corresponding to childhood in the human being."

---

1. *Deficient Calcification Produced by Diet* by F. Pottenger Jr M.D. and D. Simonsen Trans. Am. Therapeutic Society, 39, p. 21-31, 1939.

Why did only those cats fed cooked meat have all these troubles?

We must remember that all protein contains nitrogen and sulphur, which when released in the body combines with water and other matters to form destructive uric acid and sulphurous or sulphuric acids, all of which must immediately be neutralized by the alkaline minerals to prevent cell destruction. If no minerals are instantly available, they will destroy living tissue to get them. This in turn will release more nitrogen and sulphur, continuing the process *ad infinitum*.

Furthermore, all forms of animal flesh contain proteins and acids which are broken down during the process of digestion, and these experiments prove conclusively that cooking meat breaks down a great deal *more* protein, causing the formation of more of these acids, which clearly were what wrecked the cats' lives. If humans want to avoid the same or equivalent results, they must give up cooked meat, and I believe should give up *all* meat, for the rest of their lives.

These acids break down body tissues, and germs arise merely as scavengers; if we can stop the breakdown of tissue through a diet free from these acids, we can also end the danger from germs, as well as the troubles from decalcification and eliminating meat. Reducing the total protein eaten would accomplish this in a large measure.

Dr M. Hindbede, a famous Danish dietician, says a 150-lb. man can live on 3/4 oz. of protein a day, and be healthier than a person eating a greater amount; and he adds that it should be *vegetable* protein.

Dr J. Bitner, of Yakama, Washington, has cured intestinal infections in young children[1] by witholding all milk and protein from the patient for two days, and giving a quantity of apple pulp, which has considerable antiseptic effect. He cured about 90% of his cases with this two-day treatment, although he had many relapses among the 10% when they were allowed milk and protein.

This, I believe, was due to the short treatment not completely eliminating all of the waste protein in the system. Four, six or eight days or even longer periods without milk or protein in the more severe cases could have better results.

However, he had only one death in 946 cases, a far better record than the average physician usually has in such troubles. See my book *Prolongation of Life Through Diet*.

There are many authorities who maintain that a well mineralized system such as we would have on a vegetarian or fruitarian diet would be absolutely immune to germ action of every kind.

---

1. *Therapeutic and Preoperative Actions of Raw Apple Pulp*, J. Bitner M.D., Dec. 1936.

Dr J. Greer says in *The Physician in the House* and also in *The Drugless Road to Perfect Health* that in cases of diphtheria, if the patient gargles the throat with lemon juice every hour, it will cut the false membrane loose so that it will come out.

Possibly more frequent gargling would be better, and an exclusive fruit juice diet for a few days would quickly restore normal health.

> "A very high percentage of all physical disturbances in the tropics are intestinal – some wrong food, some wrong drink, a few germs.
>
> All in all the chief danger is with what is eaten and what is drunk; and the thing is so simple, unless you are a glutton, that it seems absurd that everybody traveling along the equator should not be fit all the way."

In an article entitled *Lemon Squashing Around the World* in the *Saturday Evening Post* of July 24, 1926, (p.68), Samuel Blythe advises all visitors not acclimatised to tropical countries to entirely avoid meat and liquor, to reduce to a minimum the amount of proteins and starches eaten, and to subsist principally on fruits and vegetables. He adds:

> "Lemon squash is a panacea in the tropics. It is the regulator, the reviver, the protector against fever, the assassin of germs, the foe of tropical acidity, the enemy of rheumatic conditions, the quencher of thirst, the general efficient hygenic handyman within the body.
>
> There is no doubt that the two most beneficial fruits known to man are the orange and the lemon, and it is in the tropics that the lemon shines with the greatest effulgence.
>
> It is a hygenic policeman that polices the body, paying strict attention to the liver, supplies richly the needed mineral salts, and when burned in the process of digestion leaves an alkaline ash that neutralizes the acids that are so copiously the result of tropical living conditions. The lemon is a friend, aid and companion, and the way to utilize it is in squash."

He goes on to say that lemon squash is a lemonade as we know it, made from fresh lemons, while bottled lemonade in the tropics is a citric acid preparation usually artificial in composition, and should be avoided. He also advises no sugar or very little, and to see that the squash is made from the fresh fruit and good water. He adds:

> "Get it and drink it by the quart. Drink 5 or 6 or 7 or 10 lemon squashes a day. Drink one every time you feel thirsty, but always between meals, never at meals ... lap them up. They

are cool, they are refreshing, they taste good, and they surely are life-preservers ... you will be better off without tea and coffee.

Literally I lemon-squashed my way around the world. Not a day passed when I was in the tropics that I did not drink 8 or 10 of them, and in the cooler climates I took 2 or 3. I drank them straight, without sugar... fruit and sugar do not make a good food or drink combination.

The result was marvelous. The lemon squashes kept all bodily functions regular, kept me in perfect health, and I am quite a way past my 50th birthday. I did not have an ache, a pain, a digestive disturbance, a physical qualm of any sort... and was perfectly fit and perfectly well all the way. Just a little care about food and the assiduous consumption of lemon squash did it."

The same drink – lemon squash – as well as others, such as pineapple juice, grapefruit, oranges, and the cold pressed juices of the green leafy vegetables, and beets, carrots, tomatoes, etc., are all rich in the minerals needed to control acidity.

And we can use smaller quantities of them if we avoid meats and liquors and hold the quantity of acid-forming proteins and starches to the minimum needs of the body.

A correct diet will control any infection as well as most other forms of ill health.

THE END

Antoine Béchamp with his wife Clementine and son Joseph.

BÉCHAMP.
Chimie médicale et Pharmacie.

9 MÉDAILLES D'OR

.ce, Porto, Liverpool, New-Orléans, 1884, 85, 86

Diplôme d'Honneur 1886

Professor Béchamp (r) and an unknown colleague

Louis Pasteur

E. Douglas Hume

BOOK TWO

Béchamp or Pasteur?

A Lost Chapter in the History of Biology

Ethel Douglas Hume

Based on a manuscript by
Dr Montague R. Leverson, *M.A., Ph.D.*

First published in 1923 and
revised in subsequent editions.

Author's preface

Many years ago in New York, Dr. Montague Leverson chanced to come upon the writings of Professor Antoine Béchamp. So greatly did he become imbued with the views of the French scientist that he seized the first opportunity to travel to Paris for the purpose of making the latter's acquaintance. Leverson arrived some months before Béchamp's death, and was able to receive from him in person an account of his discoveries and his criticisms of science, both ancient and modern.

After attending in Paris in 1908 the funeral of Professor Béchamp, Dr. Leverson found his way again to England. A year or two later I had the pleasure of making his acquaintance. We were both speakers at a meeting arranged by Lady Kathleen Bushe.

Dr. Leverson was still full of vigour; so much so that a little later, aged 80, he married for the second time. His enthusiasm for Antoine Béchamp was exceeded only by his detestation of Pasteur. He talked much to me about *microzymas*, but without explaining what was meant by this term. It was therefore incumbent on me to find out for myself.

I went to the reading room of the British Museum and sent for my long-suffering friend, Mr. R. Stretfeild.

"Have you ever heard of a French biologist, Professor Antoine Béchamp?" I asked him.

"Never", he answered. "These are all works on biology. I am afraid that is all I can do to help."

He left me standing in front of a row of large volumes on a main shelf. As though impelled by some external agent, I stretched out my arm and withdrew one. I opened it at random. On the page before me I saw the name *Béchamp*. My search was ended the moment it had begun. From that one short reference to the great Frenchman I was enabled to investigate further and discover that *microzymas* are the cell granules observed by many cytologists.

After some days of study, I put the results together in the form of an article. This I lent to Dr. Walter R. Hadwen, who then wrote on the subject in a subsequent issue of *The Abolitionist*, a magazine he edited. I, however, was dissatisfied with my first treatment of the matter, and entirely rewrote my treatise, which, under the title *Life's Primal Architects*, was accepted for publication in *The Forum*. It was afterwards reproduced in *The Homoeopathic World*, and translated into Spanish for *Hispania*, a South American periodical.

The late Mr. Arnold Lupton, at one time Liberal Member of Parliament for Sleaford in Lincolnshire, then asked to be allowed to publish it as a pamphlet. In this form it ran through a couple of editions.

In 1915, I had an invitation from Mr. Lupton to attend with him and his wife, as his guest, the meetings of the British Association in Manchester. I was delighted to accept. Time passed quickly. It was not until the morning of the day of departure that Mr. Lupton made known the real purpose of his kind hospitality.

Without seeing it, he had promised to publish a work on Béchamp by Dr. Leverson. On receiving the typescript he found that this would be impossible because of the state it was in, and so he asked me to edit it. In the circumstances it was difficult for me to refuse, although I, too, was in ignorance of the nature of the proposed task. When the manuscript reached me, I found that it was little more than a jumble of quotations, chiefly from Béchamp's writings, without any references.

"There is no book to edit," I was forced to tell Mr. Lupton. "The book has still to be written."

He pressed me to carry out the work.

Immediately, a divergence of opinion arose with Dr. Leverson. He wished an account to be given of what he termed a 'fake experiment' by Pasteur. Both Mr. Lupton and I considered Pasteur's misdemeanours to be of less consequence than Béchamp's achievements, except where the two had bearings one on the other, so the 'fake experiment' was left out, which vexed Dr. Leverson. He asked for his manuscript to be returned, along with most of the books that he had lent me. I kept a few that were essential for my purpose, and sent off the rest together with his manuscript, which had been in my keeping for only a few weeks and which I never saw again.

I had secured for myself Béchamp's works from Paris, and, at my request, the authorities in the Department of Printed Books bought and included the same in the Library of the British Museum, where they continue to be available.

After naming the work on which I was engaged *Béchamp or Pasteur? A Lost Chapter in the History of Biology*, my first efforts were concentrated on acquiring details about Béchamp's life. A long correspondence followed with his relations, and finally, from his son-in-law, Edouard Gasser, I obtained all the particulars that are included in the introductory chapter of this book.

A thorough examination of the reports of the meetings of the French Academy of Science was my next task. In this I was greatly helped by the kindness of the British Museum authorities, who put at my disposal a long table in the North Library, where the massive volumes of the *Comptes Rendus* were allowed to remain until I had done with them.

When I came to the end of my work, I read it through with Mr. Lupton, who made some helpful criticisms. The manuscript was also submitted to Mr. Judd Lewis, who checked the scientific matter and kindly enabled me to see the workings of the polarimeter, the instrument of which, in his investigations, Béchamp made such great use. In another laboratory I was shown under the microscope the different stages of *Karyokinesis*.

All this occurred while World War I was raging. The period was unsuitable for publication. My manuscript was relegated to the bottom of a trunk, while I married and went to live in Scotland. For the moment my mind was distracted from Professor Béchamp.

Eventually, on my return to England, I rewrote the whole book; indeed I redid a great part of it for a third time. Then came tiresome business arrangements, in which I could not have done without the help of my husband. As my *Life's Primal Architects* had already, without reference to me, been made use of as a chapter in an American work on therapeutics, it seemed necessary for *Béchamp or Pasteur?* to be published in the United States for the sake of obtaining the American copyright.

At last, in 1923, the first edition appeared. Dr. Leverson, though still alive, was past knowledge of the event. When the first two thousand copies were sold, Mr. Lupton was eager for a second edition. This came into being not long after his death in 1930. A few days before his end I was privileged to see him. Never shall I forget the wonderful blessing he bestowed upon me for my pains. I shall always be grateful to him for forcing upon me an attempt that has succeeded far better than I would have dared to hope.

My gratitude also goes out to others most kind in their assistance, particularly to Her Grace, Nina, Duchess of Hamilton and Brandon.

Much encouragement has come from Béchamp's own country. First and foremost from Dr. Paul Chavanon, author of *Nous les ... Cobayes* and other eminent medical books. He is anxious that *Béchamp or Pasteur?* should be translated into French. The book also met with high approval from Dr. Gustave Rappin, Director of the Pasteur Institute of Nantes. As a young man he was present at the stormy sessions of the Academy of Science, when Pasteur thundered at all who dared to oppose his views. The subsequent investigations of Dr. Rappin confirmed him in his strong support of the opinions of Béchamp. Gustave Rappin died during the Second World War at the age of 92.

Ethel Douglas Hume

1.
Introduction

Antoine Béchamp

At Villeneuve l'Etang, not far from Paris, on the 28th September, 1895, the death took place of a Frenchman who has been acclaimed as a rare luminary of science, a supreme benefactor of humanity. World-wide mourning, national honours, pompous funeral obsequies, lengthy newspaper articles, tributes public and private – all attended the passing of Louis Pasteur. His life has been fully recorded; statues preserve his likeness; his name has been given to a system, and institutes that follow his methods have sprung into being all over the world. Never has Dame Fortune been more prodigal with bounties than in the case of this chemist who, without ever being a doctor, dared nothing less than to profess to revolutionise medicine. According to his own dictum, the testimony of subsequent centuries delivers the true verdict upon a scientist, and, adopting Pasteur's opinion as well as, in all humility, his audacity, we dare to take it upon ourselves to search that testimony.

What do we find?

Nothing less than a lost chapter in the history of biology, a chapter which it seems essential should be rediscovered and assigned to its proper place. For knowledge of it might tend, firstly, to alter our whole understanding of modern medicine and, secondly, to prove the outstanding French genius of the nineteenth century to have been actually another than Louis Pasteur!

For indeed this astonishing chapter *denies* the prevalent belief that Pasteur was the first to explain the mystery of fermentation, the cause of the diseases of silkworms, and the cause of vinous fermentation; moreover, it shows that his theories of micro-organisms differed in basic essentials from those of the observer who seems to have been the real originator of the discoveries to which Pasteur has always laid claim.

And so, since Truth is our object, we venture to ask for patient and impartial consideration of the facts that we shall bring forward regarding the life-work of two French scientists, one of whom is barely known to the present generation, though much of its knowledge has been derived from him, while the name of the other has become a household word.

Twelve and a half years after the death of Pasteur, on 15th April, 1908, there passed away in a modest dwelling in the student quarter of Paris an old man in his ninety-second year. His funeral was attended by a platoon of soldiers, for the nonagenarian, Professor Pierre Jacques Antoine Béchamp, had a right to this honour, as he had been a Chevalier of the Legion of Honour. Otherwise, the quiet obsequies were attended only by the dead man's two daughters-in-law, several of his grandsons, a few of his old friends and an American friend.[1] No pomp and circumstance in the last ceremonies indicated the passing of a great scientist, but, after all, it was far from the first time that a man's contemporaries had neglected his worth. Rather more than a century earlier another Antoine, whose surname was Lavoisier, had been done to death by his countrymen, with the comment:

"The Republic has no need of savants!"

And now, with scant public notice, was laid in its last resting place the body of perhaps an even greater scientist than the great Lavoisier, since this other Antoine, whose surname was Béchamp, seems to have been the first clear exponent of the fermentative mysteries and the pioneer of authentic discovery in the realm of microscopy.

In the year in which he died, eight pages of the *Moniteur Scientifique* were required to set forth a list of his scientific works. To list his titles gives an idea of the stupendous labours of his long career:

— Master of Pharmacy.

— Doctor of Science.

— Doctor of Medicine.

— Professor of Medical Chemistry and Pharmacy at the Faculty of Medicine at Montpellier.

— Fellow and Professor of Physics and of Toxicology at the Higher School of Pharmacy at Strasbourg and Professor of Chemistry of the same town.

— Corresponding Member of the Imperial Academy of Medicine of France and of the Society of Pharmacy of Paris.

— Member of the Agricultural Society of Hirault and of the Linnaean Society of the Department of Maine et Loire.

---

1. Dr. Montague R. Leverson.

- Gold Medallist of the Industrial Society of Mulhouse (for the discovery of a cheap process for the manufacture of aniline and of many colours derived from this substance).
- Silver Medallist of the Committee of Historic Works and of Learned Societies (for works upon the production of wine).
- Professor of Biological Chemistry and Dean of the Faculty of Medicine of Lille.

Honorary Titles

- Officer of Public Instruction.
- Chevalier of the Legion of Honour.
- Commander of the Rose of Brazil.

Long though his life was, it can only seem incredibly short when compared with a list of discoveries phenomenal for the lifespan of one man. And as both the history of the foundations of biology and the work of Louis Pasteur are both intricately connected with this extended career, we will now sketch an outline of the life story of Antoine Béchamp.

He was born during the epoch that had just seen the finish of the Napoleonic wars, on 16th October, 1816, at Bassing, in Lorraine, where his father owned a flour mill. The boy was only eleven when a change in his life occurred. His mother's brother, who held the post of French Consul at Bucharest, paid the Béchamps a visit and was struck by the intelligence and aptitude of young Antoine. He grew anxious to give him better opportunities than he would be likely to meet with in his quiet country home. We have not heard much of Antoine's mother; but when we find that his parents unselfishly allowed him, for his own good, to be taken away from them at the early age of eleven, we may be fairly certain that she was a clever, far-seeing woman, who might perhaps confirm Schopenhauer's theory that a man's mother is of more importance to him than his father in the transmission of brains! Be that as it may, when the uncle's visit ended, the small nephew went with him, and the two undertook together the long and, in those days, arduous coach journey from Nancy to Bucharest.

It thus came about that the young Antoine saw much of the world and gained a thorough knowledge of a fresh language, advantages that strengthened and developed his intellect. Unfortunately, his kind uncle died after a few years, and the boy was left to face the battle of life alone.

Friends came to his aid, and placed him as assistant to a chemist, who allowed him to attend classes at the University, where his brilliance made all learning easy; and in 1833, without any difficulty, he obtained a diploma in pharmacy.

(In his youthful proficiency he presents a contrast to Pasteur, who in his schooldays was pronounced to be only an average pupil, and later, by an examiner, to be mediocre in chemistry.)

Antoine was still under twenty when he returned to his native land and, after visiting his parents, started work at a chemist's in Strasbourg, which at that time, along with the rest of Alsace and Lorraine, was part of France.

His extraordinary powers of work were soon made manifest. Much of his spare time was devoted to the study of his own language, in which he acquired the polish of style that was to stand him in good stead in his future lectures and literary labours. All the while he continued his University course at the Academy of Strasbourg, until he became qualified as a chemist. On obtaining his degree he set up independently at Benfield in Alsace, where he met and married Clementine Mertian, the daughter of a retired tobacco and beet-sugar merchant, who made him a capable wife. Science claimed so much of her husband's time that the training of their four children and the whole management of the household were left almost entirely to Mme. Béchamp.

Soon after the marriage, Antoine returned to Strasbourg to set up as a chemist; but this work did not nearly satisfy his vigorous energy, and he now prepared himself to occupy a Professor's chair. He soon realised his aim. In a short time he acquired the diplomas of Bachelor of Science and Letters and of Doctor of Medicine, and was nominated Professor at the School of Pharmacy in the Faculty of Science, where for a time he took the place of his colleague Pasteur.

These notable rivals both worked in the full flush of early enthusiasm in the capital of Alsace. But a difference already marked their methods. Pasteur seems never to have left an effort of his unrecorded; every idea as to the tartaric and racemic acids, with which he was then occupied, appears to have been confided to others; letters detailed his endeavours; his invaluable patron, the scientist Biot, was especially taken into his confidence, while his approaching honour and glory were never allowed to absent themselves from his friends' minds. He wrote to Chappuis that, on account of his hard work, he was

"...often scolded by Mme. Pasteur, but I console her by telling her that I shall lead her to fame." [1]

From the start, Antoine Béchamp was utterly indifferent to personal ambition. Never of a pushing temperament, he made no effort to seek out influential acquaintances and advertise his successes to them. Self-oblivious, he was entirely concentrated upon nature and its mysteries, never resting till something of these should be revealed. Self-glorification never occurred to him, and while the doings of Pasteur were being made public property Béchamp, shut in his laboratory, was immersed in discoveries which were simply published in scientific records without being heralded by self-advertisement.

The work that he accomplished at Strasbourg was prolific in benefits for France in particular and for the world at large. It was there that his studies led him to the discovery of a new and cheap method of producing aniline, which up to 1854 had been so costly as to be useless for commercial purposes. The German chemist August Wilhelm von Hofmann, who for many years carried on work in England, after investigating the results of earlier discoveries, produced aniline by subjecting a mixture of nitro-benzene and alcohol to the reducing action of hydrochloric acid and zinc. Béchamp, in 1852, showed that the use of alcohol was unnecessary, and that zinc could be replaced by iron filings, also that either acetic or hydrochloric acid may be used. [2]

By thus simplifying and cheapening the process he conferred an enormous benefit on the chemical industry, for the cost of aniline fell at once to 20 francs and later to 15 francs a kilogram; while, moreover, his invention has continued in use to the present day. It is still the foundation of the modern method of manufacture in the aniline dye industry, which has been all too much appropriated by Germany. The *Maison Renard*, of Lyons, hearing of Béchamp's discovery, applied to him and with his help succeeded in a cheap production of fuchsin, or magenta, and its varieties. The only return made to Béchamp, however, was the award, ten years or so later, of a gold medal from the Industrial Society of Mulhouse.

Neither does any recognition seem to have been made to him for his discovery of a compound of arsenic acid and aniline, which, under the name of atoxyl, is used in the treatment of skin diseases and of sleeping sickness.

---

1. *The Life of Pasteur*, René Vallery-Radot, p.58.
2. Confirmed in Richter's *Organic Chemistry* and in Thorpe's *Dictionary of Applied Chemistry* (1921).

Another work of his that was to prove especially prolific in results was his application of polarimetric measurements to his observations on the soluble ferments. The polarimeter, the instrument in which light is polarised or made to vibrate in one plane by means of one Nicol prism and examined by means of a second Nicol prism, was utilised by him in experiments, the general results of which were that he was enabled before any other worker to define and isolate a number of ferments to which he was also the first to give the name of *zymases*. In dealing with this work later on we shall show how his discovery, and even its nomenclature, has been attributed to somebody else.

So interminable were Béchamp's labours, so numerous his discoveries, that it is hard to know which to single out. He studied the monobasic acids and their ethers, and invented a method of preparing the chlorides of acid radicles by means of the derivatives of phosphorus. He made researches upon lignin, the characteristic constituent of the cell walls of wood cells, and showed clearly the difference between the substituted organic nitro-compounds, like ethyl nitrite and the nitro-paraffins. As we shall see subsequently, he was the first really to establish the occurrence in, and distribution by, the atmosphere of micro-organisms, such as yeast, and to explain the direct agent in fermentation to be the soluble ferment secreted by the cells of yeast and other such moulds. Cleverest of chemists and microscopists, he was also a naturalist and a doctor, and gradually his chemical work led him on to his astonishing biological discoveries.

The explanation of the formation of urea by the oxidation of albuminoid matters and his clear demonstrations of the specificity of the latter formed part of the strenuous labours that led to his opinion that the 'molecular granulations' of the cells assist in fermentation, that some are autonomous entities, the living principle, vegetable and animal, the originators of bodily processes, the factors of pathological conditions, the agents of decomposition – while, incidentally, he believed them to be *capable of evolving into bacteria*.

These conclusions may not all yet be adopted, but as so many of Béchamp's other teachings have come, through the independent work of some and the plagiarisms of others, to be generally accepted, it is certainly reasonable to hope that his amazing conception of Nature's biological processes will advance further discovery; and we wish to ensure the recognition of its legitimate parentage.

He showed that the cell must no longer be regarded (as was Virchow's view) as the fundamental unit of life, since it is built up by the cell-granules within it. He was, it seems, the first to draw attention to the union of these same cell-granules, which he called *microzymas*, and to the rod-like groupings that result, which now go by the name of *chromosomes*. He laid great stress upon the minuteness of his microzymas, and from his teaching we can well infer his agreement with the belief that myriads must be ultra-microscopic, although he had far too exact a mind to descant in modern airy fashion upon matters that are purely conjectural. Where he exhibited his practical genius was that, instead of drawing fancy pictures of primeval developments of chromatin, he endeavoured to trace the actual building up of cells from the 'molecular granulations', that is, *microsomes*, or microzymas.

It was never his method to draw conclusions except from a sure experimental basis.

It was while Béchamp was undertaking his researches upon fermentation, at the very time that he was engaged upon what was to become part of his *Beacon Experiment*, that he was called from Strasbourg to Montpellier to occupy the Chair of Medical Chemistry and Pharmacy at the University there.

The period that followed seems to have been the happiest of his life. Filling an important position, he carried out his duties with the utmost distinction, his demonstrations before students gaining great renown.

He had already made and was further developing extraordinary discoveries which were attracting attention both in and beyond France. These gained him the devoted friendship of his future collaborator, Professor Estor, a physiologist and histologist who combined the duties of physician and surgeon at the Montpellier Hospital. Béchamp, also, had the advantage of medical training, and though he never practised as a doctor, his pathological studies were continuous and he was daily in touch with the work of physicians and surgeons, such as Courty as well as Estor, and he himself took full advantage of the experience to be obtained in hospital wards. His and Estor's more theoretical studies were checked and enlarged by their intimacy with the vast experiments that Nature carries out in disease. Both men were accustomed to the strictness of the experimental methods of Lavoisier, and their clinical and laboratory work progressed side by side, the one confirming and establishing the other.

Without ever neglecting his professorial duties, sufficiently arduous to absorb the whole time of any ordinary mortal, Béchamp laboured incessantly, both by himself and with Professor Estor, at his researches.

A small band of pupils gathered around, helping them, while far into the night the two enthusiasts constantly worked, often, as Béchamp tells us,[1] quite awestruck by the wonderful confirmation of their ideas and verification of their theories.

Such toil could only be continued by one possessed of Professor Béchamp's exuberant health and vitality, and it possibly told upon Professor Estor, whose early death was attributed partly to his disappointment that the popular germ theory of disease, in all its crudity, should have seized public attention instead of the great microzymian doctrine of the building up of all organised matter from the microzymas, or 'molecular granulations' of cells.

His incessant work, which kept him apart from his family, was the only hindrance to Béchamp's enjoyment of a happy domestic life. An excellent husband and father, he was always thoughtful towards others, and in all his dealings was as kind as he was firm. His lectures were made delightful by his easy eloquence and perfect enunciation, no less than by the clearness of his reasoning; while his social manner possessed grace and courtliness. Well above medium height, his clear eye and ruddy complexion gave unstinted proof of the perfect sanity of mind and body that he was blessed with throughout the whole course of his long life.

To the physiognomist, a comparison of the looks of the rivals, Béchamp and Pasteur, gives a key to their respective scientific attitudes. Alert determination is the chief characteristic of Pasteur's features; intellectual idealism of Béchamp's.

Pasteur approached science from the commercial, that is to say, the utilitarian standpoint, no less self-advantageous although he professed to benefit the world.

Béchamp had the artist's outlook. His thirst was for knowledge, independent of profit; he longed to penetrate the unexplored realms of Nature's secrets; the outer world was forgotten. It never occurred to him to indite compliments to influential acquaintances and announce at the same time the dawning of a new idea. The lessons he learned in his quests he duly noted and communicated to the French Academy of Science and at first ignored the fact that his observations were pirated. When finally his silence changed to protest, we shall see, as we proceed, that his patience had been stretched to snapping point. Himself so exact in his recognition of every crumb of knowledge owed to another, he could only feel contempt for pilferers of other men's ideas, while

1. *La Théorie du Microzyma*, A. Béchamp, p.123.

his exuberant vigour and energy fired him with uncompromising opposition to those who, not content with reaping where he had sown, trampled with their distortions upon a harvest that might have been so abundant in results.

It was during the years spent at Montpellier that his open rupture came with Pasteur, on account, as we shall see further on, of the latter's appropriation of Béchamp's explanation of the causes of the two diseases that were then devastating silkworms and ruining the French silk industry. There was no escaping the fact that Pasteur's opinions on the subject had been erroneous until Béchamp had provided the proper solution, yet no voices were raised in condemnation of the former's methods. Pasteur had already gained the ear of the public and acquired Imperial patronage. In all ages, the man of influence is a hard one to cross swords with, as Béchamp was to find.

But at Montpellier he had not yet drained the cup of life's bitterness. Hope still swelled high for the future, especially when, as time passed, a new assistant rose up, and Béchamp's elder son, Joseph, became a sharer in his work. This young man, whose lovable character made him a general favourite, took at an early age his degree in science, including chemistry, besides qualifying as a doctor. It seemed certain that he would some day succeed his father at the University.

But for France a sad day was dawning, and for Béchamp a disastrous change in his career. The year 1870 saw war with Prussia, and the humiliation of France. The districts of Alsace and Lorraine, the home of Béchamp's young boyhood and early manhood, were lost to Germany.

A longing stirred to show that, though despoiled of territory, France could yet dominate the world of thought. So it came about that, as an intellectual stimulus, universities were founded in different places under ecclesiastical patronage. It was hoped that the Church of Rome might hold sway over mental activities.

Lille was one such centre, and about the year 1874 Béchamp was invited to take the post there of Dean of the Free Faculty of Medicine. Some wise friends advised him not to leave Montpellier; but, on the other side, he was bombarded with entreaties to take up work at Lille. Finally, and due entirely to patriotic motives, he allowed himself to be persuaded to leave the University of Montpellier, and its happy memories of successful work. His altruistic wish to benefit both France and science brought about his acquiescence in the change. He moved to the north with his son Joseph, the latter having been appointed Professor of Toxicology at Lille.

All might have gone well had it not been for the clerical directors at Lille. They failed to understand Béchamp's teaching or their implications. They were apprehensive of the novelty of views that in reality were lamps, with which religious faith could have illuminated the mysteries of creation. Still in the dark as to these, the anxious prelates protested against the Professor's exposition of the microzymas, the infinitesimal cellular granules now known as *microsomes*, or *microzymes*, which he considered to be the formative agents of the cells that constitute all forms, both animal and vegetable.

It was tragic that his ground-breaking conception of Nature's processes should have been regarded not as a torch of enlightenment but rather as a dangerous fuse to start a conflagration. In Béchamp was seen a man who dared to investigate Nature's methods, instead of complacently resigning them to hackneyed formula.

Pasteur, however, seems never to have fallen foul of the ecclesiastical authorities; partly, perhaps, because he did not come into the same close contact, but also because, with his worldly wisdom, he was content to profess leadership in science and discipleship in religion; besides, had he not also gained influential patronage?

Béchamp's deep insight had taught him the connection between science and religion – the one a search after truth, and the other the effort to live up to individual belief. His faith had widened to a breadth incomprehensible to those who even suggested the appointment of a Commission to recommend the placing on the Roman Index of his book *Les Microzymas*, which culminates in the acclamation of God as the Supreme Source. Béchamp's teachings are in direct opposition to materialistic views. But his opponents had not the insight to see that the Creator is best demonstrated by understanding the marvels of Creation.

Impatient of petty bickerings, like most men of high intellect, Béchamp found himself more and more at a disadvantage in surroundings where he was misinterpreted and misunderstood. Nor were these his only worries. He was suffering from the jealousy he had inspired in Pasteur, and was smarting from the latter's public attack on him at the International Medical Congress in London, which they had both attended in 1881. Such behaviour on the part of a compatriot before a foreign audience had seared the sensitive spirit of Béchamp and motivated him to reply to Pasteur's plagiarisms. As he writes in the preface to *Les Microzymas*:[1] 'The hour to speak has come!'

---

1. p.8.

Another hour was soon to strike for him. After enduring for about eleven years the prejudices and persecutions of the Bishops and Rectors of Lille, he felt unable to continue to submit to the restraints placed on his work. No cause of complaint could be upheld against him; the charge of materialism in his views could not be supported; but rather than have his work continually hampered, Béchamp regretfully decided to send in his resignation, and his son Joseph, for his father's sake, felt impelled to do the same. Thus father and son, the shining lights of Lille's educational circle, found their official careers cut short and experienced that bitterness of spirit understood only by those whose life has been their work.

The younger Béchamp during his stay at Lille had married a Josephine Lang from Havre, and, owing to this new connection, the Béchamp family moved to the seaboard town and set up in business as chemists. A scientific laboratory enabled the two strenuous workers to undertake medical analyses and continue their research.

But again the hand of Fate dealt heavily with Antoine Béchamp. His son Joseph, well known as a clever chemist, was constantly employed in making chemical assays, and this work occasionally took him out to sea. On one of these expeditions he caught a severe chill. Double pneumonia set in, and in a few days ended his comparatively short and most promising life of 44 years.

It was Antoine Béchamp's sad lot to outlive his wife and his four children. Quite against his wishes, his younger daughter had been persuaded into taking the veil, and the severity of life in a convent caused her death at an early age. His elder daughter had married, at Montpellier in 1872, a M. Edouard Gasser, who owned vineyards in Remigny, and left five children, one daughter and four sons, one of whom was at an early age carried off by typhus, while the other three lived to do service for France in World War I.

Joseph Béchamp left six children, four daughters and two sons, one of whom died young. The other son had no taste for science, and disposed of his father's pharmacy and laboratory. He died a bachelor in 1915.

Antoine Béchamp's younger son, Donat, who died in 1902, married a Marguerite Delarue, and left three sons, the two younger of whom were destined to lay down their lives in the Great War. The eldest, then a doctor in the Russian Army, narrowly escaped death by drowning through the sinking of the hospital ship *Portugal* by a German submarine. Sole living male representative of his grandfather, he is said to inherit the same genius. Without the least effort he has taken diplomas in medicine, chemistry and microscopy, and with the same facility has qualified in music and drawing, the arts being as easy to him as the sciences.

We now return to Antoine Béchamp at the point where we left him at Havre, suddenly bereft of the gifted son on whom not only his family affections but his scientific hopes were placed. Antoine Béchamp was indeed experiencing the rigorous discipline of which the Chinese philosopher Mencius speaks:

> "When Heaven demands of a man a great work in this world, it makes his heart ache, his muscles weary, his stomach void and his mind disappointed; for these experiences expand his heart to love the whole world and strengthen his will to battle on where others fall by the way."

Havre had become a place of sorrowful memories, and Professor Béchamp was glad to move to Paris. Here he could continue his biological work in the laboratory of the Sorbonne, generously put at his disposal by his old colleague, M. Friedel, who with another old friend, M. Fremy, had never ceased to deplore his patriotic unselfishness in abandoning his great work at Montpellier.

Up to 1899, that is to say, until he was 83 years of age, this grand old man of science never ceased his daily labours in the laboratory. After that time, though no longer able to continue lab work, he worked no less diligently to within a few days of his death, collecting and arranging the literary results of his long years of toil, while he continued to follow and criticise the course of modern science.

Up to the very end, his brilliant intellect was undimmed. Patriarchal in dignity, he was always ready to discuss old and new theories and explain his own scientific ideas. Though sorrow and disappointment had robbed him of his natural cheerfulness, he was in no sense embittered by the lack of popular recognition. He felt that his work would stand the test of investigation, that gradually his teaching would be proved true and that the verdict of coming centuries could not fail to raise him to his proper place. Even more indifferent was he to the lack of riches. For him, labour was its own reward, and success was defined by the results of work and not by financial profit, which as often as not falls to the share of plagiarists and charlatans, at the expense of men of real worth.

And so, in 1908, came the April day when, worn out by labour, Antoine Béchamp could no more rise from his bed. His belief was proved, to quote his own words,[1] in Him 'whom the founders of science, the greatest geniuses that are honoured by humanity from Moses to our own day, have called by the name God!'

"My faith!" was one of his last whispered utterances as his life ebbed away; and of faith he was well qualified to speak, he who had delved so deeply into Nature's marvels and the mysteries of the invisible world. Calm and confident to the end, his trust was immovable.

Well does the *Moniteur Scientifique* predict that time will do justice to his discoveries and that once the living actors have passed from the stage and impartial judgment brought into play, Béchamp's genius will be revealed to the world.

He taught that which was marvellous and complex, like all Nature's workings, and public ignorance snatched instead at what was simple and crude. But error, having the canker of destruction within itself, falls to pieces by degrees.

Already the need arises for a saner solution to disease than the mere onslaughts of venomous microbes and a fuller explanation of the processes of biological growth and disruption, of life and death.

And to whom should the world go, rather than to the inspirer of what was correct in Pasteur's teaching, the true revealer of the mystery of fermentation, the exponent of the role of invisible organisms, the chemist, naturalist, biologist and physician – Professor Antoine Béchamp?

---

1. *Les Microzymas*, A. Béchamp, p.926.

PART 1

THE MYSTERY OF FERMENTATION

2.
A Babel of Theories

Before starting any examination of the contributions of Béchamp and Pasteur to the scientific problems of their age, it may be well to consider the utter confusion of ideas then reigning in the scientific world in regard to the mysteries of life and death, and to the phenomenon of fermentation.

This chapter will give a quick outline of the absence of clarity surrounding these leading questions; and though the work of earlier scientists invariably led up to subsequent discovery, yet in the days when Antoine Béchamp and Louis Pasteur commenced their work, the understanding of the subject was, as we shall see, in a state of confusion.

Three paramount problems faced scientific inquirers of the time:

1. What is living matter, this 'protoplasm' (so-called from Greek words meaning *first* and *formed*)? Is it a mere chemical compound?

2. How does it come into being? Can it arise spontaneously, or must it always be derived from pre-existing life?

3. What causes matter to undergo the change known as 'fermentation'?

Among Professor Béchamp's prolific writings, much discussion may be found of the confused babel of theories on these subjects.

To start with the first question:

What is living matter?

There was merely the vague explanation that protoplasm is the living matter from which all kinds of living beings are formed and to the properties of which all are ultimately referred.

There was belief in a substance called *albumen*, best represented by the white of egg, which was said to mix with certain mineral and other matters without changing its nature. J. Dumas demonstrated that such 'albuminoids' comprise not one specific thing, but many different bodies; but the contrary opinion prevailed, and for such substances 'protoplasm' was adopted as a convenient term.

It was 'the physical basis of life', according to Huxley; but this hardly illumined the difficulty, for to pronounce protoplasm to be living matter *per se* was not to explain the mystery of *how* it was so, or its origin and composition. True, Huxley further declared all living matter more or less to resemble albumen, or white of egg; but this latter was also not understood by either biologists or chemists.

Charles Robin regarded it as being of the type of the mucoids – that is to say, as resembling mucus, which itself was so shrouded in mystery that Oken called it *Urschleim* (primordial slime), and the botanist Hugo Mohl identified it with protoplasm, thus dignifying mucus as the physical basis of all things living!

Claude Bernard tried to determine the relation of protoplasm to organisation and life, and combated the general idea that every living body must be morphologically constituted, that is to say, have some structural formation. He argued that protoplasm gave the lie to this belief by its own structural indefiniteness. Charles Robin followed the same view, and gave the name of *blastéme*, from the Greek word meaning *to sprout*, to the supposed primordial source of living forms.

This was nothing but the old idea of living matter, whether called *protoplasm* or *blastéme*. A cell, a fibre, a tissue – any anatomical element – was regarded as living simply because of its formation by this primordial substance. Organisation was said to be its 'most excellent modification'.

In short, formless matter was supposed to be the source of all organised living forms. In a kind of despair of any experimental demonstration of organisation and life, a name was invented for a hypothetical substance magically alive, although structurally deficient. Imagination played more part in such a theory than deduction from tangible evidence. Thus we find that the physician Bichat, who made a name for himself in science before he died in 1802, at the early age of 31, could not accept such an explanation, and declared that the living parts of a living being were the organs formed of the tissues.

A great step was gained when Virchow thought he saw the cell in the process of being built up, that is, structured, and thus jumped to the conclusion that it is self-existent and the unit of life, from which proceed all organised forms of developed beings.

But here a difficulty arose, for the cell proved as transitory as any other anatomical element. Thus many scientists returned to the belief in primordial unstructured matter, and opinion oscillated between the views held by 'cellularists' and 'protoplasmists', as the opposing factions came to be known. Confusion reigned among the conflicting theories as they struggled to explain how a purely chemical compound, or mixture of such compounds, could be regarded as living, and all sorts of powers of modification and transformation were ascribed to it with which we need not concern ourselves here.

Instead, let us consider the second problem that faced Béchamp and Pasteur when they started work:

How does this mysterious living substance come into being? Can it arise spontaneously, or must it always be derived from pre-existing life?

It is hard to realise nowadays the heated controversy that raged in the past around this perplexing mystery. The opposing camps of thought were mainly divided into the followers of two eighteenth-century priests; Needham, who claimed that heat was sufficient to produce animalcule from putrescible matter, and Spallanzani, who denied their appearance in hermetically sealed vessels. The first were named *Sponteparists* because of their belief that organised life is in a constant state of emergence from chemical sources, while the second were named *Panspermists* because of their theory of a general diffusion of germs of life, originally brought into being at some primeval epoch.

For the latter view the teaching of Bonnet, following upon that of Buffon, was chiefly responsible; while Buffon's ideas are reminiscent of the ancient system ascribed to Anaxagoras, according to whom the universe was formed of various elements as numerous as its different substances; e.g. gold was supposed to be formed of particles of gold; and a muscle, a bone, a heart, to be formed of particles of muscle, of bone, of heart. etc.

Buffon taught that a grain of sea salt is a cube composed of an infinite number of other cubes, and that there can be no doubt that the primary constituent parts of this salt are also cubes, which are beyond the powers of our eyes and even of our imagination.

This was an experimental fact, says Béchamp,[1] and was the basis of the system of crystallography of Hauy.

Buffon argued in the same strain that

> "in like manner that we see a cube of sea salt to be composed of other cubes, so we see that an elm is but a composite of other little elms."

---

1. *Les Microzymas*, p.30.

Bonnet's ideas[1] were somewhat similar; the central theme of his teaching being the universal diffusion of living germs:

> "...capable of development only when they meet with suitable matrices or bodies of the same species fitted to hold them, to cherish them and make them sprout – it is the dissemination or panspermy that, in sowing germs on all sides, makes of the air, the water, the earth and all solid bodies vast and numerous magazines in which Nature has deposited her chief riches."

He further maintained that

> "the prodigious smallness of the germs prevents them from being attacked by the causes that bring about the dissolution of the mixtures. They enter into the interior of plants and of animals, they even become component parts of them, and when these composites undergo the law of dissolution they issue from them unchanged to float in the air, or in water, or to enter into other organised bodies."

Such was the imaginative teaching with which Bonnet combated the doctrine of spontaneous generation. When it came to practical experimental proof, one party professed to demonstrate the origin of living organisms from putrescible matter in scaled vessels; the other party denied any such possibility if air were rigorously excluded; while a pastry cook named Appert put this latter belief to a very practical use, and started to preserve fruits and other edibles by this method.

And here we are led to the third conundrum:

What causes matter to undergo the change known as fermentation?

It is a puzzle that must have been brought home to many a housewife unaware of scientific problems. Why should the milk left in the larder at night have turned sour by the morning? Such changes, including the putrefaction that takes place after the death of an organism, were so much of a mystery that the causes were considered occult for a long time.

Newton had suggested that the effect was due to catalysis – a process in which a substance called a catalytic agent assists in a chemical reaction but is itself unchanged. The myriads of minute organisms revealed later on by the microscope in fermenting and putrefying matter were at first believed to be mere results of the general process of

---

1. See *Ire partie; Oeuvres d'Histoire Naturelle de Bonnet*; pp.83-86. Neuchatel, 1779.

putrefaction and fermentation.

A new idea was introduced by Cagniard de Latour, who suggested that fermentation is an effect accompanying the growth of the ferment. That is to say, he looked upon the ferment as something living and organised, by which fermentation is rendered a vital act. It was the microscopic study of beer yeast, undertaken about the year 1836, which brought him to the opinion that the oval cells he observed were really alive during the production of beer, decomposing sugar into carbonic acid and alcohol.

Turpin, the botanist, interpreted this as meaning that the globule of yeast decomposes sugar in the act of nourishing itself. J. B. Dumas maintained the necessity for nitrogenised albuminoid matter, as well as sugar, for food for yeast cells.

Schwann, the German, went farthest of all by declaring that all fermentation is induced by living organisms, and undertook experiments to prove these to be airborne.

But in spite of other experiments confirming Schwann's work, for a time this teaching was set aside for the view that vegetable and animal matters are able to alter *of themselves*. For instance, the theory was held that by dissolving cane sugar in water it changes of itself into grape sugar, or glucose; or, using technical terms, cane sugar undergoes inversion spontaneously.[1]

Such, roughly speaking, were the scientific ideas in circulation at the middle of the nineteenth century, when Antoine Béchamp and Louis Pasteur appeared on the scene with details of their respective experiments.

As Pasteur is renowned as the first to have made clear the phenomenon of fermentation, besides being appraised as the one who overthrew the theory of spontaneous generation, let us now, instead of taking this on trust, turn to the old French scientific documents and see for ourselves what he had to say in the year 1857.

---

1. The usual product of this hydrolysis, or inversion of cane sugar, is invert sugar; but, as this was formerly described as grape sugar, that expression is usually retained here.

3.
Pasteur's Memoirs of 1857

Louis Pasteur, the son of a tanner, was born at Dole in 1822. Intense strength of will, acute worldly wisdom and unflagging ambition were to be the prominent traits of his character.

He first came into notice in connection with crystallography, by discovering that the crystalline forms of the tartrates are hemihedral. His son-in-law has recorded his jubilation over his early achievement, and has told us how he left his experiment to rush out of the laboratory, fell upon the neck of a curator whom he met accidentally, and then and there dragged the astonished man into the Luxembourg garden to explain his discovery.[1]

Work so well advertised did not fail to become a topic of conversation, and the news eventually reached the ears of M. Biot. On hearing of this, Pasteur wrote to ask for an interview with this well-known scientist, with whom he had no previous acquaintance but upon whom he now showered every attention likely to be appreciated by the rather misanthropical old worker, whose influential patronage undoubtedly became the first contributing factor in the triumphal career of the ambitious young chemist.

All the same, Biot's persuasions never succeeded in gaining Pasteur a place in the Academy of Science. This he obtained only after the former's death, when nominated by the Mineralogical Section; and then, oddly enough, exception began to be taken at once to his early conclusions on crystallography.[2]

This, however, was not until the end of 1862.

Meanwhile, in 1854, Pasteur was appointed Professor and Dean of the new Faculty of Science at Lille. In 1856 a request for advice from a local manufacturer of beetroot alcohol made him turn his attention to the problem of fermentation, which was then exercising the minds of the learned. His observations were interrupted by a journey to Paris to canvass for votes for his election to the Academy of Science. Obtaining only sixteen and completely failing in his attempt to enter that select

---

1. *The Life of Pasteur*, René Vallery-Radot, p.39.
2. *ibid*, pp.101–2.

circle of Academicians, Pasteur returned to Lille and to his study of fermentations.

In spite of the work done by Cagniard de Latour, Schwann and others, the idea was prevalent that animal and vegetable matters are able to alter spontaneously, while the authority of the famous German chemist Liebig carried weight when he asserted that yeast induces fermentation by virtue of progressive alteration in water in contact with air.[1] Another German named Ludersdorff, so we learn from Béchamp,[2] had undertaken experiments to prove that yeast ferments sugar because it is living and organised. An account had been published in the fourth volume of the *Traite de Chimie Organique*, which appeared in 1856.

Now let us examine Pasteur's contribution towards this subject the following year, since at that date popular teaching assigns to him a thorough explanation of fermentation.

During 1857, Pasteur left Lille to work at the *Ecole Normale* in Paris; but we are not here concerned with his movements, but simply with what he had to reveal on the subject of fermentation.

His son-in-law tells us[3] that it was in August 1857, after experimenting in particular with sour milk, that Pasteur first made a submission on *Lactic Fermentation* to the Scientific Society of Lille. Be this as it may, we find his extract from a memoir on the subject in the *Comptes Rendus* of the French Academy of Science, 30th November, 1857.[4] The entire memoir was printed in April 1858 in the *Annales de Chimie et de Physique*,[5] and from this latter we gain full details.

The experiment consisted of Pasteur taking the substance developed in ordinary fermentation, nourished by sugar, chalk, casein or fibrin, and gluten (an organic matter occurring in cereals) and placing it in yeast broth (a complex solution of albuminoid and mineral matters), in which he had dissolved some sugar and added some chalk.

There was nothing new in the procedure, as Béchamp points out;[6] it was the same experiment that Liebig had undertaken some sixteen or seventeen years previously. However, unlike Liebig, he did not ignore microscopic examination, and so made observations that had been missed by the German chemist. Thus Pasteur is able to tell us that a

---

1. *Traite de Chimie Organique,* traduit par Ch. Gerhardt, Introduction, p.27. 1840.
2. *Les Grands Problémes Medicaux*, A. Béchamp, p.62.
3. *The Life of Pasteur*, p.83.
4. *Comptes Rendus* 45, p.913. *Memoire sur la fermentation appelee lactique.*
5. *Annales de Chimie et de Physique, 3e serie*, 52, p.404.
6. *Les Grands Problémes Medicaux*, p.56.

lactic ferment is obtained which, under the microscope, has the appearance of little globules, which he named 'lactic yeast', no doubt because of their resemblance to yeast, although in this case the little globules are much smaller. In short, he saw the minute organism known today to be the cause of lactic acid fermentation.

Now let us go on to his remarkable explanation of the phenomenon. He tells us that it is not necessary to introduce the lactic ferment in order to prepare it, as

"it takes birth spontaneously, as easily as beer yeast every time
that the conditions are favourable."[1]

This assertion surely demonstrates Pasteur's belief in the spontaneous generation both of beer-yeast and of that which he called 'lactic yeast'. It remains to be seen what the 'favourable conditions' are, according to his teaching. He tells us before long:

"These globules of lactic yeast take birth spontaneously in the
body of the albuminoid liquid furnished by the soluble part
of the (beer) yeast."[2]

There is certainly nothing in this to overthrow the general belief in spontaneous generation. But, in fairness, we must not overlook a note that he added to the full edition of his memoir, as we find it in the *Annales de Chimie et de Physique*.[3] Before this account appeared in April 1858, Professor Béchamp, as we shall find, had provided the French Academy of Science with an illuminating explanation of the origin of ferments. In the face of Béchamp's irrefutable views, Pasteur may have thought it only wise to add a proviso to a memoir that from start to finish has no solution whatever to offer as to the appearance of moulds except as a spontaneous origin.

Therefore, by the sentence 'it (lactic yeast) takes birth spontaneously as easily as beer yeast' we see a star and, looking below, find a footnote in which he says he uses the word 'spontaneously' as 'the expression of a fact', but reserves the question of spontaneous generation.[4] Certainly any denial of it is completely excluded from this memoir, with its assertion of the spontaneous appearance of beer yeast and 'lactic yeast'.

---

1. *"elle prend naissance spontanement avec autant de facilite que la levure de biere toutes les jois que les conditions sont favorables."* A. de Ch. et Ph. 3e serie, 52, p.413.

2. *"Les globules prennent naissance spontaniment au sein du liquide albuminoid fourni par la partie soluble de la levure."* A. de Ch. et de Ph. 3e serie, 52, p. 415.

3. *Annales de Chimie et de Physique* 3e serie, 52, p.413.

4. *"Je me sers de ce mot comme expression du fait, en reservant completement la question de la generation spontanee."*

Where Pasteur differed from other Sponteparists was in omitting to attempt any explanation of such a marvel.

His followers, ignoring the confusion of his views, have seized upon the concluding statement in this same memoir as a triumphant vindication of the correctness of his teaching, since he said:

> "Fermentation shows itself to be correlative of life, of the organisation of globules, not of the death and putrefaction of these globules; still more that it does not appear as a phenomenon of contact."[1]

But this was only what others had said and had gone some way to prove years before him. So devoid was he of proof that he had to make the following admission in regard to his hypothesis that 'the new yeast is organised, that it is a living being', namely:

> "If anyone tells me that in these conclusions I am going beyond facts, I reply that this is true, in the sense that I frankly associate myself with an order of ideas[2] that, to speak correctly, cannot be irrefutably demonstrated."

We have therefore in Pasteur's own words his confession of his non-comprehension of a problem that the experiments of Professor Béchamp, had already, as we shall shortly see, solved with an irrefutable demonstration. The reason why Pasteur should get the credit for demonstrating that which he admitted he could not demonstrate is as much a puzzle to anyone insisting on historical accuracy as was, apparently, the phenomenon of fermentation to Pasteur.

However, we will not deny ourselves a thorough examination of his work, and so let us now consider his *Memoir on Alcoholic Fermentation*, of which his son-in-law, M. Vallery-Radot, tells us[3] that Pasteur said:

> "The results of these labours (on lactic and alcoholic fermentation) should be put on the same lines, for they explain and complete each other."

We find the author's extract from this latter memoir among the reports of the French Academy of Science of 21st December, 1857.[4]

Pasteur's procedure in this experiment was as follows: he took two equal quantities of fresh yeast, washed in water. One was left to ferment with pure sugared water; and after having extracted from the other all

---

1. *ibid.*, p.418.
2. *Annales de Chimie et de Physique,* 3e serie, 52, p.417.
3. *The Life of Pasteur*, p.85.
4. *Comptes Rendus*, 45, p.1032.

its soluble part by boiling it with plenty of water and filtering it to get rid of the globules, he added to the limpid liquor as much sugar as he used in the first fermentation and then a trace of fresh yeast.

He expressed his conclusions as follows:

> "I am just establishing that in beer yeast it is not the globules that play the principal part, but the conversion into globules of their soluble part; because I prove that one can suppress the globules that are formed and the total effect on the sugar remains sensibly the same. Thus certainly, it matters little if one suppresses them by means of filtration with the separation of their soluble part, or if one kills them by a temperature of 100° and leaves them mixed with this soluble part."[1]

In view of the fact that he was supposed to be discussing the hypothesis that yeast is organised and living, there was so much that was extraordinary in this that he pauses to reply to inevitable criticism.

> "But how, it will be asked, can the fermentation of sugar take place when yeast is used that is heated to 100°, if it is due to the organisation of the soluble part of the globules and these have been paralysed by a temperature of 100°? Fermentation then takes place as it does in a natural sugared liquid, juice of the grape, of sugar cane, etc., that is to say, *spontaneously*..."

Here is seen the prevalent idea of spontaneous alteration, though Pasteur goes on to state that...

> "in all cases, even those *most liable in appearance* to drive us from belief in the influence of organisation in the phenomena of fermentation, the chemical act that characterises them is always correlative to a formation of globules."

His final conclusions are held up for admiration:

> "The splitting of sugar into alcohol and carbonic acid is an act correlative of a vital phenomenon, of an organisation of globules, an organisation in which sugar plays a direct part by furnishing a portion of the elements of the substance of these globules."

---

1. *Comptes Rendus*, 45, p.1034. "Je viens d'etablir que dans la levure de biere, ce ne sont point les globules qui jouent le principal role mais 'la mise en globules de leur partie soluble; car je prouve que l'on peut supprimer les globules formes, et l'effet total sur le sucre est sensiblement le meme. Or, assurement, il importe peu qu'on les supprime de fait par une filtration avec separation de leur partie soluble ou qu'on les tue par une temperature de 100 degres en les laissant meles a cette partie soluble."

But, far from understanding this process, we find that Pasteur admits three years later, in 1860:

> "Now in what does this chemical act of decomposition, of the alteration of sugar consist? What is its cause? I confess that I am entirely ignorant of it."

In any case, the critical mind inquires at once: How can fermentation be explained as a vital act by the operation of a dead organism; or by the conversion into globules of its soluble part – whatever that may mean – or by spontaneous alteration? No wonder that Béchamp comments:[1]

> "Pasteur's experiments were so haphazard that he, who acknowledged with Cagniard de Latour the fact of the organisation and life of yeast, *boiled* this living being to study its soluble part!"

Indeed, Béchamp's account of Liebig's and Pasteur's closely allied work is well worth perusal in pages 56–65 of *Les Grands Problémes Médicaux*.

The chief point to be noted is that as Pasteur made use for these experiments of substances with life in them, such as yeast broth, etc., they could not, in any case, furnish evidence as to the foremost question at stake; namely, whether life could ever arise in a purely chemical medium. That problem was never so much as touched upon by Pasteur in 1857. If we had only his explanation of fermentation, made during that year, we should indeed have a strange idea of the phenomenon. We should believe in the spontaneous generation of alcoholic, lactic and other ferments. We should be puzzled to understand how fermentation could be a vital act and yet be effected by dead organisms. Of the air-borne origin of ferments we should not have an inkling, that is, as far as Pasteur was concerned, for either he was ignorant of, or else he ignored the truth already propounded by others, particularly by Schwann, the German. Pasteur passed over with slight allusion the contacts with air that were involved in his experiments, because his aim was to disprove Liebig's theory that the alteration of yeast broth was due to an oxidation by air, and he seems to have had no idea of the important part that air might play, although for a very different reason from the one imagined by Liebig.

Clearly, in 1857 Pasteur was a Sponteparist, without, however, shedding light upon the controversy. The housewife, puzzled by the

1. *Les Grands Problémes Médicaux*, p.60.

souring of milk, could have learned from him only that living globules had put in a spontaneous appearance; the same explanation that had been generally accepted many years earlier to account for the maggots found in bad meat – until it had occurred to the Italian, Francesco Redi, to keep flies from contact.

Here the reader may interpolate that Pasteur's vision, although still obscured, was gradually piercing the fogs of the mystery. But, as it happened, those fogs were by this time entirely dispersed in other quarters: Béchamp's 'Beacon Experiment' had already shed much light on the difficulty.

In 1855 and in 1857 there had been presented to the French Academy of Science memoirs that were to become the lode-star of future science, and it seems high time that now, nearly a century afterwards, credit should be given where credit is due in regard to them.

And here let us turn to the outcome of work undertaken in a quiet laboratory by one who, perhaps unfortunately for the world, was no adept in the arts of politics or advertisement and was too much immersed in his discoveries to be at that time concerned about his proprietary rights to them.

Let us again open the old French documents and see for ourselves what Professor Antoine Béchamp had to say on the subject of fermentation.

4.
Béchamp's 'Beacon Experiment'

We may recall that it was in the Alsatian capital, Strasbourg, that Professor Béchamp achieved his first scientific triumphs, to which we have already alluded. It was there, during the course of his chemical studies, that the idea occurred to him to put the popular belief in the spontaneous alteration of cane sugar into grape sugar[1] to the test.

In those days, organic matter derived from living bodies, whether vegetable or animal, was looked upon as being dead and, according to the views held at that time, therefore liable to spontaneous alteration.

This was the belief that Pasteur combated in the way that we have already criticised. Béchamp was before him in attacking the problem by methods obviously more rigid and with results that we think will now appear to be considerably more illuminating.

An experiment upon starch made Béchamp doubt the truth of the popular theory that cane sugar dissolved in water was spontaneously transformed at an ordinary temperature into invert sugar, which is a mixture of equal parts of glucose and fructose, the change being technically known as the *inversion of sugar*. Here was a puzzle that needed investigation, and in addressing this mystery, the Professor had no idea of the consequences that were to ensue.

In May 1854, he started a series of observations to which he later gave the name of *Expérience Maitresse*, and finally called his *Beacon Experiment*. It was on 16th May 1854 that the first of the series was commenced in the laboratory of the School of Pharmacy in Strasbourg. The experiment was concluded on 3rd February, 1855.

In this experiment, perfectly pure cane sugar was dissolved in distilled water in a glass bottle with an airtight stopper but containing a little air. This was left on the laboratory table at ordinary temperature and in diffused light.

At the same time, control experiments were prepared. These consisted of solutions of distilled water and cane sugar, to one of which was added a little zinc chloride and to the others a little calcium chloride; in each one a small amount of air was left, just as in the

---

1. See note to p.186.

bottle containing the first, or test, solution. These bottles were stoppered in the same way as the first, and all were left alongside each other in the laboratory.

In the course of some months, the cane sugar in the distilled water was partially transformed into grape sugar, and the polarimeter showed that alteration had taken place in the medium, since there was a change in the angle of rotation. In short, an alteration had taken place, but possibly not spontaneously, for on 15th June moulds had put in an appearance, and from that date alteration progressed much more rapidly. The following table is a brief summary of the results of Béchamp's experiments.

	Rotation						
Solvent	May 16 1854	May 17 1854	May 20 1854	June 15 1854	Aug. 20 1854	Feb. 3 1855	Remarks
Distilled water	23.88°	23.17°	22.85°	22.39°*	17.28°	7.80°	*Moulds appeared but did not greatly increase.
25% solution of Chloride of Zinc.	22.32°	22.20°	22.10°*	22.14°	22.27°	22.28°	*The solution began to get cloudy. Later there was found a slight deposit of Oxy-Chloride of Zinc.
A solution of Calcium Chloride containing an amount of Calcium Chloride equivalent to the Chloride of Zinc.[2]	22.34°	22.13°	22.17°	22.25°	22.22°	22.29°	No moulds appeared.
25% solution of Calcium Chloride.	22.34°	22.15°	22.10°	22.08°	22.14°	22.28°	No moulds Appeared.

Table 1 – Béchamp's Beacon Experiment[1]

Béchamp prepared solutions of cane sugar:16.365g in 100cc of various solvents, and polarised each of these solutions several times at varying intervals, obtaining certain variations in the angle of rotation.

---

1. *Les Microzymas*, p.48.
2. The original is 'Solution de chlorure de calcium equivalente au poids du chlorure de zinc'. From this it is inferred that the concentration of $CaCl_2$ was molecularly equivalent,

   i.e. $25\% \times \dfrac{\text{molecular weight of } CaCl_2}{\text{molecular weight of } ZnCl_2}$ i.e. $25\% \times \dfrac{111.0}{136.3} = 20\%$

Professor Béchamp took particular note of the moulds, and found it significant that none had appeared in the solutions to which he had added zinc chloride and calcium chloride; moreover, that the change in rotation in these had been almost negligible, or, as he put it:

"The plane of polarisation underwent no change other than accidental variations."[1]

Béchamp published this experiment in the report of the French Academy of Science on 19th February, 1855.[2] He mentioned the moulds, without attempting to explain their appearance. He reserved their further consideration for future experiments, feeling it important to find the explanation as a probable clue to the cause of what had up to that time been regarded as evidence of spontaneous generation. He was also anxious to discover what was the chemical mechanism of the alteration of sugar, and why a change had not been effected in the solutions to which the chlorides had been added.

Meanwhile another observer, M. Maumené, was also experimenting, and though Béchamp disagreed with his conclusions he was much struck by the observations that were presented to the Academy of Science on 7th April, 1856, and published in the *Annales de Chimie et de Physique* in September 1856.[3]

Maumené's experiments were also concerned with polarimetric measurements. The following table sumarises his principal results:

Variety of sugar 16.35 gr. in 100cc of solution	Initial rotation in 200mm tube, January 4th, 1854	Rotation at the end of 9 months in 200mm tube	Remarks
White candy	+100.0°	+22.0°	Slight mould
Another sample	+100.0°	+23.0°	Idem.
Loaf sugar	+98.5°	+31.5°	Mould a little larger.
Another sample	+96.5°	+88.0°	Slight mould.

Table 2 – **Experiment by M. Maumené**[4]

Béchamp here saw his own observations borne out. On pages 50 and 51 of *Les Microzymas* he tells us the two questions that had arisen in his mind through his own and Maumené's experiments:

Are moulds endowed with chemical activity? and
What is the origin of the moulds that appear in sugared water?

---

1. *Les Microzymas*, A. Béchamp, p.48.
2. *Comptes Rendus* 40, p.436.
3. *Annales de Chimie et de Physique,* 3e serie, 48, p.23.
4. *Les Microzymas*, A. Béchamp, p.50.

With a view to finding an answer to these questions, he commenced at Strasbourg on 25th June, 1856, a fresh series of experiments that were completed at Montpellier on 5th December, 1857. Thus it was during the course of this work that he left Strasbourg to continue his career at the famous southern university.

The following table shows his new observations:

Solvent	Rotation of the Plane of Polarisation						Remarks
	June 25 1856	July 13 1856	Nov. 26 1856	Mar. 19 1857	July 13 1857	Dec. 5 1857	
Pure water	+22.03°	+21.89°	+16.6°	+15.84°	+10.3°	+1.5°	Nov. 26 – a slight flocculent deposit, gradually becoming a bulky mould.
Very pure, arsenious acid, very little	+22.04°	+21.65°	+12.24°	+10.8°	+7.2°	+0.7°	Mould on Nov. 26 which increased and became more abundant than in solution of sugar alone.
Mercuric chloride, very little	+22.03°	+22.0°	+21.9°	+22.03°	+22.04°	+22.1°	Liquid remains transparent.
Pure water, creosoted, one drop.	+22.03°	+22.0°	+22.1°	+22.2°	+22.2°	+22.2°	Idem.
Sulphate of zinc	+22.04°	–	–3.12°	–	–7.2°	–	Idem.
Sulphate of aluminium	+22.02°	–	–8.7°	–	–	–	Nov. 26 large green mould.
Nitrate of Potassium	+22.05°	+21.6°	+3.0°	–	–	–	Enormous quantity of moulds developed Nov. 26.
Nitrate of zinc	+22.01°	+22.0°	+22.1°	–	+22.0°	+22.2°	Liquid limpid.
Phosphate of sodium	+20.23°	+19.16°	–9.7°	–	–	–	Nov. 22 a bulky mould.
Carbonate of potassium	+20.0°	+20.0°	+20.0°	–	+20.3°	–	Liquid remains limpid.
Oxalate of potassium	+22.0°	+20.34°	+10.5°	–	–	–0.2°	Red moulds.

Table 3 – Béchamp's Beacon Experiment[1]

15.1 gm. of cane sugar dissolved in 100cc of water either with or without the addition of certain chemical substances.

---

1. *Les Microzymas*, p.52.

The results clearly demonstrated the varying effects of different salts upon the medium, which Béchamp himself has pointed out in the second chapter of *Les Microzymas*.

As also shown by the earlier experiment, zinc chloride and calcium chloride prevented the alteration of cane sugar; and a very small quantity of creosote, or of mercuric chloride, had the same preventive influence.

This was not the case with arsenious acid when present in very small proportion, or with certain other salts, which did not hamper the appearing of moulds and the alteration of the cane sugar. Indeed, some of the salts seemed to stimulate the advent of moulds; while, on the contrary, creosote, which has only since the date of these experiments been distinguished from carbolic acid, was particularly effective in the prevention of moulds and of alteration in the sugar.

With his characteristic precision, Professor Béchamp determined to investigate thoroughly the role of creosote, and with this aim in view started on 27th March, 1857 another series of experiments, which he also continued up to 5th December of the same year.

His account of the procedure followed in these experiments is as follows:

> "I prepared several sugared solutions according to the technique of the anti-heterogenists; that is to say, the water used was boiled and cooled in such a manner that air could enter only after passing through tubes containing sulphuric acid.
>
> This water dissolved the sugar very rapidly, and several jars were completely filled with the carefully filtered solution, so as to leave no air in them. Another part of the solution, having no creosote added to it, was poured into jars in contact with a considerable quantity of common air, without any care other than that of cleanliness. One of the jars contained also some arsenious acid.
>
> One jar of the creosoted solution and one without creosote were set apart, not to be opened throughout the whole course of the experiment."[1]

---

1. *Les Microzymas*, A. Béchamp, p.53.

The following table gives a summary of the observations:

Rotation of the Plane of Polarisation							
			1857				
Solvent	Mar. 27	April 30	May 30	June 30	July 30	Dec. 5	Observations
Solution not creosoted No. 1	+24°	+24°	+24°	+23°	—	+19.68°	Whitish flocula carpeted the bottom of the flasks.
No. 2	+24°	+24°	+22.8°	+21.6°	—	+15.6°	In flask No. 2 the flocula became more abundant; June 30, without filtering, one drop of creosote was added; this addition did not prevent the further progress of the inversion.
No. 3	+24°	—	+24°	—	—	—	
No. 4	+24°	—	—	+24°	+24°	—	
No. 5	+24°	—	—	—	—	+24°	
Creosoted solutions No. 1a	+24°	+24°	+24°	+24°	+24°	+24°	
No. 2a	+24°	—	+24°	+24°	+24°	+24°	
No. 3a	+24°	—	—	+24°	+24°	+24°	
No. 4a	+24°	—	—	—	+24°	+24°	
No. 5a	+24°	—	—	—	—	+24°	
Creosoted arsinated solution	+24	+24°	—	+24°	+24°	+24°	

Table 4 – Béchamp's Beacon Experiment[1]
16.365 gm of cane sugar in 100cc.

Béchamp has himself explained the results. Flasks 1 and 2 lost a little liquid during manipulation, and thus were not completely filled. Consequently, air came into contact with the solutions they held, and, in these, moulds appeared and alteration in the medium ensued, the dates differing in the two cases and the variation proving more rapid in the flask where the moulds were the more abundant.

On the contrary, the sugared water kept free from contact with air during the eight months of observation underwent no change, despite the warm climate of Montpellier during the months of June, July, August and September. This was noteworthy, for there was nothing to prevent

---

1. *Les Microzymas*, p.54.

the action of the water, had spontaneous alteration been nature's method, which was the then prevalent opinion. Furthermore, although the creosated solutions were in contact with air from the start, and these particular flasks were left open, they underwent no variation and showed no trace of moulds, not even the solution to which arsenious acid had been added.

Finally, to return to solution No. 2, moulds appeared before 30th May, with evidence on that date of a diminution of the rotation, which continued to decline, in spite of the fact that on 30th June one drop of creosote was added.

Béchamp tells us in the preface to *The Blood* that these different observations impressed him in the same way as the swing of the cathedral lamp had impressed Galileo in the sixteenth century.

At the time, it was commonly believed that fermentation could not take place except in the presence of albuminoid matter. We have already seen that Pasteur operated with yeast broth, a complex albuminoid solution.

In the media prepared by Béchamp there were, on the contrary, no albuminoid substances. He had operated with carefully distilled water and pure cane sugar, which, so he tells us, when heated with fresh-slaked lime, did not disengage ammonia. Yet moulds, obviously living organisms and thus necessarily containing albuminoid matter, had appeared in his chemical solutions.

He was awestruck by his discovery, his intellect already affording him hints of all it portended. Had he been Pasteur, the country would have rung with the news of it; he would have described the facts by letter to all his acquaintances. Instead, being Béchamp, without a thought of self, his only anxiety was to start new experiments, and consider fresh revelations.

He recorded the results of his observations in a memoir which he sent up immediately, in December 1857, to the Academy of Science, which published an extract of it among its reports of 4th January, 1858.[1] The full publication of this all-important document was deferred, for some unknown reason, for eight months, when it appeared in September 1858 in the *Annale de Chimie et de Physique*.[2]

The title of the memoir was *On the Influence that Water, either Pure or Charged with Various Salts, Exercises in the Cold upon Cane Sugar*.

---

1. *Comptes Rendus* 46, p.44.
2. *Annale de Chimie et de Physique,* 3e serie, 54, p.28.

Béchamp comments:

"By its title, the memoir was a work of pure chemistry, which had at first no other object than to determine whether or not pure cold water could invert cane sugar, and if, further, the salts had any influence on the inversion; but soon the question, as I had foreseen, became complicated; it became at once physiological and dependent upon the phenomena of fermentation and the question of spontaneous generation – thus, from the study of a simple chemical fact, I was led to investigate in turn the causes of fermentation, the nature and origin of ferments."[1]

The overall result of the experiments was to confirm that

"Cold water modifies cane sugar only in proportion to the development of moulds, these elementary vegetations then acting as ferments."[2]

Here at one stroke was felled the theory of alteration through the action of water; the change known as fermentation being declared to be due to the growth of living organisms.

Furthermore, it was proved that:

"moulds do not develop when there is no contact with air and that no change then takes place in the rotary power,"

and also that:

"the solutions that had come into contact with air varied in proportion to the development of moulds."

The necessity of the presence of these living organisms for the processes of fermentation was thus shown clearly. Béchamp further explained the action of moulds:

"They act after the manner of ferments. Whence comes the ferment?"

In these solutions there existed no albuminoid sustance; they were made with pure cane sugar, which, heated with fresh-slaked lime, does not give off ammonia. It thus appears evident that airborne germs found the sugared solution a favourable medium for their development, and it must be deduced that *the ferment is produced by the generation of fungi.*"

---

1. *Les Microzymas*, A. Béchamp, p.55.
2. *Comptes Rendus*, 46, p.44.

Here, in direct contradiction to Pasteur's account of the spontaneous origin of beer yeast and other organisms, Béchamp gave proof of Schwann's concept of airborne germs, and further specified yeast to be of the order of fungi.

Remarkable though such a clear pronouncement was at a date when scientific ideas were in chaotic confusion, Béchamp went much further in his observations. He stated:

> "The matter that develops in the sugared water sometimes presents itself in the form of little isolated bodies, and sometimes as voluminous colourless membranes which come out in one mass from the flasks. These membranes, heated with caustic potash, give off ammonia in abundance."

Here he noted the diversity of the organisms of these moulds, an observation that was to result in a deep insight into cellular life and his foundation of a first proper understanding of cytology.

He had a further definite explanation to make on the action of moulds, namely:

> "The transformation that cane sugar undergoes in the presence of moulds may be compared with that produced upon starch by diastase."

This particular conclusion, he tells us,[1] had an enormous bearing on the subject, and was such a novel idea at that epoch that Pasteur, even later, ignored and denied it.

Béchamp further explained that:

> "...cold water does not act upon cane sugar, except when moulds are able to develop in it; in other words, the transformation is due to a true fermentation and to the development of an acid that is consecutive to the appearance of the ferment."

So, it was by the acids engendered by the moulds that he explained the process of fermentation. He drew many more conclusions from the effects of various salts upon the solutions.

Had Lord Lister only followed Béchamp's teaching instead of Pasteur's, the former might have been spared his subsequent honest recantation of his invention, the carbolic spray, which proved fatal to so many patients.

---

1. *Les Microzymas*, A. Béchamp, p.57.

Béchamp taught that:

> "...creosote, in preventing the development of moulds, also checks the transformation of cane sugar."

Also:

> "...creosote, with or without prolonged contact with air, prevents at one and the same time the formation of moulds and the transformation of cane sugar. But from observation, it appears that once the moulds are formed, creosote does not prevent their action."

Drawing more conclusions from the effects of different salts, he stated:

> "The influence of saline solutions is variable, not only according to the sort or kind of salt, but moreover according to the degree of saturation and neutrality of these salts. The salts that prevent the transformation of cane sugar into glucose (grape sugar) are generally the salts reputed to be antiseptic. In all cases, a certain minimum temperature is necessary for the transformation to take place."

Thus we see that in 1857, when fermentation was such a complete mystery that Pasteur, operating with albuminoid matters, including dead yeast, looked upon this yeast and other organisms as products of spontaneous generation, Béchamp had dispelled all uncertainty on the subject.

To summarise, he taught:

1) that cane sugar was a proximate principle unalterable by solution in water.

2) that the air had in itself no effect upon it, but that owing to its importation of living organisms, the apparent effect of air was all-important.

3) that these organisms, insoluble themselves, brought about the process of fermentation by means of the acids they generated; these acids were regarded as the soluble ferments.

4) that the way to prevent the invasion of organisms in the sugared solution was by first slightly creosoting the medium; but if the organisms had appeared *before* creosote was added, he showed that its subsequent addition would have no power to arrest their development and the consequent inversion of the sugar.

For further revelations we cannot do better than quote these paragraphs from Béchamp's own summary of his discovery in the preface to *Le Sang (The Blood)*.[1] There he writes:

> "It resulted that the soluble ferment was allied to the insoluble by the reaction of product to producer; the soluble ferment being unable to exist without the organised ferment, which is necessarily insoluble.
>
> Further, as the soluble ferment and the albuminoid matter, being nitrogenous, could only be formed by obtaining the nitrogen from the limited volume of air left in the flasks, it was at the same time demonstrated that the free nitrogen of the air could help directly in the synthesis of the nitrogenous substance of plants; which up to that time had been a disputed question.[2]
>
> Thus it became evident that since the material forming the structure of moulds and yeasts was elaborated within the organism, it must also be true that the soluble ferments and products of fermentation are also secreted there, as was the case with the soluble ferment that inverted the cane sugar. Hence I became assured that that which is called fermentation is, in reality, the phenomenon of nutrition, assimilation, disassimilation, and excretion of the products disassimilated."[3]

Thus we see how clear and complete was Béchamp's explanation of fermentation as long ago as the year 1857. He showed it to be due to the life processes of living organisms so minute as to require a microscope to render them visible, and in the case of his sugared solutions, he proved them to be airborne. Not only was he clearly the first to solve the problem; his initial discovery was also to lead him a great deal farther, unfortunately far beyond the understanding of those who, lacking his understanding, became obsessed with the idea of atmospheric organisms.

But before we proceed to delve deeper into Béchamp's teachings, let us pause and return to Pasteur, and see how his work was affected by the great beacon with which his rival had illumined science.

---

1. p.16.
2. It is now considered that atmospheric nitrogen can only be utilised by a few special plants (natural order: Luguminosae) and then under special conditions.
3. In modern phraseology, these processes are known as nutrition, constructive metabolism, destructive metabolism and the excretion of the waste products of the last named process.

Who proved fermentation in a chemical medium to be due to airborne living organisms – Béchamp or Pasteur?

Béchamp	Pasteur
1855[1] and 1857[2]	*1857 – Lactic fermentation[3]*
Experiments upon perfectly pure cane sugar in distilled water, with or without the addition of different salts, (air in some cases excluded, in others admitted).	Experiment with ferment obtained from a medium of sugar, chalk, caseine or fibrin and gluten, and sown in yeast broth, in which sugar had been dissolved with the addition of chalk.

Béchamp — Conclusions

Conclusions

1) That the inversion of cane-sugar is due to moulds, which are living organisms, imported by the air, and whose influence upon cane sugar may be compared with that exercised upon starch by diastase.

2) That creosote prevents the invasion of moulds, though it does not check their development when once established.

Corollary

That here was the first clear explanation and proof of the mystery of fermentation, and the basic foundation of the knowledge of antiseptics.

Pasteur — Conclusions

Conclusions

A lactic ferment takes birth spontaneously, as easily as beer-yeast, in the body of the albuminoid liquid furnished by the soluble part of the yeast. The lactic ferment is a living being, though this conclusion is among an order of things that *cannot be irrefutably demonstrated.*

Alcoholic Fermentation[4]

Experiment with two equal quantities of fresh yeast washed in water. One was left to ferment with pure sugared water, and after extracting from the other all its soluble part by boiling it with plenty of water and filtering it to get rid of the globules, as much sugar was added in the first fermentation, and then a trace of fresh yeast.

Conclusions

In beer yeast it is not the globules that play the principal part, but the conversion into globules of their soluble part, since the globules may be killed by a temperature of 100° when fermentation takes place spontaneously. The splitting of sugar into alcohol and into carbonic acid is an act correlative of a vital phenomenon.

Corollary

The albuminoid substances used in these experiments nullified the attempt to probe the mystery of changes in a purely chemical medium. The origin of the ferments was said to be spontaneous, and while fermentation was declared to be a vital act, dead yeast was used, and the conclusions in general were pronounced to be beyond the power of proof.

---

1. *Comptes Rendus* 40, p.436.
2. *C. R.* 46, p.44. See also *Annales de Chimie et de Physique*, 3e série, 54, p.28.
3. *Comptes Rendus* 45, p.913.
4. *ibid.*, 45, p.1032. See also *Annales de Chimie et de Physique*, 3e série, 52, p.404.

5.
Claims and Contradictions

Professor Béchamp's series of observations – which indeed seem to merit the name of *Beacon Experiment* – clearly demonstrated the possibility of the appearance of ferments in a medium devoid of albuminoid matter.

As this fact had been disbelieved until then, it is evident that Béchamp was the first to establish it. We can search through the old scientific records and fail to find any such demonstration by anyone.

We can read for ourselves that Pasteur's procedure in 1857 was entirely different. Influenced by the prevalent belief, what he did, as we have already seen, was to take the ferment developed in an ordinary fermentation and sow it in yeast broth, a complex solution of albuminoid and mineral matters. Thus he obtained what he called his lactic fermentation. Neither does he seem to have been entirely successful in his deductions from his observations. He announced that the lactic globules:

> "...take birth spontaneously in the body of the albuminoid liquid furnished by the soluble part of the yeast,"

and also that:

> "...they take birth spontaneously with as much facility as beer yeast."

There can be no question of the contrast between these sponteparist views of Pasteur's and the clear, simple explanation of Béchamp. No conscientious reader can compare the two workers' original documents without being struck by their disparity.

Where Pasteur's work was more allied to Béchamp's was in an experiment recorded among the reports of the French Academy of Science in February 1859, more than a year after the publication of Béchamp's *Beacon Experiment*. So certainly, from the point of date alone, it in no way repudiates Béchamp's claim to priority in clearly explaining fermentation; indeed, it seems to have been inspired by the Professor's observations, for we find that Pasteur here *omitted to use yeast broth as his medium and ascribed the origin of lactic yeast to the atmospheric air.*

According to his own details[1] he mixed with pure sugared water a small quantity of salt of ammonia, phosphates and precipitated carbonate of lime, and actually expressed surprise that animal and vegetable matter should have appeared in such an environment. There could hardly be a greater contrast to Béchamp's rigorous deductions, while an extraordinary ambiguity follows in the conclusions. We read:

> "As to the origin of the lactic yeast in these experiments, it is solely due to the atmospheric air; we fall back here upon facts of spontaneous generation."

After asserting that by suppressing all contact with ordinary air, or by boiling the solution, the formation of organisms and fermentation are quite prevented, he winds up:

> "On this point, the question of spontaneous generation has made progress."

If he meant here that the question had progressed toward the denial of the belief, why was it that he did not say so?

In a subsequent memoir published in the *Annales de Chimie et de Physique*[2] in April 1860, he constantly refers to the spontaneous production of yeasts and fermentations. Anyone really aware of the atmospheric origin of micro-organisms of the nature of yeast would undoubtedly have steered clear of phraseology that, at that particular time, conveyed such a diametrically opposite signification.

The many experiments detailed in this latter memoir were only commenced on 10th December, 1858, whereas Béchamp first presented his *Beacon Experiment* to the Academy of Science in December 1857, and its full publication appeared in September 1858, three months before Pasteur started his new experiments. He was, undoubtedly, inspired by Béchamp in this new work, which he claimed illumined 'with a new day the phenomena of fermentation'.

Béchamp's criticism of it may be found in the preface to his book *The Blood*. There he explains that the formation of lactic acid, following upon the original alcoholic fermentation, was due to an invasion by atmospheric germs, in this case lactic yeast, their subsequent increase resulting in the starvation of the beer-yeast, which had been included at the start of the experiment. He maintains that Pasteur's deductions prove his lack of real comprehension of:

---

1. *Comptus Rendus* 48, p.337.
2. 3e série, 57-58, pp.323 to 426 inclusive, esp. from pp.283 to 392.

> "the chemical and physiological phenomena of transformation, called fermentation, which are processes of nutrition, that is to say, of digestion, followed by absorption, assimilation, excretion, etc..."

and his lack of understanding of the living organism and how it would:

> "...at last reproduce itself if all conditions dependent upon nutrition are fulfilled."[1]

Over and above Béchamp's scientific criticism of this memoir, any critic must be struck by the inexactitude of Pasteur's descriptions. For example, if we turn to the third section, we find that for these observations Pasteur's medium included the ashes of yeast and that he makes mention of the addition of fresh yeast. Yet in the title of one such experiment, he gives the following misleading description:

> "Production of yeast in a medium formed of sugar, a salt of ammonia, and phosphates."[2]

All reference to the original inclusion of yeast, admitted on p.383, is omitted in the above heading and in the final summary:

> "All these results, though the majority were obtained by acting upon very small quantities, establish the production of alcoholic and lactic yeast and of special fermentations corresponding to them, in a medium *formed only* of sugar, a salt of ammonia and of mineral elements."[3]

The actual medium, mentioned only two pages beforehand, consisted of:

> "10 grammes of sugar.
> 100 cubic centimetres of water.
> 0.1 gm of ammonium tartrate.
> The ash from 1 gm of beer-yeast.
> Traces of *fresh yeast*, the size of a pin's head."[4]

Altogether, it is clear that even by 1860 Pasteur had no clear teaching to put forward such as that contained in Béchamp's epoch-making observations.

And here we have an illuminating view of the characters of the two men. Béchamp could not but be aware that his knowledge exceeded

---

1. *Le Sang*, A. Béchamp, preface, p.41.
2. *Annales de Chimie et de Physique*, 3e serie, 57-58, p.381.
3. *ibid*, p.392.
4. *ibid*, p.390.

that of Pasteur, yet all the same, in his lectures to students, we find nothing but courteous allusions to his rivals.

We need only refer to the Professor's *Lessons on Vinous Fermentation*, a work published in 1863, before his actual demonstration in explanation of the phenomenon. In this book are Béchamp's views, which he was careful always to carry into practice, on the subject of giving honour where honour is due in scientific revelations.

> "One can only have either *inspired* ideas or *communicated* ideas, and it is by working upon one and the other that new ones are conceived. That is why a seeker after truth should give credit to the ideas of those who preceded him in his work, because those, great or small, had to make their effort, and herein lies their merit, to bring their share of truth to the world. I cannot conceive of a superior title than this of proprietary right, because it is this that constitutes our personality and often genius, if it be true that this sublime prerogative, this rare privilege, is nothing but a long patience, fecundated by the spark God has set in us. This right must be respected all the more, in that it is of the nature of the only riches, the only property, that we can lavish without impoverishing ourselves. It is in thus spending it that we enrich ourselves more and more." [1]

Unfortunately we find a great contrast in Pasteur, who, from the start – according to the old records – repeatedly arrogated to himself the discoveries of Béchamp, beginning with those of 1857.

The *Beacon Experiment* had flashed illumination into the darkness of sponteparist views at a time when the controversy on spontaneous generation was destined to flare up.

At the end of December 1858, M. Pouchet, Director of the Natural History Museum of Rouen, sent up to the Academy of Science a memoir entitled *A Note on Vegetable and Animal Proto-Organisms Spontaneously Generated in Artificial Air and in Oxygen Gas*.

The subject again gripped public interest. Professor Béchamp, seizing every spare moment for continued research, was too much occupied working to take much part the debate. Pasteur, on the contrary, kept everyone well acquainted with the experiments he proposed to undertake. There were said to be living organisms – germs – in the atmosphere, so he decided to investigate air microscopically. The method of doing so – by filtering it into glass flasks – had already been

---

1. *Lecons sur la Fermentation Vineuse et sur la Fabrication du Vin*, A. Béchamp, pp.6,7.

inaugurated by two Germans, Schroeder and Dusch.

Experimenting in the same way, Pasteur made comparisons between the different contents of phials, which, according to him, varied with the admission of atmospheric dust and remained unaltered in examples where this was excluded. But he was not content with laboratory and cellar experiments, and planned to make observations that would be more striking and picturesque.

Keeping everyone well notified of his proceedings, in September 1860 he started on a tour armed with 73 phials, which he opened and then summarily sealed at different places and at varying altitudes. The last 20 he reserved for the Mer de Glace, above Chamonix, with the result that in only one of the twenty were the contents found to be altered.

From this time, the autumn of 1860, Pasteur, the former Sponteparist, veered round to a completely opposite standpoint, and ascribed almost all phenomena to the influence of atmospheric germs.

His immediate opponent, meanwhile, experimented on air on mountains, on plains, on the sea, and, as everybody knows, Pasteur never succeeded in convincing M. Pouchet.

Of these Pasteurian experiments, Béchamp writes:

> "From his microscopic analysis he comes to conclusions, like Pouchet, without precision (*sans rien préciser*); there are organised corpuscles in the collected dust, only he cannot say 'this is an egg, this is a spore,' but he affirms that there are a sufficient number to explain all the cases of the generation of infusoria. Pasteur thus took up the position of explaining by germs of the air all that he had explained before by spontaneous generation."[1]

He was naturally entitled to hold any opinions that he chose, whether they were superficial or otherwise, and also to change his opinions, but we think it obvious that he was *not* entitled to claim for himself discoveries made by another worker.

Yet, in a discussion on spontaneous generation, which took place at the Sorbonne during a meeting on the 22nd November, 1861 of the *Sociétés Savantes*, Pasteur, in the presence of Professor Béchamp, took to himself the credit of the proof of the appearance of living organisms in a medium devoid of albuminoid matter.

The Professor, with that distaste for self-advertisement which so often accompanies the highest intellect, listened in amazed silence

---

1. *Les Grands Problémes Médicaux*, A. Béchamp, p.13.

until his own turn came, when, instead of putting forward the legitimate seniority of his work, he merely gave an account of the experiments described in his memoir and the conclusions that had resulted from them. On returning to his seat, which happened to be next to Pasteur's, he asked the latter to be so kind as to admit his knowledge of the work that had just been under description. The report of the meeting tells us of Pasteur's method of compliance:

> "M. Béchamp quoted some experiment (*those of the memoir of 1857 – ed.*) wherein the transformation of cane sugar into grape sugar effected under the influence of the air is always accompanied by moulds. These experiments agree with the results obtained by M. Pasteur, who hastened to acknowledge that the fact put forward by M. Béchamp is *one of the most rigid exactness.*"[1]

We cannot help but think that Pasteur might also have added an admission that his associate had been in the field *before* him. A further point to be noted is Pasteur's later contradiction of his own words – Béchamp's work, described by him in the quote above as being 'rigidly exact', was later to be accused by him as being guilty of 'an enormity'.

We turn to the *Études sur la Biére*:

> "I must repudiate a claim of priority raised by M. Béchamp. It is known that I was the first to demonstrate that living ferments can be entirely constituted from their germs deposited in pure water into which sugar, ammonia and phosphates have been introduced and protected from light and green matter.
>
> M. Béchamp, relying on the old fact that moulds arise in sugared water and, according to him, invert the sugar, pretends to have proved that organised living ferments can arise in media deprived of albuminoid matters.
>
> To be logical, M. Béchamp should say that he has proved that moulds arise in pure sugared water without nitrogen, without phosphates or other mineral elements, for that is an enormity that can be deduced from his work, in which there is not even the expression of the least astonishment that moulds have been able to grow in pure water with pure sugar without other mineral or organic principles."[2]

---

1. *Revues des Sociétés Savantes 1*, p.81 (1862).
2. p.310 (note).

How was it, then, that Pasteur should, as we have already seen, have earlier described that self-same work as possessing 'rigid exactness'? Can it be that it is only when it is likely to eclipse Pasteur's that it turns into 'an enormity'? And how did Pasteur come to omit *all reference to the admittance of air, without which the formation of moulds would have been impossible?*

At a time when Pasteur was using yeast broth and other albuminoid matters for his experiments, Béchamp, on the contrary, gave a clear demonstration that in media devoid of albuminoid matters moulds would appear which, when heated with caustic potash, set free ammonia. By the same set of experiments, the Professor proved that moulds, living organisms that play the part of ferments, are deposited from the air and appear in pure water to which nothing but sugar, or sugar and certain salts, have been added. Therefore by this criticism,

> "To be logical, M. Béchamp should say that he has proved
> that moulds arise in pure sugared water, without nitrogen,
> without phosphates or other mineral elements, for that is an
> enormity that can be deduced from his work..."

M. Pasteur seems to have committed the enormity himself, by thus apparently misunderstanding the facts proved by Béchamp! The latter had noted that the glass flasks filled completely with the solution of sugar and distilled water, and into which *no air whatever* was allowed to enter, moulds did not appear and the sugar was not inverted; but in the flasks in which air had remained, or into which it had been allowed to penetrate, moulds had formed, despite the absence of the albuminoid matters included in Pasteur's experiments: moreover, Béchamp had found these moulds to be more abundant when particular salts, such as nitrates, phosphates, etc., had been added.

The Professor, in *Les Microzymas*[1], cannot resist an allusion to Pasteur's extraordinary criticism:

> "A chemist, *au courant* with science, ought not to be surprised
> that moulds are developed in sweetened water contained, in
> contact with air, in glass flasks. It is the astonishment of M.
> Pasteur that is astonishing!"

When a war of words ensued, Pasteur was no match for Béchamp, and the former quickly saw that his own interests would be best served by passing over the latter's work as far as possible in silence. This human weakness of jealousy was no doubt one of the contributory causes of

---

1. *Les Microzymas*, p.87.

the setting aside of important discoveries which, afterwards ascribed to Buchner in 1897,[1] were actually made by Béchamp before 1864, in which year he first publicly employed the name *zymase* for the soluble ferment of yeasts and moulds.

And it is to these researches of his that we shall now turn our attention.

---

1. See pp.158, 160, 177, 236.

6.
The Soluble Ferment

Before we can form an idea of the magnitude of Béchamp's discoveries, we must first establish an understanding of the scientific views of the period. Not only were physical and chemical influences believed to be involved in the spontaneous generation of plant and animal life, but Dumas' physiological theory of fermentation had been set aside for the belief that this transformation anteceded the appearance of micro-organisms.

We have already seen that light was thrown upon this darkness by Béchamp's *Beacon Experiment*; we shall now see just what he deduced from his observations.

At the date of the publication of his memoir, scientists were so little prepared to admit that moulds could appear apart from the co-operation of some albuminoid matter that it was at first insisted that Béchamp must have employed impure sugar. On the contrary, he had made use of pure sugar candy, which did not produce ammonia when heated with soda lime.

Yet his critics would not be satisfied, even by the fact that the quantity of ammonia set free by the moulds far surpassed any that could have been furnished by any impurity. Further evidence was given by the experiments that showed the development of micro-organisms in mineral media, and these could not be accused of connection with anything albuminoid.

Béchamp was not, of course, the first to view and notice the moulds, the micro-organisms. That had been done before him. What he did was to demonstrate conclusively their atmospheric origin, and, above all, to explain their function. Anyone interested in this important subject cannot do better than study the second chapter of *Les Microzymas*, where the matter is explained fully. Here we can only briefly summarise some of its teaching.

The outstanding evidence that faced the Professor in his observations was the fact that the moulds, which appeared in sweetened water exposed to air, set free ammonia when heated with caustic potash. This was evidence that a nitrogenised organic substance, probably albuminoid, had been produced and had served to constitute one of the materials necessary for the development of an organised being.

From where had it arisen?

The Professor finds his answer through a study of nature. He describes how the seed of a flowering plant will germinate and the plant that appears will grow and develop, always weighing more than the seed sown originally.

From where were the chemical compounds derived that were not to be found in the seed?

The answer, he says, is elementary, and he goes on to explain how the organs of the young plant are the chemical apparatus in which the surrounding media (i.e. the water in the soil, in which it strikes its roots, supplying nitrogenous salts, and the atmosphere providing its leaves with carbonic acid and oxygen) are enabled to react and produce, according to chemical laws, the compounds whereby the plant is nourished and with which it builds up its cells and hence all its organs.

In the same way behaves the spore of the mucorina, which the air carried to the sweetened solution. It develops, and in the body of the microscopic plant the air, with its nutrient contents, the water and the dissolved materials in the sweetened solution all react, and the necessary organic matter is constructed and compounds are produced which were non-existent in the original medium. He goes on to explain that it is because the mucorina is a plant, with the faculty of producing organic matter, that it is able to develop in a medium that contains nothing organised.

For this production of organic matter, the presence of certain minerals is indispensable. Béchamp here reverts to Lavoisier's explanation of the way in which water attacks glass and dissolves a portion of it, and himself shows how the moulds are thus supplied with the earthy and alkaline materials they need. The amount thus furnished is very small, so that the harvest of moulds is correspondingly limited. If, however, certain salts – such as aluminium sulphate, potassium nitrate or sodium phosphate – were added to the sweetened water, large moulds resulted and the inversion of the sugar was proportionately rapid. Béchamp says:

> "The meaning of this is that each of these salts introduced a specially favourable condition and perhaps helped in attacking the glass, which thus yielded a greater quantity of its own substance." [1]

------

1. *Les Microzymas*, p.84.

But, even still, the mystery of fermentation was not quite clear without an explanation of the actual way in which the change in the sugar was brought about, that is to say, cane sugar transformed into grape sugar.

Here again, as we have already seen, Béchamp solved the difficulty by a comparison, and likened the influence of moulds to the effects exercised upon starch by diastase, which, in solution, possesses the property of causing starch to break up at a high temperature, transforming it first into dextrin and then into sugar.

Béchamp proved his comparison to be correct by rigorous experiments. By crushing the moulds which appeared in his solutions he found that the cells that composed them secreted a soluble ferment and that the latter was the direct agent in transforming the sugar, and he made a very clear demonstration of this also in regard to beer yeast.

For instance, just in the same way the stomach does not work directly upon food, but only indirectly through a secretion called gastric juice, which contains pepsin – a substance more or less analogous to diastase, and which is the direct agent of the chemical changes that take place in the digestive organ. Thus it is by a soluble product that beer yeast and certain other moulds bring about the chemical change that alters the type of sugar. Just as the stomach could not transform food without the juice it secretes, so yeast could not change sugar without a soluble ferment secreted by its cells.

On p.70 of *Les Microzymas*, Béchamp commences an account of some of the experiments he undertook in this connection. Here may be found the description of an experiment with thoroughly washed and dried beer yeast, which was mixed with a little more than its weight of cane sugar and the mixture carefully creosoted, the whole becoming soft and by degrees completely fluid.

Béchamp provides a full explanation of the experiment.

He shows that the yeast cell is like a closed vesicle, or a container enclosing a content, and that it is limited in space by a membranous envelope. In the dried state, which he used for his experiment, it yet contained more than 70% of water, no more perceptible to touch than the amount – on an average 80% of the body weight – contained in the human body. He explains how the living yeast, in its natural state, on contact with water allows nothing of its content to escape except excretory products, but in contact with the sugar it is, as it were, irritated and the enveloping membrane permits the escape of water with certain other materials held in solution, and it is this fluid that liquefies the mixture of yeast and sugar. The escape of the fluid Béchamp shows to be due to the physical process *osmosis*, by which a solution passes through a permeable membrane.

Thus having obtained his liquid product, he diluted it with water and left it to filter.

Meanwhile, Béchamp performed another experiment; namely, he dissolved a small piece of cane sugar in water, and found that no change was produced when this was heated with alkaline copper tartrate. He then took another small piece of sugar and heated it to boiling point with very dilute hydrochloric acid; he neutralised the acid with caustic potash and made the solution alkaline; he then added his copper reagent and heated it, whereupon reduction took place, a precipitate being produced which was at first yellow, and then red. By means of the acid the sugar had been inverted, that is to say, transformed into a mixture of glucose and levulose (a constituent of fruit sugar), which reduced the cupric copper of the blue reagent to cuprous copper which was precipitated as the red oxide.

Béchamp then returned to the liquid that had been filtering, and found that when he barely heated it with the alkaline copper tartrate reagent, the change in the sugar was effected. This proved to him that something besides water had escaped from the yeast; something that, even in the cold, had the power of rapidly inverting the sugar.

Professor Béchamp here points out[1] two facts that must be clearly demonstrated.

First, that without the escaping element yeast in itself is inoperative, for when steeped in water, with the alkaline copper tartrate reagent added, reduction is not affected.

Secondly, that heat destroys the activity of the escaping element, for yeast brought to the boil with a little water to which sugar is added does not, even after time has been allowed for it to take effect, produce the inversion; the alkaline copper tartrate reagent is not reduced.

In short, he discovered that heat destroys the activity of the ferment secreted by yeast and moulds of all sorts, just as heat destroys the activity of sprouted barley, of diastase and of other soluble ferments, that is, ferments capable of being dissolved in a fluid.

Béchamp further discovered sodium acetate to be another agent especially efficient in promoting the passage of the soluble contents through the call walls. To dried yeast he added some crystals of that salt, experimenting on a sufficiently large quantity. The mixture became

1. *Les Microzymas*, pp.71,72.

liquid and was thrown upon a filter. One part sodium acetate to ten or more of yeast he found sufficient to effect the liquefaction.

He then took the filtered liquid and added alcohol to it, and a white precipitate appeared. He collected this in a filter, and washed it with alcohol to free it from the sodium acetate. The alcohol being drained off, the precipitate was dried between folds of filter papers and was then taken up with water. There resulted a solution and an insoluble residue. This last was coagulated albumen, which came from the yeast in solution, but was rendered insoluble by the coagulating action of the alcohol.

Béchamp says of this:

> "As to that portion of the precipitate which has been dissolved, alcohol can precipitate it again; this new precipitate is to beer yeast what diastase is to sprouted barley, or synaptase to almonds; it is the principle that in the yeast effects the inversion of the cane sugar.
>
> If some of it is dissolved in water, cane sugar added and the solution kept for several minutes in the water bath at 40°, the alkaline copper tartrate proves that the sugar has been inverted.
>
> The action is also very rapid at the ordinary temperature, but slower in proportion to a lesser amount of the active product; which explains the slowness of the reactions obtained with certain moulds that I could only utilise in small quantity. All this proves that the cause of the inversion of the sugar is pre-formed in the moulds and in the yeast, and as the active matter, when isolated, acts in the absence of acid, this shows that I was right in allying it to diastase."[1]

It was after Professor Béchamp had established these facts that he gave a name to this active matter. He called it *zymase*, from the Greek for 'ferment'. The word, applied by him at first to the active matter of yeast and of moulds, has become a generic term. Later on, he specially designated the *zymases* of yeast and of moulds by the name of *zythozymase*.

Béchamp's first public employment of the name *zymase* for soluble ferments was in *A Memoir on Fermentation by Organised Ferments*, which he read before the Academy of Science on 4th April, 1864.[2]

The following year he resumed the subject[3] and showed that there

---

1. *Les Microzymas*, p.72.
2. *Comptes Rendus 58*, p.601.
3. *Comptes Rendus 59*, p.496.

were *zymases* in microzoaires and microphytes, which he isolated, as Payen and Persoz isolated the diastase from sprouted barley. These *zymases*, he found, possessed generally the property of rapidly transforming cane sugar into glucose, or grape sugar. He discovered the *anthrozyma* in flowers, the *morozyma* in the white mulberry and the *nephrozyma* in the kidney of animals.

Finally, the following year, 1866, he gave the name *microzyma*[1] to his crowning discovery, which was to him the basic explanation of the whole question, and which had not yet been made apparent to him when he immortalised his early experiments in his memoir of 1857; but this we must leave for future consideration. We have here given them dates to show how long ago Professor Béchamp made a complete discovery of the nitrogenous substance formed in the yeast cell, to which he gave the name of *zymase*.

Apart from the justice of giving credit where credit is due, for the mere sake of historical accuracy it is desirable that his own discovery should be publicly accredited to him. Instead, in the *Encyclopedia Britannica*[2] we find, in the article on *Fermentation* by Julian Levett Baker:

> "in 1897, Buchner submitted yeast to great pressure and isolated a nitrogenous substance, enzymic in character, which he termed *zymase*."

Again, we take up *A Manual of Bacteriology*,[3] by R. Tanner Hewlett, and we read:

> "Until 1897, no enzyme had been obtained which would carry out this change (alcoholic fermentation); it only occurred when the living yeast cells were present, but in that year Buchner, by grinding up the living yeast cells, obtained a juice which decomposed dextrose with the formation of alcohol and carbonic acid. This *zymase* Buchner claimed to be the alcoholic enzyme of yeast."

Yet, once more, Professor and Mrs. Frankland, in their book *Pasteur*,[4] while apologising for certain of the latter's erroneous views, write as follows:

---

1. *Comptes Rendus 63*, p.451.
2. Eleventh edition.
3. Sixth edition, p.36.
4. See Chapter 9.

"In the present year (1897) the discovery has been made by E. Buchner that a soluble principle giving rise to the alcoholic fermentation of sugar may be extracted from yeast cells, and for which the name *zymase* is proposed. This important discovery should throw a new light on the theory of fermentation."

But this 'important discovery', as we have here seen, was made nearly half a century before by Antoine Béchamp!

It is true that Pasteur accused Béchamp of having taken his ideas from Mitscherlich. Not only was Béchamp able to disprove this, but he also showed that it was Pasteur who had followed the German's views, and that, moreover, on a point on which the latter appeared to have been mistaken.[1]

Thus it is clear that Béchamp was the first to give tangible proof not only of the airborne origin of yeasts and moulds, but also of the means by which they are physiologically and chemically active.

When he started work, there was no teaching available for him to plagiarise – had plagiarism been possible to such a deeply versed and honest student of scientific history who, step by step, traced any observations that had preceded his own.

Unfortunately, it was he who was preyed upon by plagiarists, and, sad to relate, foremost among these seems to have been the very one who tried to detract from his work and the one who bears the world-famous name of Pasteur!

Let us pause here to document Pasteur's progress and the way in which he gained credit for Béchamp's great discovery of the invading hordes from the atmosphere – micro-organisms with their fermentative powers.

---

1. *Les Microzymas*, pp.76,77.

7.
Rival Theories and Workers

Undoubtedly, one of the main factors of Pasteur's success was the eagerness with which he pushed to the forefront of any scientific question, thus focusing public attention upon himself.

Béchamp's illuminating explanations of ancient problems were conveniently to hand at just the moment that Pouchet brought the controversy on spontaneous generation again into the limelight of general interest. Pasteur, seizing the opportunity, entered the debate, and, as Béchamp comments, Pouchet's observations being as wanting in precision as Pasteur's, it was not hard for the latter to emerge as victor, genuinely impressing the world of scientists.

Thus he who had taught the spontaneous origin of yeast and of micro-organisms of all sorts now discoursed enthusiastically upon the germs of the air, and began to make life synonymous with atmospheric organisms. Not only, according to his new views, was fermentation caused by pre-existing germs of airborne origin, but each germ induced its own definite specific form of fermentation.

Here he fell foul of Béchamp, for according to the latter's physiological explanation, each micro-organism may vary its fermentative effect in conformity with the medium in which it finds itself; it may even *change in shape*, as modern workers are discovering.

Pasteur, however, proceeded to label each with a definite and unalterable function. In 1861, claiming to discover a special butyric vibrio, which he thought could live only *without air*, he divided living beings into two classifications, the *aerobic* and the *anaerobic*, or those that require air and those that flourish without it. Fermentation he defined as life without oxygen.

The verdict of time, to which he himself has relegated all scientists for final judgment, is scarcely in his favour. To quote, for instance, from one of his eulogists in the article *Fermentation* by Julian Levett Baker, in the *Encyclopaedia Britannica*[1] we read:

> "According to Pasteur... 'fermentation is life without air, or
> life without oxygen'. This theory of fermentation was

---

1. Eleventh edition.

materially modified in 1892 and 1894 by A. J. Brown, who described experiments which were in disagreement with Pasteur's dictum."

Pasteur himself, in controversies with both M. Trécul and the Turin Commission (which investigated his prophylaxis for anthrax), was forced to admit that anaerobics could gradually be induced to live with air without becoming ferments and that aerobics could become ferments. Thus he himself destroyed his own classification. Yet this untenable description was Pasteur's chief support for his later equally untenable claim that he had been the first to regard fermentation as a phenomenon of nutrition and of assimilation. In a statement of his made in 1872 and repeated in his *Études sur la Biere*, we find quite contrary teaching:

> "That which separates the chemical phenomenon of fermentation from a crowd of other acts *and especially from the acts of ordinary life* is the fact of the decomposition of a weight of fermentative matter much superior to the weight of the ferment." [1]

What more inevitable act of 'ordinary life' could there be than that of nutrition and digestion, from which the famous chemist thus separated the phenomenon of fermentation? Pasteur was here only appropriating the same singular idea of physiology that had already been voiced in 1865 by a follower of his, Duclaux:

> "When in our alcoholic fermentation we see a certain weight of sugar transformed into alcohol by a weight of yeast one hundred, nay, a thousand times smaller, it is very difficult to believe that this sugar made at any time a part of the materials of the yeast, and that it (the alcohol) is something like a product of excretion." [2]

It seems strange that scientists should have required the following simple physiological explanation from Professor Béchamp:

> "Suppose an adult man to have lived a century, and to weigh on average 60 kilograms: he will have consumed in that time, besides other foods, the equivalent of 20,000 kilograms of flesh and produced about 800 kilograms of urea. Shall it be said that it is impossible to admit that this mass of flesh and of urea could at any moment of his life form part of his being?

---

1. *Comptes Rendus* 75, p.785 (1872).
2. *Annales Scientifiques de l'École Normale*, 2, 6. 249 (1865).

Just as a man consumes all that food only by repeating the same act a great many times, the yeast cell consumes the great mass of sugar only by constantly assimilating and dissimilating it, bit by bit.

Now, that which only one man will consume in a century, a sufficient number of men would absorb and process in a day. It is the same with the yeast; the sugar that a small number of cells can consume in a year, a greater number will destroy in a day. In both cases the more numerous the individuals, the more rapid the consumption." [3]

By the need of such an explanation evidence is given that Pasteur had failed to understand fermentation to be due to physiological processes of absorption and excretion. It would take too long to follow the varying examples that substantiate this criticism, and, naturally, difficult scientific intricacies were beyond the comprehension of the general public, a great part of whom, having no idea of the processes required for the food they put into their own bodies, were still far less likely to fathom the nutritive functions of organisms invisible except through the microscope.

It was nothing to them that, among the learned reports of the Academy of Science, treatises were to be found, by a professor working at Montpellier, that clearly explained the why and the wherefore of the intricate chemical changes that go by the name of fermentation. But, on the contrary, more or less everyone had heard, so widely had the subject been ventilated, of the controversy as to whether life, in its lesser forms, sprang invariably from antecedent life, or whether chemical combinations could produce life independently of parents.

The public, too, could follow the account of Pasteur's holiday tour in pursuit of the question. Very little embellishment was needed to make anyone understand the point of the flasks that he unsealed, some by a dusty roadside, some on an Alpine summit. Since visible dust could cloud a fluid, it was easy to realise that invisible aerial germs could also affect the contents of the scientist's phials. Minute living things afloat in the atmosphere were not hard to imagine, and Pasteur put his case so enthusiastically that it was not remarkable that the impression was created that he had been the first to demonstrate them; especially since the obstinacy with which a number of scientists declined to endorse his views made him appear as a champion in the battle against the sponteparists, whose opinions he had cast off so recently.

1. *Comptes Rendus* 75, p.1523.

All this time, in spite of Biot's influential patronage, Pasteur had remained outside the select circle of Academicians. But at the end of 1862, as we have said before, he was at last nominated by the Mineralogical Section. No sooner was his candidature commenced than exception began to be taken to his early conclusions on crystallography. None the less, by 36 out of 60 votes, he secured his coveted place in the Academy of Science; and, advised to drop crystallography, he proceeded to experiment further in connection with his new views on airborne organisms.

To secure matter free from atmospheric dust, he made observations upon muscle, milk, blood, etc., taken from the interior of bodies. From the start, he cannot but have been handicapped by his lack of medical training. His viewpoint was that of the chemist. According to Pasteur's conception, as Béchamp points out,[1] the marvellous animal body was likened to wine in the cask or beer in the barrel. He looked upon muscle, milk, blood, and so forth as mere mixtures of chemical proximate principles. He did, it is true, draw some distinction between the interior of an organism and that of a barrel of beer, or a cask of wine, for we find that he said that the first is:

"endowed with powers of transformation that boiling destroys."[2]

Béchamp here shows how Pasteur's mind reverted to the old-fashioned belief in spontaneous alteration. Recognising nothing inherently alive in the composition of animal and vegetable bodies, it was his aim to show that meat, milk, blood, etc., would remain unchanged if completely secured from invasion by aerial organisms. And when, later on, he copied an experiment that Béchamp had undertaken on meat, and found in his own observation that, in spite of precautions against germs of the air, the muscular masses of the meat yet became tainted, he was driven to fall back for an explanation upon vague, occult 'powers of transformation'.

In the same way, for the wonderful evolution of an egg into a bird he had no explanation, except these same mysterious 'transformative powers'. How can it be said that he had destroyed belief in spontaneous generation, when he could only ascribe to a spontaneous change the amazing development of, for instance, the cells of an egg to a circulatory apparatus, bony and nervous systems, glands, organs, and finally a bird covered with feathers? For a spontaneous change it must be, if

1. *Les Microzymas*, p.754.
2. *ibid*, p.390.

the substance of an egg is only a chemical mixture of the same order as wine or beer.

What are Pasteur's 'powers of transformation', if not the same as Bonnet's 'excellent modification', which produces the organisation of matter, or if not the same as the *'nisus formativus'* or productive forces, vegetable and plastic, with which Needham, and, later Pouchet, the believers in spontaneous generation, explained the phenomenon?

Pasteur has merely provided fresh terms for old theories.

But such intricacies were beyond the comprehension of the general public. The 'man in the street' delved no deeper than the surface test that alterable substances could be preserved by excluding air, and that as the atmosphere was said to be filled with living germs, there was no need to confuse the issue with the possible emergence of life from mere chemical sources. The religious felt duly grateful for views that appeared to controvert the materialistic tendencies of the nineteenth century, and were blandly innocent of the superficial character of the contradiction. Meanwhile, the talk of the controversy and the exploits of Pasteur reached the ears of the Emperor, who, like most rulers, felt it incumbent upon him to patronise contemporary science. Soon after his election to the Academy of Science, Pasteur, in March 1863, had the honour of being presented to Napoleon III at the Tuileries.

As usual, his numerous correspondents seem to have been notified at once of the interview, for his son-in-law tells us:

> "Pasteur wrote the next day: 'I assured the Emperor that all my ambition was to arrive at the knowledge of the causes of putrid and contagious diseases.'"[1]

Here we have an interesting illustration of the contrast between the methods of Pasteur and Béchamp. As we have seen, right up to 1860, Pasteur's memoirs contained sponteparist opinions. It was now only 1863, but he had already changed his standpoint; and it is clear that – before any proofs could have been brought into bearing on the subject – Pasteur was already connecting the ferments of the air with the idea, voiced by earlier workers (Linné, Raspail and others) that specific organisms might be the cause of specific diseases.

The best and the worst of us invariably preach against our own individual weaknesses; and therefore Pasteur rightly quoted a great writer as having declared that:

---

1. *The Life of Pasteur*, René Vallery-Radot, p.104.

> "the greatest derangement of the mind is to believe things because one wishes them to be so." [1]

He could well apprehend this danger, since it was one to which we find he was particularly susceptible.

Béchamp's attitude to his work was diametrically opposite. He gave his imagination no play until he had interrogated Nature. Not until he had received a direct reply to a direct demand did he allow his mind to be carried away by possibilities, and even then experiments punctuated the course to his conclusions. In short, he did not direct Nature, or decide what he wished to discover. He allowed Nature to direct him, and made his discoveries follow her revelations.

Fortunately for Pasteur, however, Imperial patronage was no dead letter. Four months after his presentation to Napoleon, in July of the same year, he received direct encouragement from the latter to turn his attention to the vinous diseases that were then interfering with the trade in French wines. Once more Pasteur started on a scientific tour during the holidays, this time to vineyards, and with the Emperor's blessing to clear his path.

Meanwhile his opponents, Pouchet, Joly and Musset, followed his example and climbed mountains, testing air collected in small glass flasks. They returned triumphant, for although they had scaled one thousand metres higher than Pasteur, there was alteration in their phials.

We have no need here to discuss the wagging of tongues on the subject, and Flourens' pronouncement in favour of Pasteur at the Academy of Science. It suffices to mention that the deep problem of spontaneous generation became so popular that when Pasteur entered the lecture room of the Sorbonne on the evening of 7th April, 1864, to discourse on the subject, every seat available was filled, not simply by learned professors, but also by literary celebrities, Alexandre Dumas and George Sand among them, and also Princesse Mathilde and all the well-known votaries of fashion, the 'smart set' of Paris. And happily for these worldlings, Pasteur had nothing very abstruse to set before them. He simply asseverated the impossibility of dispensing with parents, a subject likely to provoke banter rather than very deep reasoning. He wound up by explaining an experiment in which dust from the air had been excluded from a putrescible liquid and in consequence no animalcule had become apparent.

---

1. *Comptes Rendus* 80, p.91 (1875).

To quote his own words:

> "It is dumb because I have kept it from the only thing man
> cannot produce, from the germs that float in the air, from
> Life, for Life is a germ and a germ is Life. Never will the
> doctrine of spontaneous generation recover from the mortal
> blow of this simple experiment." [1]

There was never a word as to how this partial truth had been
originally arrived at years before, as far back as 1857, by his
contemporary, Professor Béchamp. There was also no acknowledgment
made of Béchamp's memoir that had enlightened Pasteur's progress
and revealed to him early errors.

He took to himself all the credit, and with that which is taken
sufficiently forcibly, the public will seldom argue. We can picture the
fashionable audience dispersing, proud of having understood the subject
under discussion (as they no doubt imagined), and delighted with the
lecturer for having proved them so much more scientific and clever
than they had ever supposed themselves.

Pasteur became the toast of society; the Church gave him its blessing;
the Emperor invited him at the end of 1865 to spend a week at the
Palace of Compiégne. His name and fame were established. Can we
wonder that scientists who had never received such honours should
have felt reluctant to oppose this favourite of fortune.

But let us pause for an instant and consider his noted lecture at the
Sorbonne – what was in it? He had merely ascribed to the germs of the
air a mysterious quality – 'life' – that he denied to the component parts
of more complicated animal and vegetable beings. For the origin, the
source of his atmospheric germs, he provided no explanation, neither
has any since been found by his innumerable followers, for whom the
description 'life is a germ and a germ is life' was soon to evolve
into 'disease is a germ and a germ is a disease' – an infinitely more
lugubrious axiom.

Was Pasteur correct even in his denial of alteration apart from
airborne organisms? In his own experiment upon meat, he had to admit
that the latter became tainted. To assume that this was caused by some
faultiness in operation is not to explain the appearance of micro-
organisms in cases where no airborne germs could possibly account
for their origin. Thus it is that Pasteur's boast in his lecture at having
struck a 'mortal blow' at the doctrine of spontaneous generation has

---

1. *The Life of Pasteur*, by René Vallery-Radot, p.109.

not met with real fulfilment. Not only was his contemporary Pouchet never satisfied, but the later work of Gustave le Bon and of Dr. Charlton Bastian affected to demonstrate, according to their view, the production of organised beings from inorganic matter.

Professor Bastian asserts:

> "Living matter may have been continuously coming into being ever since the time of man's first appearance; and yet the fact that no member of the human race has ever seen (or is ever likely to see) such a birth throws no doubt upon the probability of its occurrence." [1]

Professor Bastian based this belief upon such observations as his experiment with the '*cyclops quadricornis*, one of the *Entomostraca* so commonly to be found in ponds':

> "If we take one of these little creatures, and put it in a drop of distilled water, on a glass slip with a fragment of a No. 2 cover-glass on each side of it, and place over it all a cover glass, it will be found that the animal is soon killed by the weight of the glass.
>
> We may then place the microscope slip in a Petri dish containing a thin stratum of water (so as to prevent evaporation from beneath the cover-glass), and fixing upon one of the tail *setae* (these being larger than those of the abdominal feet), we may examine it from time to time.
>
> What may be observed is this. After an interval of two or three days (the duration depending upon the temperature of the air at the time) we may see, under our microscope, scarcely visible motionless specks gradually appear in increasing numbers in the midst of the structureless protoplasm, and, still later, we may see some of these specks growing into bacteria...
>
> At last the whole interior of the spine becomes filled with distinct bacteria...
>
> Later still, all the bacteria, previously motionless, begin to show active swarming movement.
>
> It is clear we have here no process of infection from without, but rather a *de novo* origin of bacteria from the protoplasmic contents of the spines or *selae*. The fact that they appear in these situations as mere separate motionless specks, and gradually take on the forms of bacteria (also motionless at first) is, as I have previously indicated, just what we might

---

1. *The Evolution of Life*, H. Charlton Bastian, p.31.

expect if they had actually taken origin in the places where they appear. On the other hand, such a mode of appearance is totally opposed to what might be expected if the micro-organisms had obtained an entry from without, through the tough chitinous envelope of the spines." [1]

Professor Bastian gives numerous examples of the finding of bacteria in internal animal organs and in fruit and vegetables, where he demonstrates the impossibility of an invasion.

Can the followers of Pasteur provide any solution of the mystery?

If they cannot, it must be conceded that no 'mortal blow' at the doctrine of spontaneous generation was struck by Pasteur, as he proudly boasted. The dealer of the blow, or, at any rate, the provider of an explanation, apart from heterogenesis, was not the French chemist, performing for a fashionable audience which included 'all Paris', but a hard-working French professor and physician, who was also a chemist and a naturalist, and who was taking little part in all the talk because he was so hard at work wresting fresh secrets from Nature.

Even admitting that he demonstrated before Pasteur, and far more thoroughly, the role of airborne organisms, it may yet be asked how Béchamp's observations enlightened any better the depths of the heterogenetic mystery.

The answer to this is that, in his memoir of 1857, the Professor did not include certain of his observations. His reason for the omission was that the results he obtained seemed too contradictory to be accurate. Believing that he had made some mistake, he set aside these particular experiments for the time being.

In the end, as the following pages will set forth, his apparent failure was ultimately to provide the solution of the problem, and was also to explain the development of organised life from the most minute commencements.

It was, in fact, according to him, to be the nearest elucidation ever given of animal and vegetable upbuilding, of the processes of health, disease and final disruption. In short, it was to wrest from Nature the stupendous truth:

"Nothing is the prey of death; everything is the prey of life!"

---

1. *The Nature and Origin of Living Matter*, H. Charlton Bastian, p.110.

PART 2

THE MICROZYMAS

8.
The 'Little Bodies'

Just as certain musicians seem born with a natural facility for a particular instrument, so in the world of science from time to time arise men who appear specially gifted in the use of technical instruments.

It was, no doubt, Professor Béchamp's proficiency as a microscopist, as well as the insight of genius, that enabled him from the start of his work to observe so much that other workers ignored when employing the microscope; while his inventive brain led to an application of the polarimeter which greatly assisted him. His powers combined in a remarkable degree the practical and theoretical.

From the time of his earliest observations, he was quick to notice the presence of minute microscopic objects much smaller in size than the cells of the organisms he examined. He was by no means the first to observe these; others had done so before him, but although they applied to them such names as 'scintillating corpuscles', 'molecular granulations', and so forth, no one was any the wiser as to their status and function.

Most of what had been said about them was summed up in Charles Robin's definition in the *Dictionary of Medicine and Surgery* (1858), in which he described the minuteness of 'very small granulations formed of organised substance' found in the tissues, cells, fibres and other anatomical elements of the body, and in great abundance in tuberculous substances and other disease matters.

Béchamp, always careful to avoid unsubstantiated conclusions, did not allow his imagination to run away in regard to these 'very small granulations'. At first he merely noted them, and bestowed upon them the noncommittal name of 'little bodies'. He did no further work in regard to them when his new duties took him to Montpellier, and he there brought to a close the observations that he had commenced at Strasbourg and which he recounted and explained in his memoir of 1857.

It will be remembered that for many of these experiments, the Professor employed various salts, including potassium carbonate, in the presence of which the inversion of cane sugar did not take place, in spite of the absence of creosote.

Another experiment that he made was to substitute calcium carbonate in the form of chalk for potassium carbonate. Great was his surprise to find that in spite of the addition of creosote, to prevent the intrusion of atmospheric germs, cane sugar none the less underwent inversion, or change of some sort.

In regard to creosote, Béchamp had already proved that though it was a preventive against the invasion of extraneous organisms, it had no effect in hampering the development of moulds that were already established in the medium. The experiments in which he had included chalk seemed, however, to contradict this conclusion, for in these cases creosote proved incapable of preventing the inversion of sugar. He could only believe that the contradiction arose from some faultiness of procedure; so he determined to probe further into the mystery and meanwhile to omit from his memoir any reference to the experiments in which chalk had proved a disturbing factor.

The work that Professor Béchamp undertook in this connection is an object lesson in painstaking research. To begin with, he had first chalk and then a block of limestone conveyed to his laboratory with great precautions against any air coming into contact. He then proved by innumerable experiments that when all access of air was entirely prevented, no change took place in a sugar solution even when chemically pure calcium carbonate ($CaCO_3$) was added; but as soon as ordinary chalk, even from his specially conserved block, was introduced, fermentation took place even though the entry of atmospheric germs had been guarded against completely. No addition of creosote even in increased doses could then prevent the inversion of the sugar.

Béchamp was naturally extremely surprised to find that a mineral, a rock, could thus play the part of a ferment. It was clear to him that chalk must contain something over and above just calcium carbonate. Working with the most powerful microscope obtainable, he undertook a minute investigation both of pure calcium carbonate and of the chalk he had used for his experiments.

Great was his amazement to find in the chalk 'little bodies', similar to those he had noted in other observations, while nothing of the sort was to be seen in the pure calcium carbonate.

Also, while in the microscopic preparation of the calcium carbonate everything was opaque and motionless, in that of the chalk the 'little bodies' were agitated by a movement similar to that known as 'Brownian' after the naturalist Robert Brown, but which Béchamp differentiated from it.[1] These 'little bodies' were further distinguishable by the way in which they refracted light from their opaque surroundings. They were smaller than any of the microphytes seen up to that time in fermentations, but were more powerful as ferments than any known; and it was because of their fermentative activity that he regarded them as living.

To form any correct estimate of the magnitude of the discovery upon the brink of which Béchamp hovered, we should remind ourselves of the scientific opinions of the time. The Professor's observations were made when most believed in Virchow's view of the cell as the unit of life in all forms, vegetable and animal, and spontéparist opinions were held by a large body of experimenters, including at that time Pasteur. In the midst of this confusion of ideas, Béchamp clung firmly to two axioms:

1) that no chemical change takes place without a provocative cause.

2) that there is no spontaneous generation of any living organism.

Meanwhile, he concentrated his mind upon the 'little bodies'.

He realised at the start that if those he had discovered in chalk were really organised beings, with a separate independent life of their own, he ought to be able to isolate them, prove them to be insoluble in water, and find them composed of organic matter.

He succeeded in isolating them, then proved carbon, hydrogen, etc., to be their component parts, and then demonstrated their insolubility.

If they were living beings it followed that it must be possible to kill them. Here again he found the truth of his contention, for when he heated chalk together with a little water to 300°C (572°F), he afterwards proved it to have become devoid of its former fermentative power, and the 'little bodies' were now quite devoid of the movement that before had characterised them.

Among other points, he discovered that if, during the process of fermentation by these minute organisms, all foreign invasions were guarded against by rigid precautions, the little bodies nevertheless increased and multiplied. This observation was to stand him in good stead in his subsequent[2] researches.

Béchamp observed that the chalk he had used seemed to be formed mostly of the mineral remains of a microscopic world long since

---

1. *La Théorie du Microzyma*, A. Béchamp, p.115.
2. *ibid*, pp.113-14.

vanished, the fossil remains of which, according to Ehrenberg, belong to two species called *Polythalamis* and *Nautilae*, and which are so minute that more than two million could be found in a piece of chalk weighing just one hundred grams.

But, over and above these remains of extinct beings, the Professor saw that the white chalk contained organisms of infinitesimal size, which according to him are living and which he thought might be of immense antiquity. The block of limestone he had obtained was so old that it belonged to the upper lacustrian chalk formation of the Tertiary Period; yet he proved it to be possessed of wonderful fermentative properties which he satisfied himself to be due to the presence of the same 'little bodies'. [1]

He continued a persistent examination of various calcareous deposits, and not only found the same minute organisms, but discovered them to possess varying degrees of ability to cause fermentation.

The calcareous tufa and the coal areas of Bessége had very little power either to liquefy starch or to invert cane sugar; while on the other hand the peat bogs and the waste moors of the Cévennes, as well as the dust of large cities, he proved to contain 'ittle bodies' possessing great powers for inducing fermentation.

He continued his investigations and found the entities in mineral waters, in cultivated land (where he saw that they would play no inconsiderable role), and he believed them to be in the sediment of wines. In the slime of marshes, where the decomposition of organic matter is in progress, he found the 'little bodies' in the midst of other inferior organisms, and, finding also alcohol and acetic acid, attributed to these minute living beings the power that effects the setting free of marsh gas.

Nature having confided such wonderful revelations, the time had come for Professor Béchamp to allow his mind to interpret their meaning. The experiments he had omitted from his 1857 memoir, instead of being faulty, now seemed to hold marvellous suggestions. The 'little bodies' he had discovered in the chalk appeared to be identical with the 'little bodies' he had observed in the cells of yeast and in the body cells of plants and animals – the 'little bodies' that, for the most part, went by the name of 'molecular granulations'.

He remembered that Henle had in a vague way considered these granulations to be structured and to be the builders of cells; and Béchamp saw that, if this were true, Virchow's theory of the cell as the

---

1. *Les Microzymas*, A. Béchamp, pp.940,944.

unit of life would be shattered completely.

The granulations, the 'little bodies', would be the anatomical elements, and those found in the lime stone and chalk he believed might even be the living remains of animal and vegetable forms of past ages. These must be the constituent parts, the building blocks, of plant and animal bodies, and these might survive when such corporate bodies have long since undergone disruption.

At this point, we may draw attention to the cautiousness of Béchamp's proceedings. Although his investigations of chalk were commenced at the time of the publication of his Beacon memoir, he continued to work at the subject for nearly ten years before giving publicity to his new observations. Meanwhile the proverb about the ill wind was exemplified in his case, for diseases affecting vines were becoming the scourge of France, and led him to undertake some experiments that helped in widening the new views that he was gradually formulating.

We have already seen how, in 1863, Pasteur had been despatched with the Emperor's blessing to investigate the troubles of the French wine growers. There was no official request for Professor Béchamp's assistance, but, nonetheless, with his unfailing interest in all scientific problems he started to probe into the matter, and in 1862, a year before Pasteur, he began his researches in the vineyard.

He exposed to contact with air at the same time and place

1) grape-must, decolourised by animal charcoal;
2) grape-must, simply filtered; and
3) grape-must, not filtered.

The three preparations fermented, but to a degree in an inverse order from the above enumeration. Further, the moulds or ferments that developed were not identical in the three experiments.

The question thus arose: 'Why, the chemical medium being the same in the three cases, did it not act in the same manner upon the three musts?'

To solve the riddle, the Professor instituted more experiments. Whole healthy grapes, with their stalks attached, were introduced direct from the vine into boiled sweetened water, cooled in a current of carbonic acid gas, while the gas still bubbled into the liquid. Fermentation took place and was completed in this medium, protected during the whole process from the influence of air. The same experiment succeeded when the grapes were introduced into must, filtered, heated and creosoted.

From these researches, it was evident that neither oxygen nor airborne organisms were the cause of the fermentation, but that the grape carried with it the provocative agents.

Professor Béchamp communicated the results of his experiments to the Academy of Science in 1864, and among its reports the subject was exhaustively treated.[1] He had come to the conclusion that the agent that causes the must to ferment is a mould that comes from the outside of the grape, and that the stalks of grapes and the leaves of vines bear organisms capable of causing both sugar and must to ferment; moreover, that the ferments borne on the leaves and stalks are sometimes of a kind to injure the vintage.

The year 1864, when Béchamp presented his memoir to the Academy, marks an era in the history of biological research, for on the 4th April of that year, he read before the Academy of Science his explanation of the phenomena of fermentation. He showed the latter to be due to the processes of nutrition of living organisms, that absorption takes place, followed by assimilation and excretion, and for the first time he used the word *zymase* to designate a soluble ferment.

It was the following year that Duclaux, a pupil of Pasteur's, tried to cast scorn upon Béchamp's explanation, thus supplying documentary proof that his master had no right to lay claim to having been a pioneer of this teaching.

Béchamp, who in 1857 had so conclusively proved airborne organisms to be agents of fermentation, now in 1864 equally clearly set forth the manner in which the phenomenon is induced.

All the while, he was at work on Nature's further mysteries, undertaking experiments upon milk in addition to many others, and in December of the same year he informed Dumas of his discovery of living organisms in chalk.

Later, on the 26th September, 1865, he wrote to Dumas on the subject, and by the latter's request his letter was published the next month in the *Annales de Chimie et de Physique*. Here he stated:

> "Chalk and milk contain living beings already developed, which fact, observed by itself, is proved by this other fact that creosote, employed in a non-coagulating dose, does not prevent milk from finally turning, nor chalk, without extraneous help, from converting both sugar and starch into alcohol and then into acetic acid, tartaric acid and butyric acid." [2]

---

1. *Comptes Rendus* 59, p.626.
2. 4e série, 6, p.248.

Thus we clearly see the meaning in every single experiment of Béchamp's and the relation that each bore to the other. His rigid experiments with creosote made it possible for him to establish further conclusions. Since creosote prevented the invasion of extraneous life, living organisms must be pre-existent in chalk and milk *before* the addition of creosote. These living organisms were the 'little bodies' that he had seen associated in cells and singly in the tissues and fibres of plants and animals. Too minute to differentiate through the microscope, Béchamp tells us that:

> "The naturalist will not be able to distinguish them by description; but the chemist and also the physiologist will characterise them by their function." [1]

He was thus not checked in his investigations by the minuteness of his objects of research, so infinitesimal as in many cases, no doubt, to be ultra-microscopic. Neither was he disturbed by the ridicule with which many of his contemporaries received his account of the 'little bodies' in chalk and milk. Being a doctor, he was much helped in his research work by his medical studies. In the year 1865, he found in fermented urine that, besides other minute organisms, there were little bodies so infinitesimal as to be only visible by a very high power of the microscope. Soon afterwards, he found these same 'little bodies' in normal urine.

The following year, 1866, he sent up to the Academy of Science a memoir entitled *On the Role of Chalk in Butyric and Lactic Fermentations and the Living Organisms Contained in It.* [2]

Here he detailed experiments and proposed for the 'little bodies' the name *microzymas* from Greek for 'small' and 'ferment'. This descriptive nomenclature portrayed them as ferments of the minutest perceptible order. To the special 'little bodies' found in chalk he gave the name *microzyma cretae.*

Without loss of time, he continued his investigations on the relation of the microzymas of chalk to the molecular granulations of animal and vegetable cells and tissues, and also made numerous further geological examinations.

The results of the latter were partly incorporated in the memoir *On Geological Microzymas of Various Origin*, an extract of which was published among the Reports of the Academy of Science.

---

1. *La Théorie du Microzyma*, A. Béchamp, p.124.
2. *Comptes Rendus* 63, p.451. *Les Microzymas*, A. Béchamp, p.940.

In this he asks:

"What is now the geological significance of these microzymas and what is their origin?"[1]

He answers:

"I believe that they are the organised and yet living remains of beings that lived in long past ages. I find proof of this both in these researches and in those that I have carried out by myself and in collaboration with Professor Estor on the microzymas of actual living beings. These microzymas are morphologically identical, and even though there may be some slight differences in their activity as ferments, all the components that are formed under their influence are nevertheless of the same order.

Perhaps one day geology, chemistry and physiology will join in affirming that the great analogies that there are stated to be between geological fauna and flora and living fauna and flora, from the point of view of form, exist also from the point of view of histology and physiology.

I have already set forth some differences between geological microzymas of various origin: thus, while bacteria may appear with the limestone of Armissan and that of Barbentane, these are never developed in the case of chalk or of Oolithic limestone under the same circumstances.

Analogous differences may be met with among the microzymas of living beings.

It is remarkable that the microzymas of limestones that I have examined are almost without action at low temperatures, and that their activity only develops between 35 and 40 degrees. A glacial temperature, comparable to that of the valley of Obi, would completely arrest this activity."

Though many ridiculed such new and startlingly original ideas and though many nowadays continue to do so, we have to remember that the mysteries of chalk could bear much more investigation.

Modern geologists seem ready to admit that chalk possesses some remarkable qualities, that under certain conditions it produces movements that might evidence life and induce something like fermentation. Professor Bastian, though his inferences differ completely from Béchamp's, again confirms the latter's researches.

---

1. *Comptes Rendus* 70, p.914. *Les Microzymas*, A. Béchamp, p.944.

We read in *The Origin of Life*:

"We may, therefore, well recognise that the lower the forms
of life – the nearer they are to their source – the greater is
likely to have been the similarity among those that have been
produced in different ages, just as the lowest forms are now
practically similar in all regions of the earth.

How, otherwise, consistently with the doctrine of evolution,
are we to account for the fact that different kinds of bacilli
and micrococci have been found in animal and vegetable
remains in the Triassic and Permian strata, in Carboniferous
limestone and even as low as the Upper Devonian strata?
(See *Ann. des Sciences Nat. (Bot.)*, 1896, II, pp.275-349.)

Is it conceivable that with mere lineal descent such variable
living things could retain the same primitive forms through
all the changing ages? Is it not far simpler and more probable
to suppose, especially in the light of the experimental evidence
now adduced, that instead of having to do with unbroken
descent from ancestors through these aeons of time as Darwin
taught, and is commonly believed, we are instead dealing,
in the case of bacteria and their allies, with successive new
births of such organisms throughout these ages as primordial
forms of life, compelled by their different but constantly
recurring molecular constitutions to take such and such
recurring forms and properties, just as would be the case
with successive new births of different kinds of crystals ?"[1]

We have introduced this quotation merely to show the confirmation
by Bastian of Béchamp's discovery of living elements in chalk and
limestone, and we must leave it to geologists to determine whether
infiltration or other extraneous sources do or do not account for
the phenomena.

If they do not, we might be driven to believe in Professor Bastian's
explanation of successively recurring new births of chemical origin –
were it not for Professor Béchamp's elucidation of all organised beings
taking their rise from the microzymas, which we may identify with
what are now known as microsomes when found in cells, whether
animal or vegetable.

Thus we see that Béchamp's teaching can explain appearances which
without it can only be accounted for by spontaneous generation, as
shown by Professor Bastian. Whether Béchamp was correct in his belief
that the microzymas in chalk are the living remains of dead beings of

---

1. *The Origin of Life*, H. Charlton Bastian, pp.67,68.

long past ages is not a point that we care to elaborate. We wish to leave the subject of chalk to those qualified to deal with it and have only touched on it here because these initial observations of Professor Béchamp were what led to his views of the cell – since confirmed by modern cytology – and to what may be termed his 'microzymian doctrine', which we are inclined to believe has been too much neglected by the modern school of medicine.

Those disposed to ridicule Béchamp may well ponder the fact that the first word rather than the last is all that has been said so far about micro-organisms. For instance, it is now claimed that in the same manner that coral is derived from certain minute sea insects, so particular micro-organisms not only aid in the decomposition of rocks and in the formation of chalk and limestone, but play an active part in the forming of iron deposits.[1]

Though, as we have said, derided by some, Béchamp's work at this time was beginning to attract a great amount of attention, and midway through the 1860s it gained for him an enthusiastic co-partner in his labours. This was Professor Estor, physician and surgeon at the hospital at Montpellier, and who, besides being involved in practical work, was a man thoroughly accustomed to research, and abundantly versed in scientific theories. He had been astounded by the discoveries of

---

1. Attention has been drawn to a remarkable and up-to-date parallel of Béchamp's discovery of microzymas in chalk. See The *Iron and Coal Trades Review* for May 4th, 1923. In this, in an article on *Coal Miners' Nystagmus*, Dr. Frederick Robson puts forward a statement by a Professor Potter that:

> "there are in coal bacteria capable of producing gases, and that the gases isolated are methane, carbon dioxide and carbon monoxide, with heating up to 2°C (35–36°F).
>
> It would appear as if wood were capable of containing in its metamorphosed state (coal) the bacteria originally present in the tree stage of its existence. It is possible, too, that different kinds of orders of flora would give rise to the presence of different species of bacteria... possibly resident in the woody-fibred coal...
>
> This idea of bacterial invasion of coal suggests that some degree of oxidation may be due to the great army of aerobic or anaerobic bacteria which may give rise to oxidation and may be the genesis of coal gases in the pits, i.e. that oxidation is due to living organisms with increase of 2°C of heat. This has been disproved, but it is evident that bacteria exist....
>
> There is evidence to show that at 100°C (212°F) all bacterial action ceases. If soft coals and bacterial invasion go hand in hand, in some kind of relationship, then as the coal measures become harder from east to west, the microbic invasion or content may diminish with the ratio of gaseous liberation."

Thus more modern corroboration is found of Béchamp's astounding discovery; while it is due to him alone that we may understand the origin of the so-called bacteria. According to his teaching, these must be the surviving microzymas, or microsomes, of the cells of prehistoric trees, known to us now in their fossilised form as coal, but still preserving intact the infinitesimal lives that once built up primeval vegetation.

Professor Béchamp, which he described as laying the foundation stone of cellular physiology. In 1865 he published in the *Messager du Midi* an article that placed in great prominence Béchamp's explanation of fermentation as an act of cellular nutrition. This conception made a sensation in Germany, for while in a sense confirming Virchow's cellular doctrine, it showed the German scientist's view to be only a partial explanation of the truth.

Béchamp's star was now at its zenith. Conscious that his great discovery, as he proceeded with it, would illumine the processes of life and death as never before in the course of medical history, he was also happy in finding a zealous collaborator who was to share in his work with persistence and loyalty, while at the same time a group of pupils gathered, full of eagerness to forward his researches.

Indistinguishable in the distance, however, loomed a tiny cloud that would soon grow to darken his horizon.

France was in trouble. Her whole silk industry was threatened by mysterious diseases among silkworms. Unsolicited and unassisted financially, Béchamp at once turned his mind to the problem, not knowing when he did so that it was to bring him into direct rivalry with the man who had been appointed officially, and that, while providing the latter with solutions to the enigma, he would receive no gratitude – but instead he would earn the undying hatred and jealousy of Fortune's favourite, Louis Pasteur.

9.
Diseases of Silkworms

At the beginning of 1865, the epidemic among silkworms had become so acute that the sericultural industry of France was seriously threatened. Eggs, worms, chrysalides and moths were all affected. The trouble was characterised by the presence of a microscopic object called the 'vibrant corpuscle', or 'Corpuscle of Cornalia', after the scientist who first observed it; while the malady became popularly known as *pébrine*, from the patois word *pébré*, pepper.

It appears to have been through the advocacy of Dumas that Pasteur was appointed by the Minister of Agriculture to investigate the matter, and no one can have attended a popular lecture on the subject without being informed that Pasteur's work redeemed for his country more money than the war indemnity wrung from France by the Germans after 1870.

What really happened was that Pasteur's luck stood him in extraordinarily good stead; for had Professor Béchamp not provided him with the solution to the silkworm mystery, a very different story might have been told.

Nothing better illustrates the acuteness of Béchamp's intellect than the rapidity with which he solved the cause of *pébrine* and suggested a preventive. Although he was entirely unassisted and obliged to defray any expenses out of his own pocket, already in the year 1865 he was able to state that *pébrine* was a parasitical disease, and that creosote could be used to prevent the attack of the parasite.

Meantime, however, Pasteur had been entrusted by the Government with the official investigation of the silkworm problems, and no one who understands anything of departmental red tape will wonder that, instead of at once accepting Béchamp's verdict, agricultural societies waited to hear the pronouncement of the official representative. Plenty of patience had to be exercised!

Pasteur arrived on his mission at Alais in June 1865, having, as he stated before long in his note to the Academy of Science,[1] 'no serious title' to his fresh employment owing to his ignorance of the subject. 'I

---

1. *Comptes Rendus* 61, p.506.

have never even touched a silkworm,' he had written previously to Dumas. The perusal of an essay on the history of the worm by Quatrefages comprised his study up to June 1865.

Yet, as some statement was expected from him, he managed to put together a submission to the Academy of Science on the 25th September of the same year, in which he provided the following extraordinary description:

> "The corpuscles are neither animal nor vegetable, but bodies more or less analogous to cancerous cells or those of pulmonary tuberculosis. From the point of view of a methodic classification, they should rather be compared to globules of pus, or globules of blood, or even granules of starch, rather than to infusoria or moulds. They do not appear to be free, as many authors think, in the body of the animal, but well contained in the cells... It is the chrysalides, rather than the worm, that one should try to submit to proper remedies." [1]

One may well appreciate that such a description evoked ridicule from Professor Béchamp, who scornfully wrote:

> "...this chemist, who is occupying himself with fermentation, has not even begun to decide whether or not he is dealing with a ferment." [2]

What Pasteur *had* done, however, was to give a detailed description that was wrong in every particular. There, for a considerable time, he left the matter, while the deaths of his father and two of his daughters intervened, and he was invited as a guest to spend a week with the Emperor and Empress at the Palace of Compiégne.

Napoleon III, we are told, was deeply interested in science. At any rate, he and the Empress listened patiently to Pasteur's discourses. The latter was not only brought into close contact with eminent diplomats and the shining lights of art and literature, but was singled out from among these celebrities for special Imperial favours. His silkworm perplexities were confided to Eugénie, and she encouraged him to fresh endeavours. Limelight is invariably thrown upon those smiled upon by Imperial personages, and so it is easy to understand the increasing deference that began to be shown to Pasteur by most of his peers.

As regards the silkworm diseases, instead of being watchful for the

---

1. *Comptes Rendus* 61, p.506.
2. *Les Grands Problémes Medicaux*, A. Béchamp, p.7.

correct verdict, the world at large merely waited to hear what Pasteur had to say on the subject.

In February 1866, Pasteur again left for that part of France then suffering from the trouble, and this time fortified himself with the company of scientific assistants. The Government again gave all the help possible, and the Minister of Public Instruction granted special leave of absence to a Professor Gemez at the College of Louis le Grand, so that he might be free to help Pasteur. Yet in spite of all this assistance, and notwithstanding extra early rising, his biographer has to admit that the results Pasteur arrived at 'were being much criticised'.[1] His actual pronouncements his son-in-law has wisely passed over, and instead has introduced various topics to divert the attention of the reader who might persist in asking: 'What was Pasteur's solution to the silkworm mystery?'

Fortunately, we can find the exact answers in the reports of the French Academy of Science. The first one to turn to, however, is a note not by Pasteur, but by Professor Béchamp, dated 18th June, 1866.[2]

In the midst of his professorial duties and his constant researches on other matters, Béchamp snatched time to send to the Academy fuller details of the disease *pébrine* and measures for preventing it. His note was entitled *On the Harmlessness of the Vapours of Creosote in the Rearing of Silkworms*. He repeated the pronouncement he had made the previous year, and clearly stated:

> "The disease is parasitical. *Pébrine* attacks the worms at the start from the outside and the germs of the parasite come from the air. The disease, in a word, *is not primarily constitutional*."

He went on to explain how he developed the eggs, or the seeds as they are called, of the silkworms in an enclosure in which the odour of creosote was produced from a very minute dose of the drug. The eggs thus hatched were all free from *pébrine*. As Professor Béchamp never committed himself to statements until he had proof positive, we find in this verdict upon *pébrine* the decisive clearness that characterises all his opinions.

Pasteur was still so much in the dark that he had not even the acumen to gauge the correctness of Béchamp's views. But this note of Béchamp's was, no doubt, a trial to him; here was another worker

---

1. *The Life of Pasteur*, René Vallery-Radot, p.133.
2. *Comptes Rendus* 62, p.1341.

pronouncing upon a subject that had been officially relegated to him by the Empress. Accordingly, on the 23rd July, 1866, Pasteur unburdened himself of a statement to the Academy of Science on the nature of *Pébrine*. It was entitled *New Studies on the Disease of Silkworms*.[1]

And here we must look for the great discovery said to have been provided by Pasteur for 'the salvation of sericulture'. It was this:

> "The healthy moth is the moth free from corpuscles; the healthy seed is that derived from moths without corpuscles."

Such an obvious conclusion is laughable.

Still, as it could not be condemned as actually being incorrect, it would have been just as well for Pasteur to have ventured no further. Instead, he proceeded:

> "I am very much inclined to believe that there is not an actual disease of silkworms. I cannot better make clear my opinion of silkworm disease than by comparing it to the effects of pulmonary phthisis. My observations of this year have fortified me in the opinion that these little organisms are neither animalcules nor cryptogamic plants. It appears to me that it is chiefly the cellular tissue of all the organs that is transformed into corpuscles or produces them."

Not a single proof did he bring forward of a fact that would, if true, have been marvellous: not a single suggestion did he give of any experiment to determine the asserted absence of life in the corpuscle or their relation to the disease. Finally, he went out of his way to contradict Béchamp, and in so doing set a definite seal on his blunder:

> "One would be tempted to believe, especially from the resemblance of the corpuscles to the spores of mucorina, that a parasite had invaded the nurseries. *That would be an error.*"

This intentional dig at another worker was singularly unlucky, for it provides proof of Pasteur's rebuttal of a correct solution – one to which he afterwards laid claim. Here was the man who had so utterly renounced his former sponteparist views as to ascribe all fermentative effects, all vital phenomena, to airborne causes, now denying the extraneous origin of a disease that was proved by Béchamp to be undoubtedly parasitic.

Béchamp at once fortified his conclusions with an account of the

---

1. *Comptes Rendus* 63, p.126–142.

experiments upon which he had based them. On the 13th August, 1866, he presented a note to the Academy of Science: *Researches on the Nature of the Prevailing Disease of Silkworms.*[1] In this he described a process of washing the seeds and worms, which gave proof that those affected had been invaded by a parasite. In answer to Pasteur he declared that the vibrant corpuscle

> "...is not a pathological production, something analogous to a globule of pus, or a cancer cell, or to pulmonary tubercles, but is distinctly *a cell of a vegetable nature.*"

Again, on the 27th August, another note to the Academy[2] described experiments that proved the vibrant corpuscle to be an organised ferment.

Later, on the 4th February of the following year, 1867, a new memoir sent to the Academy[3] detailed more experiments that not only showed the corpuscle to be a ferment, but also that after the inversion of sugar, fermentation went on, producing alcohol, acetic acid and another non-volatile acid.

In January, 1867, Pasteur, who had been away, returned to Alais, apparently at last enlightened by Professor Béchamp's explanations. In a letter to Duruy, the Minister of Public Instruction, he seems to have started to claim for himself credit for solving the mystery of the silkworm trouble. This would account for the plea put forward by Béchamp for recognition of his outstanding priority in providing a correct scientific explanation.

On the 29th April, 1867, Béchamp provided the Academy of Science[4] with an even fuller account in which he stated his opinion that the vibrant corpuscle was a spore, and demonstrated that it multiplied in an infusion of dead worms, chrysalides and moths, and that creosote diminished this multiplication. He added to this note a plate of designs of the microscopic examination of this reproduction of corpuscles. He added:

> "Thus is completed the parasitic theory of *pébrine* for the triumph of which I have struggled for nearly two years. I venture to hope that the priority of the idea and of the experiments that have demonstrated it will not be disputed."

---

1. *Comptes Rendus* 63, p.311.
2. *ibid*, p.391.
3. *Comptes Rendus* 64, p.231.
4. *ibid*, p.873.

He showed that up to the previous August, he had been alone in holding his opinion, with the exception of M. Le Ricque de Monchy, to whom he expressed gratitude for his encouragement and able assistance.

Unfortunately for Béchamp, Pasteur was devoid of the habit of rendering due honour. Convinced against his will by the Professor's irrefutable proofs, there was nothing for him to do but turn a complete about face, as he had done before when Béchamp had incontestably proved the erroneousness of belief in spontaneous generation.

On the same date, 29th April, 1867, we find among the reports of the Academy of Science[1] a letter from Pasteur to Dumas, dated Alais, 24th April. In this letter, Pasteur feebly excused his mistake on the grounds that he had held his erroneous view in good company with 'many persons of great repute', and he also pleaded the impossibility of recognising the mode of reproduction of the corpuscles. Instead of any acknowledgment to Professor Béchamp for his revelations, Pasteur coolly expressed the hope that he himself would soon be able to present an almost complete study of the disease. His omission to do so then and there seems noteworthy proof of a continued want of clear understanding.

We find among the reports[2] of the 20th May, 1867, a letter addressed to the President of the Academy of Science by Béchamp, dated the 13th May, on the subject of Pasteur's communication of the previous April. He pointed out the error of Pasteur's former views, and asserted his own priority in discovering the true nature of the corpuscles and their mode of reproduction.

On the same date he brought forward[3] *New Facts to Help the History of the Prevailing Disease of Silkworms and the Nature of the Vibrant Corpuscle.* Here he claimed that the corpuscles were airborne and to be found on mulberry leaves, the greatest care therefore being necessitated in the preparation of leaves destined for the food of the worms. But the most noteworthy fact in this memoir is that Béchamp identified another silkworm disease in addition to *pébrine.*

Observations had already been made by the naturalist Joly of the presence of vibrios in the intestinal canal of sick worms, to which the name of *morts-flats* or *resté-petits* had been given, but as much ignorance prevailed in regard to this disease, which came to be known as *flacherie,*

---

1. *Comptes Rendus* 64, p.835.
2. *ibid*, p.1049.
3. *ibid*, p.1043.

as had existed over *pébrine*.

On the 11th of the previous April, Professor Béchamp had already published a pamphlet on this second silkworm disease, and afterwards, in July 1868, forwarded his account to the Academy of Science, which inserted a reference to it.[1] In this pamphlet he wrote:

> "A non-corpuscular seed may and often does contain, as observed by de Monchy and by me, other products besides the spherules of the vitellus and the fatty globules. They are the motile points, much smaller than all the others that surround them, and often excessively numerous. We call these motile points *microzyma aglaiae* temporarily, until we determine positively their significance.
>
> To sum up, as long as their parents are unknown, the best course will be to procure seed only that is not corpuscular, either internally or externally, and that is free from the *microzyma aglaiae*."

In his communication of the 20th May he went further in his description, and showed that in this other disease the vibrant corpuscles might be entirely absent, while, instead, motile particles were noticeable – like those he had observed in chalk and equally minute, and on these he now bestowed the name *microzyma bombycis,* on account of the way in which they were coupled two by two, like a figure of eight.[2]

The next reports that we find on the subject of silkworm disease are on 3rd June, 1867.[3] They are two letters from Pasteur, addressed to Dumas.

Regarding the first, Pasteur has to make a curious explanation. It is dated 'Alais, 30th April', and in a note Pasteur says that this letter left Alais on the 4th May and that by a postal error it only reached Dumas on the 22nd May. Be that as it may, the 30th April is, anyway, posterior to the 11th April, when Professor Béchamp had put forward his first explanation of *flacherie*; neither does Pasteur in his letter do more than allude to the corpuscular malady as not being the only torment of sericulture. As a precaution against *pébrine* he put forward his system of taking seed only from moths free from corpuscles, which, as Béchamp pointed out,[4] was an absurdity, considering the parasitic nature of the complaint and the fact that the parasites abounded on mulberry leaves.

The other letter to Dumas, published on the 3rd June, 1867, was

1. *Comptes Rendus* 67, p.102.
2. *Les Grands Problémes Médicaux*, A. Béchamp, p.26.
3. *Comptes Rendus* 64, p.1109 and p.1113.
4. *Les Grands Problémes Médicaux*, p.25.

dated 'Alais, 21st May'. Here Pasteur stated that another trouble was often wrongly confused with *pébrine,*

> "...because in a great number of cases the two diseases had
> no connection, or at least not directly."

Considering the complete disparity of the two complaints, as already shown by Béchamp, the vibrant corpuscles being often entirely absent in the case of *flacherie,* this comment of Pasteur's is noteworthy as showing that he did not possess his rival's comprehension of the subject.

Béchamp, meanwhile, worked hard and sent to the Commission on Sericulture a memoir entitled *On the Transformation of the Vibrant Corpuscle of Pébrine and on the Nature of the Disease called 'Resté-Petits'.* This important communication the Academy of Science published only in abstract on the 10th June, 1867; while on the 1st July of the same year the Academy published another memoir, also first sent by Béchamp to the Commission on Sericulture, and entitled *On the Saccharification of the Vibrant Corpuscle of Pébrine.*

Here he gave a full description of the corpuscle, showing it to lose its oscillating movement in a solution of caustic potash, but to be insoluble in this liquid. He found it to be soluble in sulphuric acid on boiling, and proved that glucose could be produced from it by successive treatment with sulphuric acid, barium carbonate, alcohol and water, and came to the conclusion that the vibrant particle contains cellulose.

From Pasteur, the official inquirer into the diseases of silkworms, the reports of the Academy of Science provide no further communication on the subject for almost a year.

From Béchamp, on the contrary, a series of memoirs show the way in which his detailed, persevering work on micro-organisms led to his final comprehension of the silkworm disease called *flacherie.*

He had already, on the 2nd April, 1867, sent up a note to the Academy on *Microscopic Organisms in Saliva.* The matter was so new and unexpected that only a résumé was given.[1]

On the 24th February, 1868, he sent up a note on *The Molecular Granulations (Microzymas) of Ferments and of Animal Tissues.*[2] Here he drew attention to the micro-organisms to be found in vaccine virus, a plagiarised confirmation of which was given by Chauveau.

On the 2nd March, 1868, he sent a note on *The Molecular Granulations (Microzymas) of the Cells of the Liver.*[3]

---

1. *Comptes Rendus* 64, p.696.
2. *Comptes Rendus* 66, p.421.
3. *ibid,* p.366.

On the 4th May, 1868, he submitted *On the Origin and Development of Bacteria*.[1] This was a general demonstration of bacterial development from the anatomically elemental microzymas.

It was on the 8th June, 1868, that he applied all the preceding facts to the disease of *flacherie* in a note titled *On the Microzymian Disease of Silkworms*.[2] Here he stated *flacherie* to be hereditary, owing to the abnormal development of the inherent elemental microzymas of the silkworm. He showed that the microzymas might be seen singly or associated in chaplets, or in the form of very small bacteria. To see them a very high power of the microscope was needed, nothing less than obj. 7, Oc. 1, Nachet. He stated that the microscopes supplied to workers by the Government were not strong enough.

He showed that microzymas and bacteria might exist in the same worm, but it appeared worthy of attention that the number of microzymas was in an inverse ratio to that of the bacteria. It was useless to take seed from moths with the complaint, which was distinguishable by an examination of the contents of the abdomen. He pointed out that to isolate the microzymas, they should be treated with a preparation of caustic potash, which, dissolving everything else, would leave the elemental micro-organisms.

Thus, as he had at first fully explained the cause and the mode of prevention of *pébrine*, so now Professor Béchamp made an equally clear and complete explanation of the second silkworm disease, *flacherie*. He showed that, unlike *pébrine*, it was *not* caused by an extraneous parasitic invasion, but was due to an abnormal unhealthy development of the microzymas in the body cells of the silkworms.

The sericultural troubles had thus given him a chance to demonstrate his full understanding of disease conditions. He was able to provide a clear exposition of, on the one hand, a parasitic complaint, and on the other of one due not to a foreign agent, but to a diseased status of anatomical elements.

Pasteur was well acquainted with all the notes published by Béchamp, but, regrettably to say, had not the generosity to offer praise for his rival's scientific triumph. It is undeniable that his thought was of himself, and how he could best vindicate his own pretensions.

Béchamp's explanation of *flacherie* appeared, as we have shown, among the reports of the Academy of Science on the 8th June, 1868. On the 29th June the reports include[3] a letter to Dumas from Pasteur

1. *Comptes Rendus* 66, p.859.
2. *ibid*, p.1160.
3. *ibid*, p.1289.

dated 24th June, 1868. Here, it is extraordinary to find that *he actually dared to claim that he had been the first to draw attention to this second silkworm disease* and distinguish it from *pébrine*.

But no doubt realising that the Academy reports were destitute of any such proof, he demanded the insertion of the full text of a note that he claimed to have sent on the 1st June, 1868, to the Agricultural Society of Alais. It was duly inserted with Pasteur's letter, and was entitled *Note on the Silkworm Disease commonly known as 'Morts-Blancs' or 'Morts-Flats'*.

A perusal of these communications by Pasteur leaves one marvelling that he was able to impose upon the world the idea that it was he who had elucidated the diseases of silkworms. Just as he had been astray in regard to *pébrine*, so, even now after all the time he had been at work, he had nothing valuable to say about *flacherie*. He referred to the organisms associated with the disease without any allusion to the fact that Joly of the Faculty of Science of Toulouse, as well as Professor Béchamp, had observed them long before him. He thought there was nothing to show that these organisms caused the complaint, but that they were the result of digestive trouble. He wrote:

> "The intestine, no longer functioning, for some unknown reason, the materials it encloses are situated as though inside an immovable vessel."

Béchamp, naturally, felt obliged to answer Pasteur; and so among the reports of the French Academy of Science,[1] on the 13th July, 1868, we find a note from the Professor titled *On the Microzymian Disease of Silkworms, in Regard to a Recent Communication from M. Pasteur*.

Here, Béchamp refers to his previous pamphlet, published on the 11th April, 1867, in which he and Le Ricque de Monchy had drawn attention to the organisms associated with *morts-flats*. He refers to his past communication of the 13th May, published among the Academy reports of the 20th May, and also to his note of the 10th June, 1867. He shows how again on the 28th March, 1868, he published a second edition of his pamphlet, to which he added further opinions on the microzymian complaint, otherwise *flacherie*. He also draws attention to the fact that as far back as the 4th July, 1867, a member of the silkworm industry (M. Raibaud l'Ange) had written to ask to be allowed to visit him at Montpellier to study the disease.

Pasteur responded by calling M. Raibaud l'Ange to his help, only

---

1. *Comptes Rendus* 67, p.102.

for the latter to confess that he had visited Montpellier for the desired object. Yet such was the fear of offending the Government representative, the man honoured by Imperial patronage, that M. Raibaud l'Ange, all the same, championed Pasteur with flattery and ridiculed the microzymas.[1]

Béchamp replied to Raibaud l'Ange on the 17th August, 1868, reminding him of the table of designs that had accompanied his note of the 8th June, 1867.[2]

No one replied. As Béchamp afterwards said,[3] the Academy might submit to plagiarism, but no one could deny it. No doubt it was the total inability to set aside Béchamp's just claims that made Pasteur so hate his brilliant rival from this time henceforward. Béchamp's extraordinary success in dealing with the silkworm diseases was all the more remarkable because he had no help – pecuniary or otherwise – from the Government, and no time to expend on the problem except what he could snatch from a professorial career already filled with work quite apart from any of his scientific researches.

Pasteur, on the other hand, had Government help at his disposal, every expense defrayed and scientific assistants. Moreover, he was given complete leisure to carry out his researches. That another should have so profoundly succeeded where he had failed must have been a source of bitterness to him, and his jealousy led him into a veritable persecution of Béchamp. He was sure of his own position, which had the highest influence to back it, and we may be certain that he did not allow himself to pass from the memory of his Imperial patrons. He commenced his book on vinous fermentation with a foreword to the Emperor, while a dedication to the Empress in the same way prefaced his book on the disease of silkworms. We may search in vain through this for any generous reference to the first elucidator of these troubles. Instead, he takes all the credit to himself[4] and even goes out of his way to deride Béchamp's arguments in favour of creosote as a preventive.[5]

But there is truth in the American dictum that you may fool all the people some of the time and some of the people all of the time, but never all of the people all of the time; and so Pasteur's selfish claims must completely fail in face of the scientific reports to which we have given reference, and which are available to anyone, for instance, in

1. *Comptes Rendus* 67, p.301.
2. *ibid*, p.443.
3. *Les Grands Problémes Médicaux*, p.29.
4. *Études sur la Maladie des Vers-a-Soie*, Pasteur, p.11.
5. *ibid*, p.47.

the Library of the British Museum. These incontestably prove that the man who made such gains for France in regard to aniline dyes was also the man who provided his country with the correct diagnosis of the silkworm diseases and suggested methods of prevention.

Unfortunately, practical measures were left to Pasteur, and the best commentary upon them are facts in regard to the sericultural industry put forward by Dr. Lutaud,[1] at one time editor of the *Journal de Médecine de Paris*.

At the commencement of the silkworm trouble, about 1850, we are told that France produced annually about 30,000,000 kilograms of cocoons. In 1866-7, the production had sunk to 15,000,000 kilograms. After the introduction of Pasteur's 'preventive method', production diminished from 8,000,000 kilograms in 1873 to even as low as 2,000,000 kilograms of cocoons in certain subsequent years. Dr. Lutaud wrote:

> "That is the way in which Pasteur saved sericulture! The reputation which he still preserves in this respect among ignorami and the short-sighted has been brought into being
>
> 1) by himself, by means of inaccurate assertions;
>
> 2) by the sellers of microscopic seeds on the Pasteur system, who have realised big benefits at the expense of the cultivators; and
>
> 3) by the complicity of the Academies and public bodies, which, without any investigation, reply to the cultivators: 'But sericulture is saved! Make use of Pasteur's system!' However, not everybody is disposed to employ a system that consists of enriching oneself by the ruination of others."

Perhaps the greatest harm occasioned by Pasteur's jealousy was the barrier he set up to any notice being taken of Béchamp's work, particularly in regard to his cell doctrine and microzymian theories.

So much effort did Pasteur put into flouting these ideas that members of the Academy, influenced by friendly motives, actually begged Professor Béchamp to drop the very use of the word *microzyma*!

Thus the misfortune came about that, instead of being encouraged, science was held back, and at every turn Béchamp found himself hampered in the work that should have laid the foundations of cytology and physiology, and elucidated the processes of the anatomical elements in birth and life, in health and disease, in death and in disruption.

---

1. *Études sur la Rage*, Dr. Lutaud, pp.427,428.

Who gave the correct diagnosis of the silkworm diseases Pébrine and Flacherie – Béchamp or Pasteur?

1865

Béchamp	Pasteur
Statement before the Agricultural Society of Hérault that *pébrine* is a parasitical complaint and creosote suggested as a preventive of the parasite.	Statement to the Academy of Science[4] that the corpuscles of *pébrine* are neither animal nor vegetable. From the point of view of classification, they should be ranged beside globules of pus, or globules of blood, or better still, granules of starch!

1866

18 June[1]

Statement to the Academy of Science that the disease is parasitical; that *pébrine* attacks the worms at the start from the outside and that the parasite comes from the air. The disease is not primarily constitutional. Method given for hatching seeds free from *pébrine*.

23 July[5]

Statement to the Academy of Science that one would be tempted to believe that a parasite had invaded the chambers: however that would be an error. Inclined to believe that there is no special disease of silkworms, but that it should be compared to the effects of pulmonary phthisis. Little organisms neither animalcules nor cryptogamic plants.

13 August[2]

Statement to the Academy of Science describing the parasite as a cell of a vegetable nature.

27 August[3]

Statement to the Academy of Science proving the vibrant corpuscle, *pébrine*, to be an organised ferment.

---

1. *Comptes Rendus* 62, p.1341.
2. *Comptes Rendus* 63, p.311.
3. *ibid*, p.391.
4. *Comptes Rendus* 61, p.506.
5. *Comptes Rendus* 63, pp.126–142.

1867

Béchamp	**Pasteur**
4 February[1]	*29 April*[4]
Statement to Academy of Science on further research in connection with *pébrine* as an organised ferment.	Confession of error in having believed, in company with many persons of great repute, that the vibrant corpuscles, *pébrine*, were analogous to globules of blood, pus, or starch!
11 April	
Publication of a pamphlet in which attention was called to another silk-worm disease – *morts-flats*, or *resté-petits*, commonly known as *flacherie*.	*3 June*[5]
	A letter to Dumas communicated to the Academy of Science. Safeguard against disease is to take seed only from moths free from corpuscles (a statement that proves the parasitical nature of *pébrine* to have been still uncomprehended by Pasteur). An allusion to the corpuscular malady as not the only torment of sericulture.
29 April[2]	
Statement to the Academy of Science on the vibrant corpuscle, *pébrine*, demonstrating it to be a spore, and supplying a plate of designs. Hope expressed that the priority of his correct diagnosis will not be disputed.	
	Another letter[6] to Dumas communicated to the Academy of Science stating another trouble often to be confounded with *pébrine*, but that "in a great number of cases the two diseases had no connection or at least not directly!" (As they had no connection at all, the uncertainty of his ideas is apparent.)
20 May[3]	
Statement to the Academy on 'new facts', and the other disease, *flacherie*, clearly distinguished from *pébrine*.	
10 June	
Academy of Science published an extract from a communication on the two diseases previously sent to the Commission on Sericulture.	

---

1. *Comptes Rendus* 64, p.231.
2. *ibid*, p.873
3. *Comptes Rendus* 63, p.1043.
4. *Comptes Rendus* 64, p.835.
5. *ibid*, p.1109.
6. *ibid*, p.1113.

Béchamp

A series of publications, ending with:

8 June[1]

A communication to the Academy of Science titled *On the Microzymian Disease of Silkworms*, more fatal than *pébrine*, since creosote could be a preventive of the latter, while the former is constitutional and hereditary. The microzymas are to be seen singly or associated in chaplets or in the form of very small bacteria.

No seed should be taken from moths that have the complaint discernible by an examination of the contents of the abdomen under a very high power of the microscope, at the very least the combination obj. 7, oc. 1, Nachet.

Pasteur

29 June[2]

A letter to Dumas communicated to the Academy of Science claiming to have been the first to draw attention to the disease of *morts-flats* and demanding the publication of a communication to the Agricultural Society of Alais on the 1st of the current month.

The latter follows: Reference to the organisms associated with *flacherie*, without any acknowledgment of the prior observations of Joly and Béchamp.

Considers the organisms to be probably the necessary result of digestive trouble.

Corollary

In view of the above, Pasteur's claim of priority in a correct diagnosis of the two silkworm diseases – repeated on p.11 of his *Études sur la Maladie des Vers-a-Soie* – is entirely without foundation.

---

1. *Comptes Rendus* 66, p. 1160.
2. *ibid*, 66, p.1389.

10.
Laboratory Experiments

As we have already seen, at the time when Béchamp and Pasteur turned their attention to the subject of fermentation, only the vaguest conceptions were held in regard to living matter. Grand names were given, such as *protoplasm* and *blastéme*, but so little was known that the albuminoids were believed to be always identical.

Virchow had tried to simplify matters by declaring that the living units of animal and vegetable forms are the cells of the body, and while Henle advanced considerably further by stating that, on the contrary, the cells are themselves built up by minute atoms, the molecular granulations, just distinguishable within them. Schwann had also taught that the atmosphere is filled with infinitesimal living organisms.

Then Béchamp and Pasteur appeared on the scene, the latter first of all affirming the spontaneous origin of ferments, while at the same time Béchamp irrefutably demonstrated that yeast and other organisms are airborne.

Finally Pasteur, converted by Béchamp's illuminating views, became enthusiastic about atmospheric germs and, as we have seen, before a fashionable assembly of the elite claimed for himself all the credit for their elucidation. Yet so little was he really enlightened that we find him soon afterwards denying the parasitic origin of a complaint, *pébrine*, which was genuinely provoked by a parasite, while in the opposite direction his conception of living matter was no more advanced than the old-fashioned view that held the living body to be nothing more than a kind of chemical apparatus. For him, the body contained nothing actually alive; its wonderful workings never suggested to him living autonomous agents.

Of course, to be fair, it may be said that there was no reason why Pasteur should have understood the body. He never received any medical, physiological or biological training, and had no pretensions to being a naturalist. Chemist though he was, he seems to have had no aptitude for the branch of science to which he turned his attention. When he took his degree of Bachelor of Science, his examiner appended a note to his diploma, stating that he was only 'mediocre in chemistry'.

He does not seem even to have been particularly quick in grasping the ideas of other people, for we have seen what a long time it took before he realised the correctness of Béchamp's explanation of *pébrine*.

It was in worldly wisdom that his mind was acute. Fortune favoured him, and he was always on the alert to seize opportunities; but, sad to say, it seems that he was not above pushing himself at someone else's expense, even though the progress of science might be thereby hampered, and we can only deplore this misuse of his admirable persistence and energy.

While Pasteur learned nothing more about life than the fact that there are living organisms in the air, Professor Béchamp continued his untiring experiments. Fate was kind in bringing to his help Professor Estor, another worker fully qualified by training and experience. The two scientists were hard-working men, with their minds well exercised by their daily toil, and their discoveries were consistently founded in their clinical observations.

Béchamp made discoveries in the same way that a Beethoven composes, a Raphael paints and a Dickens writes; that is to say, because he could not help himself – he could not do otherwise. In pathetic contrast, we find men today taken away from practical work and set down in laboratories to make discoveries. In many cases, they have mediocre minds which could never originate an idea of any sort. All they can follow are routine theories and their so-called 'discoveries' are of the type that pile up error upon error. Provide a man with his practical work, and if he has the discoverer's rare insight, as night yields to day, so will practice lead to enlightenment. What is urgently needed is freedom from dogma and the encouragement of original opinions. Minds *en masse* move at a snail's pace, and the greatest impediment, no doubt, to Béchamp's microzymian doctrine was the fact that it so utterly outstripped the scientific conceptions of that period.

What he did, first and foremost, was to lay the foundations of what was then a new science; that of cytology.

Having made his surprising discovery of the minute organisms, agents of fermentation, in chalk, Béchamp's next work was an investigation of the 'molecular granulations' of cells with which he connected the 'little bodies' of chalk and limestone. Up to this date, Henle's vague views regarding the granulations had been ignored and they were widely considered to be mere formless, meaningless particles.

Calling the microscope and polarimeter to his aid and undertaking innumerable chemical experiments, Professor Béchamp, making use at first principally of such organisations as yeast, found the granulations which they contain to be agents provocative of fermentation, and then bestowed on them the explanatory name of *microzyma*.

These same granulations he found in all animal and vegetable cells and tissues and in all organic matter, even though apparently not organised, such as milk, in which he proved them to account for the chemical changes that result in the milk clotting. He found the microzymas teeming everywhere, innumerable in healthy tissues, and in diseased tissues he found them associated with various kinds of bacteria.

One axiom he laid down[1] was that though every microzyma is a molecular granulation, not every molecular granulation is a microzyma. Those that are microzymas he found to be powerful in inducing fermentation, and to be possessed of some structure. In short, it was made clear to him that microzymas, not the cell, are the primary anatomical elements.

It was never his practice to let his imagination outstrip his experiments. Invariably he propounded his question and waited for facts to provide the answer. Working with Professor Estor, observations showed that not only are the molecular granulations, the microzymas, anatomical elements, autonomously living, with organisation and life inseparably united in their minute selves, but that it is due to these myriad lives that cells and tissues are constituted living; in fact, that all organisms, whether the one-celled amoeba in its pristine simplicity or man in his varied complexity, are associations of these minute living entities.

A modern text book[2] sums up Béchamp's primary teaching:

> "Their behaviour" (that of the molecular granulations, here named *microsomes*) "is in some cases such as to have led to the hypothesis long since suggested by Henle (1841) and at a later period developed by Béchamp and Estor and especially by Altmann, that *microsomes* are actually units or bioblasts, capable of assimilation, growth and division, and hence to be regarded as elementary units of structure, standing between the cell and the ultimate molecules of living matter."

Only some such discovery could clear away the confusion on the subject of spontaneous generation. Superficial observers, among whom we are forced to include Pasteur, continued to maintain that

1. *Les Microzymas*, A. Béchamp, p.133.
2. *The Cell in Development and Inheritance*, Edmund B. Wilson, p.290.

fermentation was only induced by germs from the air; but at the same time Pasteur had to admit that meat, protected from atmospheric contact in an experiment of his own, nonetheless became tainted. Other experimenters insisted upon changes taking place for which atmospheric organisms could not be held responsible.

Béchamp, the first to make clear the fermentative role of airborne agents, was now able, according to his own views, to explain that fermentation might take place apart from these, for all organisms teem with minute living entities capable of producing ferments, and that in fact those found in the air he believed to be simply the same released from plant and animal forms, which they have first built up, but from which they are afterwards freed by that disruption we call death. Béchamp and Estor, working together, began to trace and follow life in its marvellous processes.

At the risk of being wearisome through repetition, we must remind ourselves of the order in which Béchamp achieved his early discoveries.

First, he demonstrated that the atmosphere is filled with minute living organisms capable of causing fermentation in any suitable medium, and that the chemical change in the medium is effected by a ferment engendered by them, which ferment may well be compared to the gastric juice of the stomach.

Secondly, he found in ordinary chalk, and afterwards in limestone, minute organisms capable of producing fermentative changes, and showed these to bear relation to the infinitesimal granulations he had observed in the cells and tissues of plants and animals. He proved these granulations, which he named *microzymas,* to have independent individuality and life, and claimed that they are the antecedents of cells, the genesis of bodily forms; the real anatomical, incorruptible elements.

Thirdly, he set forth that the organisms in the air, the so-called atmospheric germs, are simply either microzymas or their evolutionary forms set free by disruption from their former vegetable or animal habitat, and that the 'little bodies' in the limestone and chalk are the survivors of the living forms of past ages.

Fourthly, he claimed that, at this present time, microzymas constantly develop into the low type of living organisms that go by the name of bacteria.

We have already superficially studied the rigid experiments that established Béchamp's views on the fermentative role of airborne organisms and of those found in chalk; let us now follow a few of the innumerable experiments he carried out in the establishment of his other conclusions. His work was so incessant, and his observations so prolific, that they can only be summarised, and no attempt can be made to trace the exact chronological order of the experiments upon which he based his opinions.

At a very early stage of his researches, he demonstrated with Professor Estor that air need have nothing to do with the appearance of bacteria in the substance of tissues. Further, these investigators established the independent vitality of the microzymas of certain tissues, certain glands, and so forth, by showing that these minute granules act like organised ferments and that they can develop into bacteria, passing through certain intermediary stages which they described; these intermediate stages having been regarded by many authorities *as different species*.

We have seen that the basic solution of the whole mystery for Béchamp was his discovery of the 'little bodies' in chalk, which possess the power of inverting cane sugar, liquefying starch, and otherwise proving themselves agents of fermentation. The strata in which he found them were regarded by geologists as being at least eleven million years old, and Béchamp questioned whether the 'little bodies' he had named *microzyma cretae* could really be the surviving remains of the fauna and flora of such long-past ages. Not having centuries at his disposal to test the problem, he determined to see for himself what would remain now at this present time of a body buried with strict precautions. He knew that, in the ordinary way, an interred corpse was soon reduced to dust, unless embalmed or subjected to a very low temperature, in which cases the check to decomposition would be explained by the inherent granules, the microzymas, becoming dormant.

At the beginning of 1868, he therefore took the carcass of a kitten and laid it in a bed of pure carbonate of lime, specially prepared and creosoted, while a much thicker layer covered the body.[1] The whole was placed in a glass jar, the open top of which was closed by several sheets of paper placed in such a way that air would be continually renewed without permitting the intrusion of dust or organisms. This was left on a shelf in Béchamp's laboratory until the end of the year 1874. The upper bed of carbonate of lime was then removed and proved to be entirely soluble in hydrochloric acid. Some centimetres further down, there were to be found only some fragments of bone and dry matter. Not the slightest smell was perceptible, nor was the carbonate

---

1. See *Les Microzymas*, A. Béchamp, p.625 and onwards.

of lime discoloured. This artificial chalk was as white as ordinary chalk, and, except for the microscopic crystals of aragonite found in precipitated carbonate of lime, indistinguishable from it, and showed under the microscope brilliant 'molecules', such as those seen in the chalk of Sens. One part of this carbonate of lime was then placed in creosoted starch, and another part in creosoted sweetened water. Fermentation took place just as though ordinary chalk had been used, but more actively. Microzymas were not seen in the upper stratum of the carbonate of lime, but in that portion where the kitten's body had rested, they swarmed in their thousands in each microscopic field. After filtering the carbonate of lime through a silken sieve, it was taken up with dilute hydrochloric acid, and Béchamp thereby succeeded in separating the microzymas which had been made visible by the microscope.

At the end of this experiment, which had continued for over six and a half years, Béchamp followed it with another which lasted seven years. To meet the possible criticism that the body of the kitten had been the prey of germs of the air which might have been carried in its hair or admitted into its lungs by breathing when alive, or into its intestinal canal, Béchamp now employed more rigid precautions.

This time, in addition to burying the whole carcass of a kitten he also buried, in one case, a kitten's liver, and in another the heart, lungs and kidneys. These viscera had been plunged into carbolic acid the moment they had been detached from the slaughtered animal. This experiment, commenced in the climate of Montpellier in the month of June 1875, had to be transported to Lille at the end of August 1876 and was terminated there in August 1882.

Owing to the temperate climate of Lille, very different from that of Montpellier (which for a great part of the year is almost sub-tropical), the destruction of the body was much less advanced in this later experiment than it had been in the previous one. All the same, in the beds of carbonate of lime near the remains, in one case of the whole kitten and in the other of the viscera, microzymas swarmed and there were also well-formed bacteria. Moreover, the chalk was impregnated with organic matter, which coloured it a yellowish brown, but the whole was odourless.

In these two experiments, Béchamp found convincing confirmation of views that had been already suggested to him by many other observations.

To begin with, they supported his belief that the 'little bodies', the microzymas, of natural chalk are the living remains of the plant and animal forms of which in past ages they were the constructive cellular elements. It was shown that after the death of an organ, its cells disappear, but in their place remain myriads of molecular granulations, or *microzymas*. Here was remarkable proof of the imperishability of these builders of living forms. Neither is the fact of their own independent life denied by a longevity under conditions that would debar them from nutrition throughout immense periods, since we find prolonged abstention from food to be possible even in the animal world among hibernating creatures, while the naturalist can detail many more cases among minute organisms – for instance pond-dwellers, which fast for indefinite intervals when deprived of water, their natural habitat, and fern spores, which also are known to retain a vitality that may lie dormant for many years.

Thus, whether confined within some animal or vegetable body, or freed by the disruption of plant and animal forms, the microzymas, according to Béchamp, were proved capable of preserving vitality in a dormant state even though the period surpassed men's records. It would still be possible for different microzymas to possess varying degrees of vitality, for, as we shall see, Béchamp found differences between the microzymas of various species and organs.

But, over and above finding that the elements of the cells can live on indefinitely after the disruption of the plant or animal bodies that they originally built up, he considered that he had obtained convincing evidence of their ability to develop into the life forms known as bacteria. If not, where did these come from in the case of the buried viscera? Even if airborne germs were not completely excluded in the case of the kitten's body, the utmost precautions had been taken to exclude them in the case of the burial of the inner organs. Yet Béchamp found that the microzymas of the viscera, as well as those of the whole kitten, had evolved into associated microzymas, chaplets of microzymas, and finally into fine bacteria, among which the bacterium *capitatum* appeared in the centre of a great piece of flesh.

Here Béchamp saw how wrong first the great naturalist Cuvier and after him Pasteur had been in assuming

> "...that any part whatever, being separated from the mass of an animal, is by that fact transferred into the order of dead substances and is thereby essentially changed."

By Béchamp's researches it was seen that separate parts of a body maintain some degree of independent life, a belief held by certain modern experimenters who, unlike Béchamp, fail to provide an explanation.

His experiment showed the Professor how it is that bacteria may be found in earth where corpses have been buried and also in manured lands and among surroundings of decaying vegetation. According to him, bacteria are not specially created organisms mysteriously appearing in the atmosphere, but they are the evolutionary forms of microzymas, which build up the cells of plants and animals. After the death of these latter the bacteria, by their nutritive processes, bring about the disruption, or in other words the decomposition, of the plant or animal, resulting in a return to forms approximating to microzymas.

Thus Béchamp taught that every living being has arisen from the microzyma, and also that

"every living being is reducible to the microzyma."[1]

This second axiom of his, he says, accounts for the disappearance of bacteria in the earlier experiment, for just as microzymas may evolve into bacteria, so according to his teaching, bacteria, by an inverse process, may be reduced to the pristine simplicity of the microzyma. Béchamp believed this to have happened in the earlier case, when the destruction of the kitten's carcass was so much more complete than in the second case, when the temperate climate of Lille had prolonged the process of decomposition.

Many indeed were the lessons the indefatigable worker learned from these two series of observations:[2]

1. That the microzymas are the only non-transitory elements of the organism, persisting after the death of the latter and forming bacteria.

2. That there is produced in the organisms of all living beings, including man, in some part and at a given moment, alcohol, acetic acid and other compounds that are normal products of the activity of organised ferments, and that there is no other natural cause of this production than the normal microzymas of the organism. The presence of alcohol, of acetic acid, etc., in the tissues, reveals one of the causes, independent of the phenomenon of oxidation, of the disappearance of sugar in the organism and of the disappearance of the glucogenic matters and that which Dumas called the respiratory foods.

1. *Les Microzymas*, p.925.
2. *ibid.*, pp.628-630.

3. That without the concurrence of any outside influence except a suitable temperature, fermentation will go on in a part withdrawn from an animal, such as the egg, milk, liver, muscle, urine, or, in the case of plants, in a germinating seed, or in a fruit which ripens when detached from the tree, etc. The fermentable matter that disappears earliest in an organ after death is the glucose, glucogenic matter or some other of the compounds called carbohydrates – that is to say, a respiratory food. And the new compounds that appear are the same as those produced in the alcoholic, lactic and butyric fermentations of the laboratory; or, during life, alcohol, acetic acid, lactic or sarcolactic acid, etc...

4. That it is once again proved that the cause of decomposition after death is the same, within the organism, as that which acts, under other conditions, during life – namely, microzymas capable of becoming bacteria by evolution.

5. That the microzymas, after or before their evolution into bacteria, only attack albuminoid or gelatinous matters after the destruction of the matters called carbohydrates.

6. That the microzymas and bacteria, having effected the transformations before mentioned, do not die in a closed apparatus in the absence of oxygen; they go into a state of rest, as does the beer yeast in an environment of the products of the decomposition of the sugar, which products it formed.

7. It is only under certain conditions, particularly in the presence of oxygen, as in the experiment on the kitten buried in carbonate of lime, etc., that the same microzymas or bacteria effect the definite destruction of vegetable or animal matter, reducing it to carbonic acid, water, nitrogen, or simple nitrogenous compounds, or even into nitric acid, or other nitrates!

8. That it is in this way that the necessary destruction of the organic matter of an organism is not left to chance, to causes foreign to that organism, and that when everything else has disappeared, bacteria, and, finally, microzymas resulting from their reversion remain as evidence that there was nothing of what was primarily living except themselves in the perished organism. And these microzymas, which appear to us as the remains or residue of that which has lived, still possess some activity of the specific kind that they possessed during the life of the destroyed being.

It is thus that the microzymas and bacteria that remained from the corpse of the kitten were not absolutely identical with those of the liver or of the heart, of the lung or of the kidney.

The Professor continued:

"I do not mean to infer that in destruction effected in the open air, on the surface of the ground, other causes do not occur to hasten it. I have *never* denied that the so-called germs of the air or other causes are contributory.

I only say that these germs and these causes have not been expressly created for that purpose and that the so-called germs in atmospheric dusts are nothing else than the microzymas from organisms destroyed by the mechanism I have just explained and whose destructive influence is added to that of the microzymas belonging to the being in process of destruction.

But in the atmospheric dusts there are not only the microzymas; the spores of the entire microscopic flora may intrude, as well as all the moulds that may be born of these spores."

It must not be supposed that Béchamp founded such manifold views upon just two series of observations. From the date of his *Beacon Experiment*, he never ceased his arduous work in connection with micro-organisms.

Together with Professor Estor, he instituted many experiments upon inner organs extracted from foetuses, obtained as a result of abortions. Here again they had overwhelming proof of bacterial evolution from normal inherent particles, for, while they would find bacteria in the interiors, the surrounding liquids, which had been specially prepared as culture media, would be absolutely free from such organisms.

They spared themselves no trouble. Space does not allow a more detailed review of their continual and varied experiments; such, for instance, as those upon eggs, in which, not contenting themselves with hens' eggs, they procured ostrich eggs with their hard tenacious shells and subjected these to innumerable tests. From the latter they received evidence of the gradual evolution in the fecundated egg of the united microzymas of the male sperm and female germ cells into the organs and tissues of the resultant feathered creature. They were also shown the arrest of this development in eggs that were shaken and disturbed and the internal substitution in the rotting egg of chaplets of associated microzymas and swarming bacteria.

In the course of their work, the Professors applied every possible test to their experiments, sometimes admitting air and sometimes rigorously excluding it. Their observations began to be enthusiastically taken up by some of Professor Béchamp's pupils, among whom was M. Le Rique de Monchy, who had assisted Béchamp with his silkworm researches. In a paper called *Note on the Molecular Granulations of Various Origins*,[1] this indefatigable student demonstrated that the vibrating granulations are organisms having an energetic action similar to that of ferments upon certain of the matters with which they are in contact in their natural medium.

Meanwhile, his teacher sent up memoir after memoir to the Academy of Science. It was Béchamp who initiated the study of micro-organisms – microzymas and bacteria – in saliva and in the mucus of the nasal and other passages. The very secretions of the body afforded him proof of his opinions. Thus, in a memoir titled *On the Nature and Function of the Microzymas of the Liver*, he and Estor said:

> "Matter, whether albuminoid or other, never spontaneously becomes a zymase or acquires the properties of zymases; wherever these appear some organised (living) thing will be found."[2]

What a wonderful conception this gives of the body! Just as a household or a State cannot prosper without its different members undertaking their varied functions, so our bodies and those of animals and plants are regulated by innumerable workers whose failure in action disturbs the equilibrium of the entire organism. Just as in the State there are different experts for different forms of labour, so Béchamp demonstrated the differentiation between the microzymas of various organs, the microzymas of the pancreas, the microzymas of the liver, the kidneys, etc. Since it may be objected that it is too difficult to make such distinctions between microscopic minutiae, we cannot do better than quote the words of Béchamp:

> "The naturalist will not know how to classify them, but the chemist who studies their functions can do so. Thus a new road is opened: when the microscope becomes powerless to show us the cause of the transformation of organic matter, the piercing glance of the chemist armed with the physiological theory of fermentations will discover behind the chemical phenomena the cause that produces them."

1. *Comptes Rendus 66*, p.550.
2. *ibid*, p.421.

He also said:

> "The microzymas can only be distinguished by their function, which may vary even for the same gland and for the same tissue with the age of the animal."[1]

He also showed that they vary for each tissue and for each animal, and that the microzymas found in human blood differ from those found in the blood of animals.

These researches were attracting so much attention that in 1868 Professor Béchamp was invited by M. Glenard, the Director, to give a special lecture at the School of Medicine at Lyons. On this occasion, Béchamp discussed the experiments upon the microzymas of the liver which he and Professor Estor had conducted, as well as the role that the microscopic organisms of the mouth play in the formation of salivary diastase and in the digestion of starches. This was work he had undertaken in collaboration with Professor Estor and M. Sainte-Pierre. He also discussed the microzymas in vaccine and in syphilitic pus.

These were the days in which Béchamp was happy in his work at Montpellier, when the star of hope still gleamed, and he displayed the bright cheerfulness habitual to his temperament. There was never a word of self; of what he had done or hoped to do. Boastings or mock humilities were equally foreign to him. The mysteries of Nature, the workings of life and death; these absorbed him.

What wonderful times those were for the great teacher when his views developed with such rapidity, and continuously by day and often half through the night he worked at the unravelling of Nature's mysteries; while with him for a series of years toiled his colleague Professor Estor.

> "Ah! How moving," wrote Béchamp,[1] "were the innumerable *séances* at which we assisted, amazed by the confirmation of ideas, the verification of facts, and the development of the theory."

And with that large-hearted generosity as natural to him as it was foreign to Pasteur, he added:

> "During the period from 1868 to 1876 all that concerns the microzymas of animal organs was common to both of us, and I do not know how to distinguish between what is mine and what is Estor's."

---

1. *Les Grands Problémés Médicaux*, A. Béchamp, p.61.
2. *La Théorie du Microzyma*, p.123.

We can scarcely imagine how the discoverers must have felt as they found themselves penetrating closer to the secrets of life than any man had succeeded in doing before them.

And, since they were both doctors, their labours were not narrowed to the more or less artificial experiments they undertook in the laboratory. Their clinical work brought them constant experience, and their surest observations were those accomplished by the greatest of all experimenters – Nature!

11.
Nature's Experiments

We have taken a look at Béchamp's arduous toil in his laboratory; but he himself would have been the first to insist upon the greater importance of the experiments directly undertaken by Nature. To these he gave incessant study; whenever possible he would visit the hospital wards and make a close examination of the cases there. He carefully followed the medical work of Professor Estor and of the many other doctors with whom he was associated at Montpellier.

A cyst which had to be removed from a liver provided a wonderful demonstration of the doctrine of bacterial evolution, for in it were found microzymas in all stages of development; isolated, associated, elongated – in short, true bacteria. Dr. Lionville, one of Béchamp's medical pupils, had his interest greatly aroused, and demonstrated that the contents of a blister include microzymas and that these evolve into bacteria.

With extraordinary patience and industry, Professor Béchamp and his colleagues continued their medical researches, finding the microzymas in all healthy tissues, and microzymas and many forms of bacteria in various phases of development in diseased tissues. Punctuating his clinical study with laboratory tests, the Professor instituted many experiments – too many to include here – to prove that the appearance of bacteria was not due to external invasions.

One day an accident provided an interesting contribution to the observations.[1] A patient was brought to the hospital of the Medical University of Montpellier suffering from the effects of an excessively violent blow upon the elbow. There was a compound comminuted fracture of the articular joints of the forepart of the arm; the elbow was largely open. Amputation was imperative and was performed between seven and eight hours after the accident. Immediately the amputated arm was carried to Dr. Estor's laboratory, where he and Professor Béchamp examined it.

The forearm presented a dry black surface. Complete insensibility had set in before the operation. All the symptoms of gangrene were

---

1. *Les Microzymas*, A. Béchamp, p.181.

present. Under a high power microscope, microzymas were seen associated and in chaplets, but no actual bacteria. These were merely in the process of formation; the changes brought about by the injury had progressed too rapidly to give them time to develop. This evidence against bacteria as the origin of the mortification was so convincing that Professor Estor at once exclaimed:

> "Bacteria cannot be the cause of gangrene; they are the effects of it."

Here was the outstanding difference between the microzymian theory and its microbian version, which Pasteur and his followers were to be instrumental in promulgating.

Pasteur seems to have lacked an understanding of the basic elements of living matter. In life he compared the body to a barrel of beer or a cask of wine.[1] To him it only appeared an inert collection of chemical compounds; and after death, he recognised nothing living in it. Consequently, when life appeared he could only account for it by the invasion from without of those minute airborne organisms whose reality Béchamp had taught him to understand. But the explanation of their origin from the cells and tissues of plants and animals took him much longer to fathom, though, as we shall see, he eventually actually made an unsuccessful attempt to plagiarise Béchamp's point of view.

Béchamp and Estor, meanwhile, steadily persevered with their clinical observations, and made a special study, for instance, of microzymian development in cases of pulmonary tuberculosis. The effects they saw in their medical work they proved and tested by laboratory experiments, and with the intense caution of true scientists they carried out many tests to substantiate their belief in the development of bacteria from microzymas, and the fact that an invasion from without of those at large in the atmosphere is not required to explain their appearance in internal organs.

It was, however, one of Nature's direct experiments, a chance demonstration in the vegetable world, that offered Professor Béchamp one of his best proofs of inner bacterial development, unrelated to any atmospheric interference.

As we have said, the climate of Montpellier is almost subtropical for the greater part of the year, and various sun-lovers among plants may be found growing there, including eccentric looking cacti, with their tough surfaces and formidable prickles.

---

1. See p.164.

During the winter of 1867 and 1868, however, severe cold set in, and hard frost took liberties with the cacti to which they were quite unaccustomed.[1] On one of these cold winter days, Béchamp noticed an *Echinocactus*, one of the largest and sturdiest of its kind, frozen for two feet of its massive length. After the thaw set in, the Professor carried off the plant to examine it. In spite of the frostbite, its surface was so thick and hard that it was absolutely unbroken. The epidermis was as resistant as it had been before the misadventure, and the great density of the tissues safeguarded the interior against any extraneous invasion apart from the intracellular spaces connected with the outer air through the stomata. Yet when the Professor made an incision in the frozen part, he found bacteria teeming inside, the species that he called *bacterium termo* and *putridinis* predominating.

Béchamp at once realised that nature was carrying out remarkable tests of her workings, and when frost set in again on the 25th January and lasted until the end of the same month he proceeded to verify his preceding observation. The plants in the Botanical Gardens provided him with fine opportunities, for many of them had become frozen.

He started his observations with a cactus named *Opuntia Vulgaris*. This was only frozen in part, and on scraping the surface with a scalpel the Professor convinced himself that it was entirely unbroken. In his own words, not the minutest cleft had been formed by which an enemy could find access. Yet, all the same, under the skin and down to the deepest layers of the frozen part lurked tiny and very active bacteria, and also larger bacteria, equally mobile, of a length of 0.02mm to 0.04mm, though these were less numerous. The normal microzymas had completely given way to bacteria in the frozen parts. On the contrary, it was noteworthy that in the healthy parts, untouched by frost, there were only perfect cells and normal microzymas to be found.

Béchamp next examined a plant known as *Calla Aethiopica*. This was frozen down to the ground and so perished that the slightest touch made it crumble to powder. Microscopic study showed microzymas in the course of transformation into excessively small mobile bacteria; there were also large bacteria to be seen, measuring 0.03 mm to 0.05 mm.

Nature had also provided a valuable control experiment, for in the center of the decayed frozen plant, a bunch of young leaves was left green and healthy, and here only normal microzymas were to be found,

1. *Les Microzymas*, A. Béchamp, p.141.

in striking contrast to the scenes of transformation taking place in the surrounding parts, which the frost had shattered so ruthlessly.

A third illustration was provided by a Mexican *Agave*. In the unfrozen part, only normal microzymas were to be found, while in the blackened and frozen portion of the leaf there was a cloud of very mobile microzymas, and there also swarmed bacteria resembling the *bacterium termo*, and in small quantities bacteria that measured from 0.01 mm to 0.03 mm.

In another Mexican *Agave*, the blackened and frozen part of the leaf did not contain any microzymas, but only small bacteria and some longer varieties measuring from 0.008 mm. to 0.02 mm. In the healthy parts the microzymas were normal, but in proportion as the frozen parts were approached the microzymas were seen to be modified in shape and size.

A fifth illustration was a *Datura Suaveolens*, in which the ends of the branches were frozen. Under the epidermis, as well as deep below, were clouds of *bacterium termo*, some rare *bacterium volutans* and some large bacteria measuring from 0.03 mm to 0.04 mm. There were also long crystalline needles terminating in spindles of 0.05 mm to 0.10 mm., which were motionless and not to be found in the healthy parts. The frozen and withered portions had, all the same, remained green.

Through these and many other observations, Béchamp became convinced that the microzymas of the plant world have great aptitude for developing into bacteria. But as he never jumped to conclusions, he took the utmost care to make perfectly sure that no inoculation of extraneous organisms could be responsible.

A year later, an *Echinocactus Rucarinus*[1] supplied him with an interesting example of the absence of bacteria when their entry from without appeared likely to be facilitated, and thus he seemed to be provided yet more proof of his theory that nutritive trouble or a change of environment, like that brought about by frost, may cause the natural internal development of microzymas.

He happened to visit a conservatory in the Montpellier Botanical Gardens, where he noticed an *Echinocactus* which reminded him of the one he had examined a year before; it seemed as though this one had also been frostbitten. He questioned the gardener, who explained that the roots had rotted owing to the plant having been over-watered. Here again was a subject for the persevering student of nature. We

---

1. *Les Microzymas*, p.144.

may be sure that Professor Béchamp did not miss the opportunity. The hard thick surface seemed to him to be intact, but moulds had been formed by large cells of fungi, which had already developed mycelium. Yet, on cutting through this surface, only microzymas and not any bacteria were to be found within the cut, though everything was favourable for an invasion, for there were moulds on the surface and the roots of the plant were rotten.

It is very certain that the Professor, in all the cases we have touched upon, did not content himself with merely a microscopic examination. In each instance he applied chemical tests, and discovered that, roughly speaking, the cell sap of the normal cactus had an acid reaction, whereas that of the frozen parts was found to be slightly alkaline. There were changes, however, which varied with each plant examined, and in a memoir on the subject,[1] in which these are described, he stated the coincidence of the development of the bacteria and the alkalinity of the medium. He added:

> "Although the contrary has been believed, bacteria can develop in an acid medium, which may remain acid or become alkaline, as well as they can develop in an absolutely neutral medium."

He believed that if it be true that some species of microzymas evolve into bacteria only in neutral or slightly alkaline media, others, nonetheless, develop in media normally acid.

Béchamp, we must remember, had been the first to demonstrate with precision the development of a multiplication of airborne organisms in a suitable medium. Understanding so well the important role of the micro-organisms of the air, he was naturally curious to note the effect of their deliberate introduction into surroundings where they would encounter the microzymas, which he considered to be the living formative builders, of plant and animal bodies.

He therefore inoculated plants with bacteria and attentively studied the results of this foreign invasion. In the sugared solutions that he had used when arriving at the conclusions embodied in his *Beacon Experiment* of 1857, he had seen the invaders increase and multiply; but now, in the plant interiors, they were in contact with organisms as fully alive as they were. After inoculation, increasing swarms of bacteria were indeed observed, but Béchamp had cause to believe that these were not direct descendants of the invaders. He became convinced

---

1. *Comptes Rendus* 68, p.466 (22nd February, 1869). *Les Microzymas des Organismes Supérieures, Monipellier Médicale* 24, p.32. *Les Microzymas*, p.145.

that the invasion from without disturbed the inherent microzymas and that the multiplying bacteria he noted in the interior of the plants were, to use his own words,

"the abnormal development of constant and normal organisms."[1]

These experiments, which nature itself had carried out in the Montpellier Botanical Gardens, were to have far-reaching effects upon Professor Béchamp's pathological teaching. They were to prevent his jumping to hasty conclusions like those, for instance, formulated by Pasteur, who imagined animal and vegetable tissues and fluids to be mere inert chemical media[2] similar to the sweetened solutions in which Béchamp first displayed the part played by airborne organisms.

These botanical observations were made by Béchamp when the subject of bacteria was beginning to attract much attention. He made his special study of frostbitten plants at the beginning of the same year, 1868, in which, later, on the 19th October, Pasteur, at the early age of 45, had the misfortune to be struck down by severe paralysis, brought about, he declared, by 'excessive toil' in connection with silkworm disease.

But before this, as we have seen, the celebrated chemist had worked hard to exalt the role of what he called the germs of the air, and to take for himself the credit of the discovery. His pupils and admirers were content to follow his restricted ideas about micro-organisms, and during the 1860s, one of them, M. Davaine, more or less inaugurated what is now known as the 'germ theory' of disease.

It came about in this way. A complaint called *charbon*, or splenic fever, and later more commonly known as anthrax, made occasional ravages among the herds of cattle and flocks of sheep in France and other parts of Europe.

In 1838, a Frenchman named Delafond drew attention to the appearance of organisms resembling little rods in the blood of affected animals, and these were afterwards also recognised by Davaine and others. A theory had already been put forward in the past by Kircher, Linné, Raspail and others that special organisms might induce disease, and Davaine, becoming acquainted with Pasteur's idea that each kind of fermentation is produced by a specific germ of the air, now suggested that the little rod-like organisms, which he called *bacteridia*,

---

1. *Comptes Rendus* 66, p.863.
2. "M. Pasteur ne voyait dans un oeuf, dans le sang, dans le lait, dans une masse musculaire, que des substances naturelles telles que la vie les élabore et qui ont les vertus de transformation que l'ébullition détruit." *Les Microzymas*, p.15

might be parasitic invaders of animal bodies and the cause of splenic fever, or anthrax. He and others who tried to investigate the subject met with contradictory results in their experiments. It was later, in 1878, that the German doctor, Koch, came to their rescue by cultivating the bacteridia and discovering a formation of spores among them; while Pasteur finally took the matter up and with his fondness for dogmatising, declared:

> "Anthrax is, therefore, the disease of the bacteridium, as trichinosis is the disease of the trichina, as itch is the disease of its special acarus."[1]

Generalisations are always dangerous in a world of contradictions, but, as it has been truly said that 'there is no doctrine so false that it does not contain some particle of truth'. This wise saying has been quoted by Béchamp,[2] who goes on to say:

> "It is thus with microbian doctrines. Indeed, if in the eyes of a certain number of *savants*, doctors and surgeons, the system of pre-existing morbid germs were denuded of every appearance of truth and did not seem established on any experimental reality, its reception by these savants, who seem to me to have adopted it without going sufficiently deeply into it, would have been absolutely incomprehensible. Incontestable facts, however, seem to support it. Thus it is certain that there truly exist microscopic living beings of the most exquisite minuteness, which, undoubtedly, can communicate the specific diseased condition that is in them. The cause both of the virulence and the power of infection in certain products of the sick organism, or of bodies in a state of putrefaction after death, resides in reality in beings of this order. It is true that people have certainly discovered such beings during the development of certain complaints, virulent, infectious, contagious, or otherwise."

It is thus seen that it was Béchamp's belief that it is this particle of truth in the germ-theory that has blinded so many to its errors. He explains that the want of a fuller understanding is brought about by lack of sufficient knowledge:

> "In my eyes, it is because doctors have perceived no relation, no connecting link, between certain histological elements of the animal and vegetable organism and bacteria that they

---

1. *The Life of Pasteur*, René Vallery-Radot, p.260.
2. *La Théorie du Microzyma*, p.37.

have so lightly abandoned the laws of the great science to adopt after Davaine, and with Pasteur, Kircher's system of pre-existing disease germs. Thus it comes about that not understanding the real and essential correlation existing between bacteria and the normal histological elements of our organisation, like Davaine, or denying it, like Pasteur, they have come newly again to believe in the system of Kircher. Long before Davaine made his observation and considered the inside of the organism to be a medium for development of inoculated bacteria, Raspail said:

'The organism does not engender disease: it receives it from without... Disease is an effect of which the active cause is external to the organism.'

In spite of this, the great physicians affirm, in Pidoux's happy words:

'Disease is born of us and in us.'

But Pasteur, following the opinion of Raspail, and trying to verify the hypothesis experimentally, maintains that physicians are in error: the active cause of our maladies resides in disease germs created at the origin of all things, which, having gained an invisible entry into us, there develop into parasites. For Pasteur, as for Raspail, there is no spontaneous disease; without microbes there would be no sickness, no matter what we do, despite our imprudences, miseries or vices!

The system, neither new nor original, is ingenious, very simple in its subtlety, and, in consequence, easy to understand and to propagate. The most illiterate of human beings to whom one has shown the connection between the acarus and the itch understands that the itch is the disease of the acarus. Thus it comes about that it has seduced many people who give an unthinking triumph to it. Above all, men of the world are carried away by a specious easy doctrine, all the more applicable to generalities and vague explanations in that it is badly based upon proved and tried scientific demonstrations."[1]

Yes, unfortunately for Béchamp, the deeper knowledge embodied in an understanding of the science of cytology – so neglected, as Professor Minchin has complained,[2] even now in the twentieth century – was, and still seems to be, required to comprehend the profounder,

---

1 La Théorie du Microzyma, p.38.
2. Presidential Address – British Association, September, 1915.

more mystic and complicated workings of pathology.

Nature was performing experiments which were open to all to read with the help of the microscope. But few were sufficiently skilled to probe deep enough under what may often be misleading superficialities. Few possessed enough knowledge to understand the complexities revealed to Béchamp. Yet from the start, he warned the world against being misled by too facile judgments.

As early as 1869 he wrote:

"In typhoid fever, in gangrene, and in anthrax, the existence has been proved of bacteria in the issues and in the blood, and one was very much disposed to take them for granted as cases of ordinary parasitism. It is evident, after what we have said, that instead of maintaining that the affection has had as its origin and cause the introduction into the organism of foreign germs with their consequent action, one should affirm that one is dealing here with an alteration of the functions of microzymas, an alteration indicated by the change that has taken place in their form."[1]

Béchamp, who had already demonstrated his knowledge of real parasitic disease conditions with his discovery of the cause of *pébrine*, was surely proving himself to be the best equipped for the understanding of those experiments that nature undertakes when the normal workings of the body are reduced to chaos, and anarchy reigns in the organism. But the majority of mankind, ignorant of the cytological elements, have been delighted with a crude theory of disease which they could understand, and have ignored the profound teaching of Professor Béchamp.

It is to what appears to have been Pasteur's attempted plagiarism of these views that we will now turn our attention.

---

1. *Comptes Rendus* 75, p.1525.

12.
A Plagiarism Frustrated

A marked contrast between Béchamp and Pasteur lay in the fact that Béchamp demanded that his views formed a logical sequence, while the latter was content to put forward views that were seemingly contradictory one to another.

For instance, according to Pasteur, the body is nothing more than an inert mass, a mere chemical complex, which, while in a state of health, he maintained to be immune against the invasion of foreign organisms.[1] He seems never to have realised that this belief contradicts the germ theory of disease originally put forward by Kircher and Raspail, which he and Davaine had been so quick in adopting.

How can foreign organisms originate disease in a body when, according to Pasteur, they cannot find entry into the self-same body until after disease has set in? Anyone with a sense of humour would have noticed an amusing discrepancy in such a contention, but though Pasteur's admirers have acclaimed him as a wit, a sense of the ludicrous is seldom a strong point with anyone who takes himself as seriously as Pasteur did or as seriously as his followers take their admiration of him.

On the 29th June, 1863, he read a memoir on the subject of putrefaction[2] before the Academy of Science.

In this he said:

> "Let a piece of meat be wrapped up completely in a linen cloth soaked in alcohol" (here he copied Béchamp in an earlier experiment) "and placed in a closed receptacle (with or without air matters not) in order to obstruct the evaporation of the alcohol. There will be no putrefaction, neither in the interior, because no vibrios are there, nor on the outside, because the vapours of the alcohol prevent the development of germs on the surface; but I observed that the meat became tainted in a pronounced degree if small in quantity, and gangrenous if the meat were in considerable mass."[3]

1. "Le corps des animaux est formé, dans les cas ordinaires, a l'introduction des germes des étres inférieurs." *Comptes Rendus* 56 p.1193.
2. *ibid.* pp.1189-94
3. *ibid.* p.1194.

Pasteur's object was to show that there were no inherent living elements in meat; that if external life, the germs of the air, were quite excluded, there would be no bacterial development from inner organisms. These were the days in which, having enthusiastically adopted Béchamp's ideas of the important parts played by the atmospheric hosts, he denied equally vociferously any inherent living elements in animal and vegetable bodies.

Béchamp, knowing that his own skill with the microscope outstripped that of all his contemporaries, excused Pasteur for not having been able to detect the minute organisms in the depth of the fleshy substance. But he maintained that Pasteur's own acknowledgment of the tainted or gangrenous state of the meat should have been sufficient to have convinced him of the reality of a chemical change and its correlative necessity – *a causative agent*. Béchamp claimed that Pasteur's own experiments, while attempting to deny, on the contrary *proved* the truth of the microzymian contentions.

For instance, again, in an experiment with boiled milk, Pasteur observed a smell resembling tallow and noted the separation of the fatty matter in the form of clots. If there were nothing living in the milk, how could he account for the change in its odour and explain the cause of the clotting?

Thus it is impossible to set aside the marked contrast between Béchamp and Pasteur in regard to their attention to any phenomenon, since by Béchamp nothing was ever ignored, while Pasteur constantly passed over most contradictory evidence.

For example, in spite of all the marked changes in milk, Pasteur was content to describe it as unalterable, except through access of germs of the air, and as being nothing more than a solution of mineral salts, of milk sugar and of casein, in which were suspended particles of fat, in short, that it was a mere emulsion which did not contain any living bodies capable of causing any change in its composition. For years Béchamp studied milk, and it was not till a much later date that he finally satisfied himself as to all its scientific complexities.

We find that just as in 1857 Pasteur's sponteparist views were entirely opposed to Béchamp's, so through the 1860s Pasteur completely ignored Béchamp's teaching in regard to the microzymas, or microsomes, of the cells and the fermentative changes due to these inherent living elements. Having realised the germs of the air, he seemed blind to the germs of the body, and ignored Béchamp's prodigious work when the latter differentiated by experiment the varying degrees of heat required to destroy the microzymas of milk, chalk, etc.

Finally, it seems as though Pasteur must have been convinced against his will by Béchamp's conclusions in regard to the diseases of silkworms, and his disparagement of Béchamp was no doubt provoked by his consciousness of a dangerous rivalry. At the end of 1868, laid low with illness, who can tell what thoughts passed through his mind regarding the views of the man who had so enlightened him on the subject of airborne organisms and their part in fermentation; the man who had so incontestably proved the causes of the diseases of silkworms that his own scientific reputation had been seriously threatened – the man, in short, who would never be his disciple?

Anyway, when Pasteur rose from his sickbed, semi-paralysed, dragging one leg, the Prussian hordes had for a time interrupted the even tenor of French life and national distress overshadowed all minor controversies. Who can say whether he thought these catastrophic events might have a lethal effect on the memories of his contemporaries? Be that as it may, in the year 1872 Pasteur suddenly sprang a surprise upon the Academy of Science.

For a moment we must recapitulate. It will be remembered that as early as 1862, Béchamp took up the study of vinous fermentation and the results of his experiments were published in 1864, when he stated clearly that from the outside of the grape comes the mould that causes must to ferment and that the stalks and leaves of vines bear organisms that may produce a fermentation injurious to the vintage. Thus he showed his extensive view of fermentative phenomena. Not only did he understand the part played by airborne organisms and the role of indwelling cellular elements, but he was also able to point to organisms found on external surfaces. Subsequently, from the year 1869 to 1872, two other experimenters, Lechartier and Bellamy, bore out his views by demonstrating that the intracellular elements of fruits ferment and furnish alcohol when protected from air, the fermentation being in relation to the vegetative activity.

While this solid work was quietly progressing, Pasteur on his part was gaining great public attention. We have seen how at the start he had the benefit of the Emperor's blessing, and he dedicated to Napoleon III the book for which he was given the grand prize medal of the exhibition of 1867. Indeed, to receive it he made a special pilgrimage to Paris, where, as his biographer naively suggests,[1] 'his presence was not absolutely necessary'.

---

1. *Life of Pasteur*, by René Vallery-Radot, p.141.

One might hope that after so much worldly success, he would have been able to give at least some credit where credit was due, even to views diametrically opposed to his own unceasing invocation of atmospheric germs in sole explanation of fermentative phenomena. But such was scarcely a habit of Pasteur's; that is, not unless the others acknowledged him to be the sun, when he, in return, was ready to shed lustre on them as his satellites. Had Béchamp first bowed the knee to him, he might have been ready to accord a morsel of praise to the Professor; but as the latter outstripped and criticised him, the two were always at variance, even on points where their views might have been assimilated.

Pasteur, as we have already said, sprang a surprise upon the Academy in 1872, a year memorable for the incessant work undertaken by the School of Montpellier.

To take merely the end of the year, we find on the 7th October, 1872, an extract read before the Academy from a note of Béchamp's, entitled *Upon the Action of Borax in the Phenomena of Fermentation*.[1] This was of considerable interest at that time, and answered several questions raised by M. Dumas.

On the 21st October, 1872, Professor Béchamp and Professor Estor presented a joint memoir – *On the Function of the Microzymas during Embryonic Development*.[2] This was one of the many highly important treatises upon striking discoveries and the experiments that substantiated them.

On the 28th October, 1872, Béchamp read a memoir entitled *Researches upon the Physiological Theory of Alcoholic Fermentation by Beer Yeast*.[3]

On the 11th November of the same year he read a memoir on *Researches upon the Function and Transformation of Moulds*.[4]

Some idea of his incessant toil may be gleaned merely from the titles of these records. We can, therefore, picture his astonishment and natural chagrin when he was roused from his arduous researches by Pasteur's appropriation of views that he had put forward years previously.

First of all, on the 7th October, 1872, Pasteur described to the Academy *Some New Experiments Showing that the Yeast Germ that Produces Wine Comes from Outside the Grape*.[5]

---

1. *Comptes Rendus* 75, pp.837-839.
2. *ibid*, pp.962-966.
3. *ibid*, pp.1036-1040.
4. *ibid*, p.1199.
5. *ibid*, p.781.

Here, restated, was Béchamp's discovery, first published in 1854!

This was too much even for the subservient members of the Academy! M. Fremy interrupted, with the object of exposing the insufficiency of Pasteur's conclusions.

On the invitation of M. Dumas, Pasteur renewed his address to the Academy, under the title of *New Facts to Assist to a Knowledge of the Theory of Fermentations, Properly So-called.*[1]

Here Pasteur made the statement in which he claimed

> "to separate the chemical phenomena of fermentations from a crowd of others, and particularly from the acts of ordinary life,"

in which, of course, nutrition and digestion must be paramount. Here we clearly see that as late as 1872, while theorising upon fermentation, he had no real conception of the process, no clear understanding of it as a function of nourishment and elimination on the part of living organism. How little foundation is shown for the statement made later by his disciple, M. Roux:

> "The medical work of Pasteur commences with the study of fermentation."

Proceeding with his address, Pasteur claimed to have shown that fermentation is a necessary consequence of the manifestation of life when that life is accomplished outside of direct combustion due to free oxygen. Then he continued:

> "One perceives as a consequence of this theory that every being, every organ, every cell that lives or continues its life without the help of the oxygen of the air, or uses it in an insufficient degree for the whole of the phenomena of its proper nutrition, must possess the character of a ferment for the matter that serves as a source of heat, wholly or in part. This matter seems necessarily to contain carbon and oxygen, since, as I have shown, it serves as food to the ferment…
>
> I now bring to this new theory, which I have already several times proposed, though timidly, since the year 1861, the support of new facts which I hope will this time compel conviction."

After a description of experiments that were mere copies of those undertaken by others, he concluded triumphantly:

> "I already foresee by the results of my efforts that a new path will be opened to physiology and medical pathology."

1. *Comptes Rendus* 75, p.784.

The only timidity apparent is the wariness with which Pasteur put forward a conviction that

"...every being, every organ, every cell must possess the character of a ferment."

Such teaching was entirely opposed to the theories he had formulated since 1861, and really seems to have been nothing less than a cautious attempt to plagiarise Béchamp's microzymian doctrine. As we have seen, Béchamp, though maintaining that the grape, like other living things, contains within itself minute organisms – microzymas – capable of producing fermentation, yet ascribed that particular fermentation known as vinous to a more powerful force than these, namely, organisms found on the surface of the grape, possibly airborne.

Therefore, if Pasteur were accused of plagiarising Béchamp's microzymian ideas, he had only to deny the accusation by pointing out that the provocative cause of vinous fermentation came from outside the grape; though here again he was only following Béchamp. The reports of the Academy of Science show us how well the clever diplomatist made use of these safeguards.

Fremy was quick to return to the contest. In a note entitled *The Generation of Ferments*,[1] he said:

"I find in this communication of M. Pasteur a fact that seems to me a striking confirmation of the theory that I maintain and which entirely overturns that of my learned *confrére*. Pasteur, wishing to show that certain organisms, such as the alcoholic ferment, can develop and live without oxygen, asserts that the grape, placed in pure carbonic acid, can ferment and produce alcohol and carbonic acid.

How can this observation agree with the theory of Pasteur, according to which ferments are produced only by germs existing in the air? Is it not clear that if a fruit ferments in carbonic acid, under conditions in which it can receive nothing from the air, it must be that the ferments are produced directly under the influence of the organisation within the interior of the cells themselves and that their generation is not due to germs that exist in the air?

More than ever, then, I reject this theory of Pasteur's that derives all fermentations from germs of ferments, which, though never demonstrated, are yet said by him to exist in

---

1. *Comptes Rendus* 73, p.790.

the air; and I maintain that the phenomena due to atmospheric spores must not be confused with those produced by the actual ferments begotten by the organisation."

Pasteur replied:

"Fremy seems not to have understood me. I have carefully studied the interior of fruit used in experiments, and I assert that there were not developed either cells of yeast or *any organised ferment whatever*."

The argument between the two continued and grew heated; till Pasteur, losing his temper, accused Fremy of making himself the champion of German science; though at the same time he expressed regret at overstepping the bounds of courtesy.

After some more argument, Fremy accepted Pasteur's apology; though he hoped he would not repeat such an offensive observation as that about the Germans, for then, as again afterwards at the time of the World Wars, there was naturally such a prejudice against everything Teutonic that not even German science could be excepted.

Fremy then went on further to criticise Pasteur's contentions:

"Our friend imagines that he will issue victorious from the discussion that I sustain against him, if the exactness of the facts that he presents be not contested. M. Pasteur deceives himself strangely as to the actual basis of the discussion. It relates not only to the determination of certain experimental facts, but also to their interpretation."[1]

Pasteur, tentatively trying to put forward Béchamp's microzymian views, was now faced by Fremy with his actual theories of the past decade. Fremy tried to entangle him in them and at the same time expose the shallowness of the theory of airborne germs as the explanation of all vital phenomena.

To defend it, Pasteur was obliged, as Fremy pointed out, to account for each kind of fermentation as the work of a special organism. Then again, if fermentations were only produced by atmospheric germs, they could not take place when air has been purified by rain, or on mountain heights, which Pasteur himself had described as free from such organisms. And yet it was indisputable that fermentations are produced everywhere, even after rain and upon the highest mountains.

---

1. *Comptes Rendus* 75, pp.1059, 1060.

"If the air," said Fremy, "contained, as asserted by M. Pasteur, all the germs of ferments, a sweetened liquid capable of developing ferments should ferment and present all the successive changes experienced by milk or barley-meal – a thing that never happens."

Fremy persisted that it was established that organised bodies, like moulds, elaborate ferments; and that though Pasteur had always declared fermentation to result from the action of atmospheric corpuscles, he (i.e. Fremy) had long since demonstrated that when the seeds of barley are left in sweetened water a fermentation is produced in the interior – i.e. an *intracellular* fermentation, carbon dioxide being eliminated from the cells.

Fremy claimed that this intracellular fermentation gave the final blow to Pasteur's theory, and he derided Pasteur for declaring the production of alcohol within the cells not to be fermentation because of the absence in the fruit juices of specific beer yeast.

He pointed out that actual ferments are secreted *inside* organisms, citing as an example pepsin, secreted by the digestive apparatus, and diastase, produced during the germination of barley. He showed that in these cases the ferments themselves are not visible, but only the organs that secrete them; and that though known ferments, such as yeast, are not found in intracellular fermentations, that is no proof that fermentation does not occur.

He contended that:

"a fermentation is defined not by the ferment that causes it, but by the products that characterise it. I give the name of alcoholic fermentation to every organic modification that in decomposing sugar produces chiefly carbon dioxide and alcohol. The lactic fermentation is characterised by the transformation of sugar or dextrin into lactic acid. The diastasic ferment is that which changes starch first into dextrin and then into glucose. It is thus that fermentation must be defined. If, as desired by M. Pasteur, one rests the definition of ferments upon the description of the form that the ferments may take, serious errors are likely to arise."

Finally he wound up:

"In conclusion, I wish to refute a sort of accusation often reproduced in the communications of M. Pasteur. Our friend accuses me of being almost alone in maintaining the opinions I have above developed. I do not know that M. Pasteur is justified in saying that all savants share his opinions upon the generation and mode of action of ferments. I know a certain number of colleagues of full competence in these matters, Members of the Academy and others, who do not agree with M. Pasteur."

In the course of the controversy, Fremy distinctly showed that he did not rest his opposition to M. Pasteur on the accuracy or inaccuracy of his experiments, but upon the conclusions drawn from them, which he considered to be incorrect. Pasteur refused to consider the subject from this point of view, and called for a commission of members of the Academy to judge the accuracy of his experiments without regard to his interpretation of results! Fremy pointed out that to do this would be to beg the real question at issue,[1] and the matter ended in the two men continuing to slap at each other, Pasteur trying to make capital out of the fact that Fremy saw no use in the suggested commission.

Pasteur also fell foul of the botanist M. Trecul, in regard to a note that had not been read aloud at the session of the Academy on the 11th November.[2] At the session held on the 18th November, Trecul expressed regret that Pasteur had seen fit to add this note, which is of considerable importance, being tantamount to a complete confession that about four months previously, he began to have doubts in regard to the transformation of the cells of the organism he called *mycodermi vini* into yeast cells, and was now prepared to deny Trecul's belief in a transformation of cells.

He condescendingly warned him:

"Let M. Trecul appreciate the difficulty of rigorous conclusions in these delicate studies."

To which Trecul retorted:

"There is no need to caution me as to the causes of error that may present themselves in the course of such experiments. I pointed them out in 1868 and in 1871 in four different communications, and have since written at length upon them."[3]

He added:

"M. Pasteur said in the communication of the 7th October and in his reply to M. Fremy of the 28th of the same month, first, that the cells of grapes and of other fruits placed in

1. *Comptes Rendus* 75, pp. 1063-1065.
2. *ibid*, p.1168.
3. *ibid*, p.1219.

carbonic acid immediately form alcohol; second, that there is no appearance of yeast in their interior; third, that it is only in rare and exceptional cases that cells of yeast can penetrate from the outside to the inside."

Trecul found these statements confusing in view of another claim made by Pasteur:

"In the gooseberry, fruit of quite another nature to grapes and apples, it often happened to me to observe the presence of the small yeast of acid fruits."[1]

Trecul responded:

"How can this penetration of the beer yeast take place into the interior of fruits that have intact surfaces?"

It is not altogether surprising that such contrary statements on this and other subjects should have driven Trecul to complain of Pasteur's mode of argument,[2] which he said consisted of contradicting himself, altering the sense of words, and then accusing his opponent of the alteration. Trecul himself experienced

"many examples of the contradictions of our friend, who has nearly always two opposite opinions on every question, which he invokes according to circumstances."[3]

But while many realised that Pasteur could not support his new theory without giving the lie to his old theories, none could understand as clearly as the workers of Montpellier his tentative effort to capture Béchamp's teaching and put it forward, dressed in new words, as his own scientific offspring.

This was too much for the Professor's patience, and on the 18th November, 1872, we find a note presented by him to the Academy entitled *Observations Relating to some Communications recently made by M. Pasteur and especially upon the Subject 'The Yeast that Makes the Wine Comes from the Exterior of the Grape'*.[4]

In this memoir, Béchamp referred to his early experiments on vinous fermentation which had been published in 1864. He added:

"M. Pasteur has discovered what was already known; he has simply confirmed my work. In 1872 he has reached the conclusion arrived at by me *eight years before*; namely, that

1. *Comptes Rendus* 75, p.983.
2. *Comptes Rendus* 88, p.249.
3. *Le Transformism Médical*, M. Grasset, p.136.
4. *Comptes Rendus* 75, pp.1284–1287.

the ferment that causes the must to ferment is a mould that comes from the outside of the grape; I went further: in 1864 I established that the stalks of the grape and the leaves of the vine bear ferments capable of causing both sugar and must to ferment, and further, that the ferments borne on the leaves and stalks are sometimes of a kind to injure the vintage."

Béchamp now also took the opportunity of bringing before the Academy the conclusions of a note presented by him previously on the 13th February, 1872. This had been omitted, ostensibly on account of its length, but the need for its publication was now pressing, and its previous omission illustrates in a small degree the annoyance to which he was continually subjected.

But it was not until the session of the Academy on the 2nd December, 1872, that the Professor dealt with the deeper significance of Pasteur's newly expressed views. In a memoir entitled *Second Observation on some Recent Communications by M. Pasteur, notably on the Theory of Alcoholic Fermentation,*[1] Béchamp commenced with a restrained and dignified protest:

> "Under the title *New Facts to Forward the Knowledge of the Theory of Fermentations, Properly So-called,* M. Pasteur has published a note, the perusal of which has interested me all the more in that I have found many ideas in it that have been familiar to me for a long time. My deep respect for the Academy and consideration for my own dignity impose upon me the obligation of presenting some observations on this communication, otherwise people who are not in touch with the question might believe that I had imposed on the public by attributing to myself facts and ideas that are not mine."

He went on to show by dates and by quotations from numerous works that he had been the first to establish two essential points:

First, that organised and living ferments could be generated in media deprived of albuminoid matter; and

Second, that the phenomena of fermentation by organised or 'figured' ferments are essentially acts of nutrition.

One single fact surely deals the death stroke to the claim that Pasteur initiated a true understanding of fermentation; that in his earlier experiments – those of 1857, for instance, and again in 1860 – he employed proteid matters and thus showed that he had missed the whole point of Béchamp's great discovery that organised living ferments

---

1. *Comptes Rendus* 75, p.1519.

could arise in media totally devoid of anything albuminoid. The life at large in the atmosphere could only be demonstrated by its invasion of a purely chemical medium entirely free from the suspicion of any organised living elements. This fact alone demonstrates that Pasteur did not understand the real significance of Béchamp's demonstration.

The latter now went on to describe the physiological theory of fermentation as proved by his past experiments:

"For me, alcoholic and other fermentations by organised ferments are not fermentations in the proper sense of the term; they are acts of nutrition, that is to say, of digestion, of assimilation and of excretion.

Yeast transforms first of all, outside of itself, cane sugar into glucose by means of a substance that it contains fully formed in its organism and which I have named *zymase*: it then absorbs this glucose and nourishes itself on it: it assimilates, multiplies, increases and excretes. It assimilates – that is to say, a portion of the modified fermentable matter becomes momentarily or definitely a part of its being and serves towards its growth and its life. It excretes, that is to say, it expels the parts used by its tissues under the form of compounds that are the products of fermentation.

M. Pasteur objected that acetic acid, the constant formation of which I had demonstrated in alcoholic fermentation, had its source not in the sugar, but in the yeast. To this question on the origin of the products of fermentation, which so greatly occupied M. Pasteur and his disciples, I made answer: They ought, according to the theory, to come from the yeast in the same way that urea comes from us, that is to say, from the materials that at first composed our organism. In the same way that the sugar which M. Claude Bernard saw being formed in the liver comes from the liver and not directly from food, so alcohol comes from yeast. This is what I call the physiological theory of fermentation. Since 1864, all my efforts have been directed to the development of this theory. I developed it at a conference held at Montpellier and at another held at Lyons. The more I insisted on it, the more it was attacked. Attacked by whom? We shall see."

Béchamp then went on to show that it had been Pasteur and his pupil Duclaux who had been the chief opponents of this teaching. He quoted Duclaux as having said:

"M. Béchamp has not observed that there might be two quite distinct sources from which they (the volatile acids of fermentation) might proceed, namely, the sugar and the yeast."

He also again quoted Duclaux's extraordinary misconception of digestion as exposed by his statement:

"When one sees in an alcoholic fermentation a given weight of sugar transformed into alcohol by a weight of yeast a hundred or a thousand times smaller, it is very difficult to believe that this sugar ever made part of the material of the yeast and that the alcohol is something like a product of excretion."

This misconception Béchamp showed to be now echoed by Pasteur in the memoir under discussion, in which the latter stated:

"That which separates the chemical phenomena of fermentation from a crowd of others, and particularly from the acts of ordinary life, is the fact of the decomposition of a weight of fermentative matter greater than the weight of the ferment in action."

The Professor repeated the explanation he had given in 1867 in answer to such crude objections. He had then shown that they could only have been put forward by those ignorant of physiological processes and had used the simile of a centenarian, weighing 60 kilograms, who, in addition to other food, could have consumed something like the equivalent of 20,000 kilograms of urea. Béchamp concluded:

"Thus, it is impossible to admit that M. Pasteur has founded the physiological theory of fermentation regarded as a phenomenon of nutrition. That savant and his disciples have taken the opposite view. I ask the Academy to permit me to record this conversion of M. Pasteur."

So far, Professor Béchamp had ignored Pasteur's final attempt at plagiarism; but now, at the same session of the Academy, on the 2nd December, together with Professor Estor, he presented a joint note entitled *Observations upon the Communication made by M. Pasteur on the 7th October, 1872.*[1] They said:

"M. Pasteur, at the Academy on the 7th October last, announced new experiments on the role of cells in general, considered as agents of fermentation in certain circumstances. The principal conclusions of his communication are:

---

1. *Comptes Rendus* 75, p.1523.

1. All beings are ferments in certain conditions of their life, for there are none in which the action of free oxygen may not be momentarily suspended.

2. The cell does not die at the same time as the being or organ of which it forms a part.

3. M. Pasteur foresees, from results already obtained, that a new path is opened to medical physiology and pathology."

Béchamp and Estor showed that, for a long time past, it was they who had taught that every being – or rather every organ in such a being and every collection of cells in such an organ – could play the part of ferments, and it was they who had shown the minute cellular particles that are the agents of fermentative activity.

It was Béchamp who had demonstrated that the egg:

"...contains nothing organised except microzymas. Everything in the egg, from the chemical point of view, will be necessary for the work of the microzymas; if in this egg its ordered state should be disturbed by a violent shaking, what happens?

The albuminoid substances and the bodies of fat remain unchanged, the sugar and the glucogen disappear, and in their place are found alcohol, acetic acid and butyric acid; a perfectly characterised fermentation has taken place there.

That is the work of the microzymas, the minute ferments, which are the agents and the cause of all the observed phenomena.

And when the bird's egg has accomplished its function, which is to produce a bird, have the microzymas disappeared? No; they may be traced in all the histological elements; they pre-exist – one finds them again during the functioning and the life of the elements; one will find them yet again after death; it is by them that the tissues are made alive. The part of organised beings essentially active and living, according to the physiologists, is the granular protoplasm.

We went a step further, and said it is the granulations of the protoplasm, and though for their perception a sort of spiritual insight is required, we have based our conclusions upon experimental proofs of the most varied and positive nature.

Bichat looked upon the tissues as the elements of the bodies of the higher animals. With the help of the microscope, very definite particles, cells, were discovered, and were regarded in their turn as elementary parts, as the last term of the analysis, as a sort of living molecule.

We have said in our turn:

'The cell is an aggregate of a number of minute beings having an independent life, a separate natural history. Of this natural history we have made a complete description. We have seen the microzymas of animal cells associate two by two, or in larger numbers, and lengthen into bacteria...

We have studied the function of these microphytic ferments in physiology, in pathology and after death. We have first determined their importance in the function of secretions and shown that this functioning is, after all, only a special mode of nutrition. We have considered them as builders of cells...'

We have also announced the importance of microzymas in pathology. We said in 1869:

'In typhoid fever, in gangrene, in anthrax, the presence of bacteria has been established in the tissues and in the blood, and there has been a strong disposition to look upon this as a fact of ordinary parasitism. It is evident, after what we have said, that instead of maintaining that the disorder has for source and cause the introduction into the organism of foreign germs with their consequent action, it should instead be affirmed that it is only a matter of a deviation from the normal functioning of microzymas, indicated by the change effected in their form.'[1]

All modern works on contagion and viruses are baseless outside the doctrine of the microzymas. After death, we said again at the Medical Congress of Montpellier in 1869, it is necessary for matter to return to its primitive state, for it has only been lent for a time to the organised living being.

In these latter days, an excessive role has been ascribed to germs carried by the air; the air may bring them, true enough, but they are not essential. The microzymas in their bacterial stage are sufficient to assure, by putrefaction, the circulation of matter.

We have thus demonstrated for a long time not only that cells can behave as ferments, but also which are the parts in them that undertake this role. The cell, it is said, does not die at the same time as the being or the organ of which it forms a part. This proposition is badly expressed.

The cell dies fast enough, if one considers as such the external envelope or even the nucleus. It is known that it is impossible to study histology on a corpse, so capable is it of

---

1. *Congrés Medical de Montpellier,* 1869. Montpellier Midical, Yanvier, 1870.

varied fermentations; a few hours after death it is sometimes impossible to find a single epithelial cell intact.

What *should* be stated is that the whole cell does not die; this we have demonstrated for a long time by rearing the parts in them that survive.

M. Pasteur foresees that a new path will be opened in physiology. In 1869, we wrote as a summary of all our preceding work:

'The living being, teeming with microzymas, carries in itself with these microphytic ferments the essential elements of life, of disease, of death and of complete destruction.'

This new path we have not only foreseen, but have actually opened many years ago, and have persistently pursued it."

In face of this restrained but damning protest, Pasteur could not keep silent. So we find that on the 9th December he presented to the Academy *Observations on the Subject of Three Notes Communicated at the Last Session by Messers. Béchamp and Estor.*[1] He said:

"I have read with attention these notes, or claims of priority. I find in them only appreciations, the truth of which I believe I am authorised to dispute, and some theories, the responsibility for which I leave to their authors. Later, and at my leisure, I will justify this judgment."

But apparently the leisure was never accorded him, for Pasteur relapsed into silence.

No 'justification of his judgment' being forthcoming, Professors Béchamp and Estor sent up the following note on 30th December, 1872:[2]

"We beg the Academy to permit us to place on record that the observations inserted in the name of M. Béchamp and of ourselves, on pages 1284, 1519 and 1523 of the present volume of the *Comptes Rendus*, remain unanswered."

The facts indeed seem unanswerable. The famous chemist who had gained the ear of the public, that exceedingly credulous organ, and had put forward as his own so much of Béchamp's work, was now completely checked in his attempted incursion into the microzymian doctrine. Here he had to cry a halt and content himself with his own assertion that 'fermentation is life without air, without oxygen.' To this, applying his own approved test of time, we find his admirers regretfully acknowledging the deficiencies of his explanation. His biographers,

---

1. *Comptes Rendus* 75, p.1573.
2. *ibid*, p.1831.

Professor and Mrs. Frankland, said:

> "It would be out of place to discuss here the criticisms which at the present day are being actively carried on; one of the principal objections to the acceptance of Pasteur's views being the omission of all consideration of the element of time in estimating the fermentative power of yeast...
>
> Within the present year (1897) the discovery has been made by E. Buchner that a soluble principle giving rise to the alcoholic fermentation of sugar may be extracted from yeast cells, and for which the name of *zymase* is proposed. This important discovery should throw a new light on the theory of fermentation, as it will soon be possible to attack the problem in a new and much more decisive manner. Thus it is presumably very improbable that the action of this soluble *zymase* is influenced by the presence or absence of air..."[1]

Thus the test of time provides an answer to the pronouncements of Pasteur! And if his exponents would only study the old records of the French Academy of Science, as well as the panegyrics of a dutiful son-in-law,[2] not only might their point of view undergo a change, but they would be spared the blunder of attributing to Buchner at the end of the nineteenth century a discovery made by Professor Antoine Béchamp little decades beforehand.

1. *Pasteur*, by Professor and Mrs. Frankland, ch.9.
2. René Vallery-Radot.

Who first discovered the cause of vinous fermentation – Béchamp or Pasteur?

Béchamp	Pasteur
1864	*1872*
10 October	*7 October*
Communication to the Academy of Science[1] on *The Origin of Vinous Fermentation*. An account of experiments that prove vinous fermentation to be due to organisms on the skin of grapes and also found on the leaves and other parts of the vine, so that diseased vines may affect the quality of the fermentation and the wines that result from it.	Communication to the Academy of Science[4] on *New Experiments to Demonstrate that the Yeast Germ that makes Wine comes from the Exterior of Grapes*.

Corollary

Béchamp's discovery antedated Pasteur's by eight years, and his explanation was considerably fuller. Did Pasteur come to acknowledge Béchamp's contention that there is fermentation apart from the action of airborne organisms, but fail to substantiate any claim to this discovery?

1872

Béchamp & Estor	Pasteur
2 December	*7 October*
Communication to the Academy of Science[2] on *Observations upon M. Pasteur's Note of the 7th October*. It was shown that it was they who for many years past had taught that every being, or rather every organ in such a being and every collection of cells in such an organ, could play the part of ferments by means of the minute cellular particles, the fermentative agents. This new path to physiology they had not only foreseen, but had opened up and persistently pursued for many years.	Communication to the Academy of Science[5] that "*Every being, every organ, every cell that lives without the help of oxygen must possess the character of a ferment.*" The opening foreseen of "a new path to physiology and medical pathology."
	9 December
30 December	Expressed to the Academy of Science,[6] the hope to be able later, at his leisure, to dispute the communication of Messrs. Béchamp and Estor.
A note to the Academy of Science[3] asking for the fact to be recorded that their observations on M. Pasteur's Communication remain unanswered.	

1. *Comptes Rendus* 59, p.626.
2. *Comptes Rendus* 75, p.1523.
3. *ibid*, p.1831.

4. *Comptes Rendus* 74, p.781
5. *Comptes Rendus* 75, p.785.
6. *ibid*, p.1573

13.
Microzymas in General

So much worldly success had come to Pasteur that he was unaccustomed to hearing anything negative from his contemporaries. There seems little doubt that his rancour against Béchamp was considerably increased by the latter's determination to safeguard himself against any plagiarism of his theories concerning the cell and its formative elements. If the microzymian doctrine, suitably disguised, could not be put forward as Pasteur's, so much the worse for the microzymas and all that concerned them. The standing that Pasteur had achieved made it easy for him to trample upon any scientific development likely to overshadow his own achievements, and thanks to his extraordinary good luck, circumstances again favored him.

The time had come when Professor Béchamp relinquished his post at Montpellier, in the hope of benefiting his country. His son Joseph, who was proving a worthy helper in his researches, followed his example. The whole family, with the exception of his elder daughter, who in 1872 had been married to M. Gasser, moved to Lille. But darker pages were about to be turned in the life story of Professor Béchamp.

He no longer possessed the gift of independence, which he had hoped to increase with his transfer to the north of France. He was perpetually confounded by the priestly directors of the new house of learning, and between worry and work, his hands were soon so full that his influence began to be undermined at the Academy of Science in Paris, where, thanks to Pasteur, the very name *microzyma* had been rendered almost anathema.

How unfair destiny must have seemed to Professor Béchamp. Just when he was finishing his explanation of the processes of life, disease and disruption, unexpected opponents arose; priests, uninstructed in science, who could only find irreligion and materialism in views that (had they possessed any discernment) they would have realised could have combated far better than any of the dogmas of Rome the atheism which at that time was inclined to link itself with science.

But of this the Bishops and Rectors of Lille gleaned no idea in their complacent ignorance, and in diplomacy, sadly, Béchamp was far less accomplished than Pasteur. Subterfuge was foreign to him. He could not pretend that ignoramuses knew more than he did of the workings of life, and he made no attempt to defer to bigoted clerics.

Despite the problems, the Professor continued to put into shape the conclusions derived from the experiments he had undertaken at Montpellier and still pursued at Lille, regardless of all the interruptions. The deeper he delved into the microzymian doctrine, the better it seemed to him were the answers it gave to the puzzles of contemporary science.

One of Béchamp's earlier achievements had been a close analysis of the albuminoids and a consequent discovery of their variations. Instead of finding them alike in the innumerable species of living beings, the Professor and his collaborators found them everywhere different; so much so that they could find no limit to the number of varities.

They proved this with precise chemical tests in the application of which Béchamp seems to have so utterly outstripped his contemporaries. They found that not only did the albuminoids vary in different species, but also in the different organs of the same body.

They thus found the differentiation between species and between the organs of the body to be due both to the individuality of the inherent microzymas, and the dissimilarities of the albuminoids. For instance, in the hen's egg, they showed the complexity of the albumens that constitute the white and explained a method of separating these, while from the yolk they isolated the specific microzymas.

Dr. Joseph Béchamp, the Professor's son, took a prominent part in carrying out these particular researches. He showed by a close analysis of eggs of every description that none of the albumens contained in either the white or the yolk is identically the same as that found in the egg of any other species. A fact which his work established is that even chemically, a creature is what it is in the very egg from which it issues, both by reason of the cytological elements and also the albumens. It had been thought that the albumen of secretions was the same as the albumen of the blood: not only did Joseph Béchamp discover this not to be the case, but also that among those he isolated *none* possessed the same elementary composition as that of the serum. He showed that there exists a certain relation of cause and effect between the tissues through which the secretion passes and the nature of the albumens of the effusions. He thus disposed of Mohl's and Huxley's earlier views on the subject and of Claude Bernard's belief in a unique protoplasm. With his father, he put forward manifold instances of the elemental differences between species.

For example, they found that though the organisms of the mouth, that is, the microzymas, bacteria, epithelial cells, etc, resemble one another in form in man, dog, bull, or pig, their chemical functions are very different. Joseph Béchamp showed that the microzymas, even of the same gland, in the same animal vary according to age and condition. His father demonstrated the similarity he had found in the structure of the pancreas to that of the parotis and the dissimilarity in their products; while the secretions of the parotis he found to be different in man, horse and dog.

Béchamp senior explained that it is owing to the microzymas of allied species of animals being often functionally different in certain of their physiological centres that each animal has diseases peculiar to it and that certain diseases arc not transmissible from one species to another and often not from one individual to another even of the same species. Infancy, adult age, old age, sex, have their share in influencing susceptibility to disease conditions.

These researches of the School of Montpellier certainly seem to throw light upon the nature of infection and on the immunity constantly met with, in spite of alleged exposure, from all kinds of infectious maladies. The world might have been spared the propagation and inoculation of disease matters (i.e. Pasteur's vaccinations), had the profound theories of Béchamp been followed, instead of the cruder yet fashionable germ theory of disease, which appears to consist of distorted half-truths of Béchamp's teaching.

Another special study of the younger Béchamp was to trace microzymas in the foetus and in the organs of the body after birth; by thorough experimentation, he proved their varying multiplicity at different stages. He also showed the variation of their action in different organs – the placenta, liver, etc – and their variations of action at different ages, comparing, for instance, those of the foetus with those of the adult, and demonstrating that no extraneous organisms could effect these changes.

He also assisted his father in his researches on corpses, where the two Béchamps maintained that the inherent microzymas, apart from the assistance of foreign 'germs', bring about decomposition. They taught that when the corporate life of a being is at an end, the infinitesimal organisms that originally built up its cells continue to flourish, and by their life processes destroy the habitat of which they were the creators.

In 1880 Joseph Béchamp, as indefatigable a worker as his father, demonstrated the presence of alcohol in tissues shortly after death and its disappearance in advanced putrefaction, when he considered it to be destroyed by a continuance of fermentation due to the very microzymas that had produced the alcohol in the first instance. Thus he explained the continued vitality of the organisms that had till lately vitalised the now inert corpse or carcass, and showed that 'nothing is the prey of death; everything is the prey of life,' to quote his father.

What a different future might have awaited the microzymian doctrine had the lives of Professor Estor and Joseph Béchamp been spared, instead of both being cut off in their prime. His patriotic work foiled by bigotry, his scientific discoveries stifled by jealousy, his collaborators struck down by death – which also spared neither his wife nor the young daughter of whom the priests had robbed him – he finally made his solitary way to Paris to find his chief detractor enthroned as the idol of the public, his own genius all but unrecognised. It was a dreary outlook and might easily have daunted even a brave spirit, but Béchamp's willpower rose indomitably to meet the future, and, aided and quickened by his splendid health and vitality, spurred him on to fresh investigations.

With increasing years his incessant work never abated, and he persevered in researching the mysteries of life. Up to 1896, he continued to publish articles on milk, its chemical composition, its spontaneous changes and those occasioned by cooking. He not only maintained his early idea of its inherent autonomous microzymas, but he showed the distinctive character of various milks; human, bovine, etc. He denied the popular belief in milk being an emulsion, but was of the opinion, with which Dumas concurred, that the milk globules are vesicles of a cellular type, that is, furnished with envelopes which prevent their ready solution in ether in the milk stage, and in cream are causative of the clotting.

The crowning achievement of Béchamp's laborious and persecuted career was the publication, in his 85th year, of a work entitled *The Blood*, in which he applied his microzymian views to issues of the blood, especially that of its coagulation. We cannot do better than quote Dr. Herbert Snow's summary in the *New Age* of the 1st May, 1915:

> "It represents the blood to be in reality a flowing tissue, not a liquid. The corpuscles, red and colourless, do not float in a liquid, as is commonly thought, and as our senses indicate, but are mingled with an enormous mass of invisible

microzymas – the mixture behaving precisely as a fluid will do under normal conditions. They are each clad in an albuminous envelope, and nearly fill the blood vessels, but not quite. Between them is a very small quantity of intracellular fluid. These microzymas, in their albuminous shells, constitute the 'molecular microzymian granulations' – the third anatomical element – of the blood.

As soon as the natural conditions of life cease, and the blood is withdrawn by an incision in the vessels, these molecular granulations begin to adhere to each other very rigidly. By this adhesion, the clot is formed, and the process of coagulation is so rapid that the corpuscles are caught within its meshes before they have time to sink to the bottom, as by their weight they would otherwise do.

Then we have a second stage. The albuminous envelope of the granulation becomes condensed and shrinks. So the clot sinks *en masse*, and expels the intracellular liquor.

Finally, in the third stage, the corpuscles are crushed by the contracting clot, and the red yield their colouring to the serum without. There is no such thing as fibrin *per se;* fibrin is not a proximate principle, but a false membrane of microzymas.

There is much in this ingenious explanation of a difficult and hitherto by no means satisfactorily solved problem which seems to indicate, at any rate to the present writer, that it is worthy of far closer examination and consideration than it has received..."

Surely that could be said for the whole of Béchamp's microzymian teaching, which we can, from his writings, sum up as follows:

— The microzyma is that which is primarily endowed with life in the organised being, and that in which life persists after the death of the whole or in any excised part.

— The microzyma being thus the fundamental element of corporate life, it may become morbid through a change of function and thus be the starting point of disease.

— Only that which is organised and endowed with life can be susceptible to disease.

— Disease is born of us and in us.

— The microzymas may undergo bacterial evolution in the body without necessarily becoming diseased.

— In a diseased body, a change of function in the microzymas may lead to a morbid bacterial evolution. Microzymas morphologically identical with and functionally different from diseased microzymas may appear without a microscopic distinction being possible.

— Diseased microzymas may be found in the air, earth, or waters and in the dejecta or remains of beings in which they were once inherent.

— Germs of disease cannot exist *primarily* in the air we breathe, in the food we eat, or in the water we drink, for the diseased micro-organisms, unscientifically described as 'germs', since they are neither spores nor eggs, proceed necessarily from a sick body.

— Every diseased microzyma has originally belonged to an organism, that is, a body of some sort, whose state of health was reduced to a state of disease under the influence of various causes which determined a functional change in the microzymas of some particular centre of activity.

— The micro-organisms known as 'disease germs' are thus either microzymas or their evolutionary bacterial forms that are in (or have proceeded from) sick bodies.

— The microzymas exist primarily in the cells of the diseased body and become diseased in the cell itself.

— Diseased microzymas should be differentiated by the particular group of cells and tissues to which they belong, rather than the particular disease condition with which they are associated.

— The microzymas inherent in two different species of animals more or less allied are neither necessarily nor generally similar.

— The microzymas of a given morbidity belong to one certain group of cells rather than to another, and the microzymas of two given species of *animals are not susceptible to an identical affection.*

Such, in summary, are the propositions that form Béchamp's basis of pathology. Needless to say, he put none forward as an untried theory; each was founded upon precise experimentation and observation.

In spite of the hold of Pasteurian dogma over the Medical Faculty, scientific minds here and there confirm fragments of Béchamp's teaching, without knowledge of it, from their independent studies. In this connection may be quoted the evidence before the Royal Commission on Vivisection of Dr. Granville Bantock, whose reputation needs no comment. He said:

> "Bacteriologists have discovered that in order to convert filth or dead organic matter of any kind into harmless constituents, Nature employs micro-organisms (or microbes) as her indispensable agents.
>
> In the modern septic tank it is the action of the micro-organisms, whether aerobic or anaerobic, that dissolves the sewage, and it is the continuous action of these microbes that converts all manure matter into the saline constituents that are essential for the nutrition of plant life."[1]

After several examples, Dr. Bantock continued:

> "The microbe in its relation to disease can only be regarded as a resultant or concomitant"

and after quoting many instances of error of diagnosis through reliance on bacterial appearances, he stated:

> "Is it not therefore reasonable to conclude that these micro-organisms... are certainly *not* causative of disease?"

He also said:

> "I am bound to accept as a matter of fact the statements made as to the association of the *Loeffler bacillus* with diphtheria; but to say that their presence is the result of the disease appears to me to be the more sound reasoning."

Then, again, we may quote the practical observations of the great pioneer of nursing, Florence Nightingale.[2] She said:

> "Is it not living in a continual mistake to look upon diseases, as we do now, as separate entities, which must exist, like cats and dogs, instead of looking upon them as conditions, like a dirty and clean condition, and just as much under our own

---

1. *Report of the Royal Commission on Vivisection*, Q. 14,345-6 of the 4th Report, 1906, p.77b.
2. *Notes on Nursing*, p.19 (note).

control; or rather as the reactions of kindly Nature against the conditions in which we have placed ourselves? I was brought up by scientific men and ignorant women distinctly to believe that smallpox was a thing of which there was once a specimen in the world, which went on propagating itself in a perpetual chain of descent, just as much as that there was a first dog (or pair of dogs), and that smallpox would not begin itself any more than a new dog would begin without there having been a parent dog.

Since then I have seen with my eyes and smelt with my nose smallpox growing up in first specimens, either in close rooms or in overcrowded wards, where it could not by any possibility have been 'caught', but must have begun. Nay, more, I have seen diseases begin, grow up and pass into one another. Now, dogs do not turn into cats. I have seen, for instance, with a little overcrowding, continued fever grow up, and with a little more, typhoid fever, and with a little more, typhus, and all in the same ward or hut. *For diseases, as all experience shows, are adjectives, not noun substantives.*"

It was she who said also:

"The specific disease doctrine is the grand refuge of weak, uncultured, unstable minds, such as now rule in the medical profession. There are no specific diseases: there are only specific disease conditions."

So her personal experience gave rise to opinions that are understandable in the light of Béchamp's microzymian doctrine, which thus gains confirmation from her recounting of Nature's everyday lessons.

It seems that disease-causing entities create disease states dependent upon bad heredity, bad air, bad food, vicious living and so forth, and, provided our ancestry be good, our surroundings sanitary and our habits hygienic, our physical status lies chiefly in our own keeping, for good or evil, as our wills may determine.

Instead of being at the mercy of extraneous enemies, it rests principally with ourselves as to whether our anatomical elements, the microzymas, shall continue on the even tenor of their way, when our basic condition is healthy; or, from a change of environment in their immediate surroundings, develop morbidly, producing bad fermentative effects and other bodily calamities. *Thus, while our own shortcomings are first reflected on them, so their ensuing corruption afterwards revenges itself upon us.*

It has been argued in answer to Miss Nightingale's sound reasoning that she was only a nurse and therefore not qualified to express medical opinions. This objection comes, oddly, from the devout adherents of men such as Jenner, who bought his medical degree for 15 pounds, and Pasteur, who managed by a majority of just one vote to obtain a place among the Free Associates of the Academy of Medicine!

Let us, however, turn to the opinions of two genuine medical men and see how exactly they bear out the views of Florence Nightingale. In the eighteenth chapter[1] of *The Wonderful Century*, a work by Professor Alfred Russel Wallace, we find that he quotes the medical statistician, Dr. Farr, and Dr. Charles Creighton, greatest of epidemiologists.

> "In his (Dr. Farr's) Annual Report to the Registrar-General in 1872 (p.224) he says:
>
>> 'The zymotic diseases replace each other; and when one is rooted out, it is apt to be replaced by others which ravage the human race indifferently whenever the conditions of healthy life are wanting. They have this property in common with weeds and other forms of life: as one recedes, another advances.'
>
> This substitution theory is adopted by Dr. Creighton, who in his *History of Epidemics in Britain* suggests that plague was replaced by typhus fever and smallpox; and, later on, measles (insignificant before the middle of the seventeenth century) began to replace the latter disease."

It is interesting that the replacement of disease conditions noted by Florence Nightingale in unhealthy huts or wards, according to their changing degree of unhealthiness, exactly bears out what Dr. Charles Creighton shows to be the testimony of historic records. And this evolution or retrogression, as the case may be, of disease conditions is surely explained by Béchamp's microzymian doctrine, which teaches that upon the anatomical elements (whether called microsomes or microzymas) – the actual builders of the body cells, depends our state of wellbeing or otherwise; and that a morbid change of function in these may lead to disease conditions in us, the latter altering as the former varies, and the former influenced by surrounding conditions, whether insanitary or unhygienic.

If the microzymian teaching thus sheds light upon these mysteries, how much moreso does it do upon hereditary tendencies, too much overlooked by modern medical orthodoxy. Since the microzymas

---

1. This chapter no longer appears in the work, but was formerly to be obtained separately from Allen & Unwin.

perpetuate life from parent to child, so they carry with them parental characteristics for good or evil which may lie dormant throughout generations or be made manifest, according to the microzymas that carry the preponderating influence, thus explaining the Laws of Mendel. Yet again, disease conditions due to abnormal growth, of which cancer is an obvious example, seem to bear out Béchamp's doctrine that upon the status of the microzymas depends the status of both the whole or any single part of the corporate organism.

In place of the modern system of treating the phantom of a disease-causing entity, and trying to quell it by every form of injection, scientific procedure on Béchamp's lines would be to treat the patient taking into account his personal situation and charactersitics; for these depend upon his anatomical elements, the microzymas, which, according to Béchamp, build up his bodily frame, preserve it in health, disrupt it in disease, and finally, when the corporate association is ended by death these, with or without extraneous help, demolish their former habitat, and are set free to continue an independent existence in the earth, the air, or the water in which they happen to find themselves. Any morbidity which may be in them or in their evolutionary bacterial forms is quickly dispelled by fresh air.

And since the microzymas of different animals, different plants and different organs – lungs, kidneys, colon, as the case may be – are themselves all different, so will there be variation in their bacterial development, and so the innumerable forms of bacteria perceived everywhere are readily accounted for.

As the British Empire, or the United States of America, or the Republic of France is composed of innumerable varying individuals, so the corporate body of plant or animal is an association of living entities; and as the work of myriad individuals composes the life processes of the nation, so the action of the microzymas constitutes the life processes of all corporate beings.

What might the sciences of life and disease have been, had Béchamp's belief been developed – instead of stifled under the jealousy of Pasteur!

We will now look at some modern research that bears out various of Béchamp's teachings.

14.
Modern Confirmations of Béchamp

As we have claimed that it was Béchamp who laid the foundations of cytology, or the science of cellular life, we will now provide some examples of modern views that bear out his early conclusions. For this purpose, we cannot do better than quote the presidential address to the Zoological Section of the British Association for the Advancement of Science at Manchester in 1915, by Professor E. A. Minchin.

As we have seen, Béchamp combated Virchow's view of the cell as the anatomical unit, and did this in the 1860s.

What is Professor Minchin's opinion in the year 1915?

> "Many cytologists appear indeed to regard the cell, as they know it in the *metazoa* and *metaphyta*, as the beginning of all things, the primordial unit in the evolution of living beings. For my part, I would as soon postulate the special creation of man as believe that the *metazoan* cell, with its elaborate organisation and its extraordinary perfected method of nuclear division by karyokinesis, represents the starting point of the evolution of life."

Thus after a lapse of more than half a century, we find this expert confirmation of Béchamp's teaching.

Professors Béchamp and Estor, while working together, saw the granules – the microzymas – in cells associate, and threadlike forms develop. There seems little doubt that, all those years ago, they were already observing different stages in that complicated series of changes, known as *karyokinesis* or *mitosis*, which occur in the division of the cell nucleus, in which is effected an equal division of the substance of the nucleus of the parent cell into the two new resultant nuclei.

This process, the chief phenomenon in the cleavage of a cell, is the driving force of the cell multiplication that is responsible for the growth of the bodies of all living beings. According to the most popular modern view, it is effected by the granules which, on uniting, are known as chromatin threads, the name *chromatin* being applied to their substance because of the deeper shade it takes when stained for observation under the microscope. Staining methods greatly facilitate, although they occasionally falsify, the work of present day observers; but these were little known in the middle of the last century, so that Béchamp must have been far ahead of his generation with his technique of microscopically investigating the intricacies of cellular life and in viewing phenomena not yet noticed by his contemporaries.

The early axiom of his that minute living granules build up cells holds good today, more than half a century later, regardless of nomenclature. Indeed, when we come to names, the number and variety in use are sufficient to befog any clarity in the matter, and it is certainly unfortunate that general use has not been made of Béchamp's term *microzyma*. In regard to Béchamp's priority in demonstrating the role of the granulations and the subsequent confusion of terminology, we may quote M. Nencki, a Swiss Professor of Medical Chemistry at Berne:

> "To my knowledge, it is Béchamp who was the first to consider certain molecular granulations, which he named microzymas, to be organised ferments, and he defended his view resolutely against various attacks."[1]

In making his own acknowledgment of the molecular granulations of the pancreas, Nencki continues:

> "These are evidently the *microzymas* of Béchamp, the coccus of Billroth; the same thing as the *monas crepusculum* of Ehrenberg."

The outstanding names for the minute dots present in the cell and distinguishable under the microscope are, when arranged in chronological order: *molecular granulations, microzymas, microsomes,* and *chromatin granules*. Call them which you will, it was these Béchamp intended when he wrote:

> "The cell is a collection of little beings which have an independent life; a special natural history."[2]

Professor Minchin, in his Presidential address, without, however, rendering any acknowledgment to Béchamp, echoes his opinion:

> "To each such granule must be attributed the fundamental properties of living organisms in general; in the first place, metabolism, expressed in continual molecular change, in assimilation and in growth, with consequent reproduction; in the second place, specific individuality."

---

1. *Gesammette Arbeiten 1*, p.212 (1904).
2. *Comptes Rendus 66*, p.859. *Les Microzymas*, p.972 (Appendix).

This was exactly Béchamp's teaching, and, moreover, he showed that the microzymas are the transmitters of heredity. According to him, a plant or an animal is what it is by virtue of its microzymas. These are the link between the animal and vegetable kingdoms. Though appearing intrinsically the same, it is they that differentiate the essence of one living being from that of another. It is by reason of its microzymas that an acorn develops into an oak, or a hen's egg into a chicken; microzymian influence decides the child's likeness either to father or mother. And here again we find the supporting modern view that in the *chromatin* lies the secret of heredity.

Professor MacBride[1] thus supports Béchamp's hypothesis:

> "There seems to be no escape from the position that the *chromatin*, viewed as a whole, is the bearer of the hereditary tendencies, for the influence of the father in determining the character of the offspring is as potent as that of the mother. Now, the head of the spermatozoon is the only part of the father that enters into the constitution of the progeny, and this appears to consist practically exclusively of chromatin. May not the chromosomes be simply groups of these determiners (of characteristics, qualities, etc.) adhering by mutual chemical affinity under the peculiar chemical conditions prevailing in the cell in the period preceding karyokinesis? If this be the case, the apparent total disappearance of chromosomes during the resting period could be accounted for."

It is possible that for want of modern appliances, Béchamp may have overlooked the great importance of the cell nucleus in his cellular doctrine; but, even so, Professor Minchin confirms the correctness of his view in ascribing the supreme influence to what we may term the *microzymian*, *granular* or *chromatinic* entities. He says:

> "Already, one generalisation of cytologists has been torpedoed by the study of the *protista* (a very primitive form of micro-organism). The dictum *'omnia nucleus e nucleo'* is perfectly valid as long as it is restricted to the cells of *metazoa* and *metaphyta*, to the material, that is to say, to which the professed cytologist usually confines his observations. But in the *protista* it is now well established that nuclei can arise *de novo*, not from pre-existing nuclei, but from the extra-nuclear chromatin for which Hertwig first coined the term *chromidia*."

1. Section D. Reports of British Association. 1915.
Discussion on the Relation of Chromosomes to Heredity, by Professor E. W. MacBride.

Let us run through Béchamp's early views as we find them expressed in his *Théorie du Microzyma*:

"Microzymas are builders of cells, and by evolution become vibrios: they are histologically active; they are producers of zymases (ferments): they are physiologically active; and in noting that zymases are agents endowed with the chemical capacity of transformation or decomposition, it may be said that microzymas can generate chemical energy; it is thanks to the microzymas that we digest and that we are able to transform and assimilate the materials that serve to nourish us. They are thus *chemically* active; and placed in certain artificial surroundings (called putrescible), under favourable circumstances, they bring about decomposition (that is, fermentation); in other words, they nourish themselves while they multiply, regardless of whether they evolve into vibrios or not. They are therefore individually organisms comparable to those we call living and organised ferments, etc. Finally, they defy putrefaction, and if I add that they are not digested in the condition of animal matter where they are, one can say that they are *physiologically indestructible*."[1]

Now let us compare the modern views of Professor Minchin:

"I regard the chromatin elements as being the primary of the life and evolution of living organisms for the following reasons: the experimental evidence of the preponderating physiological role played by the nucleus in the life of the cell; the extraordinary individualisation of the chromatin particles seen universally in living organism and manifested to a degree which raises the chromatinic units to the rank of living individuals exhibiting specific behaviour, rather than that of mere substances responsible for certain chemico-physical reactions in the life of the organism; and last, but by no means least, the permanence and, if I may use the term, the *immortality* of the chromatinic particles in the life-cycle of organisms generally."

Here it may be objected that though Professor Minchin confirms Professor Béchamp's views as regards the individuality and immortality of the minute cellular granules, no confirmation is given of vibrionic – or as one would say more familiarly, bacterial – evolution.

Yet the modern Professor has no hesitation in enunciating such a belief, if relegated to primeval eras and the realm of hypothesis and

---

1. p.319.

infancy, imagining the development of living forms from the earliest living beings, 'minute, possibly ultra-microscopic particles of the nature of chromatin'. He says:

> "These earliest living things were biological units or individuals which were the ancestors, in a continuous propagative series, of the chromatinic germs and particles known to us at the present day as universally occurring constituents of living organisms."

Moreover, he tells us:

> "The evolution of living things must have diverged in at least two principal directions. Two new types of organisms arose, one of which continued to specialise further in the vegetative mode of life in all its innumerable variations, while the other type developed an entirely new habit of life, namely, a predatory existence. In the vegetative type, the first step was that the body became surrounded by a rigid envelope. Thus came into existence the bacterial type of organism."

Here is confirmation of belief in bacterial evolution from chromatinic, otherwise microzymian, granules, further supported by such statements as:

> "I agree with those who derive the bacteria as primitive, truly non-cellular organisms, directly from the biococcus (Mereschkowsky's term) through an ancestral form."

It is curious to compare this expert readiness of belief in a primeval evolution, a matter of pure conjecture, with the indifference displayed towards Béchamp's experimental demonstrations of bacterial development. In regard to this we may quote his opinion as follows:

> "But you must not imagine that the microzymas are converted into bacteria without any transition: on the contrary, there are *many* intermediate forms between the microzymas and the bacteria. What you must bear in mind is that the medium has a great influence on the appearance of the various forms in their evolution from the microzymas, and that there is an infinity of species which vary in their function; finally, that according to the nature of the medium, microzymas can produce cells in place of bacteria, true cellular microphytes, and moulds."[1]

---

1. *Les Microzymas*, p.140.

It has been argued that modern research has not confirmed Béchamp's statement:

> "We have seen the microzymas of animal cells associate two by two, or in larger numbers, and extend themselves into bacteria."[1]

But it must be remembered that other declarations of Béchamp's, strenuously combated, have since met with confirmation. Take, for instance, his claim that bacteria could change their forms, the rod-shape pass into the spheroid, etc.

This was denied by Pasteur. Nonetheless, years later, a worker at the very institute that bears the latter's name has confirmed Béchamp's statement!

We may recall the prominence given in London papers to what was described as an 'important discovery by a French lady scientist'. The *Daily News* of the 8th April, 1914, provides a simple summary:

> "*Paris, Tuesday, March 31* – Mme. Victor Henri, the lady bacteriologist, has made one of the most important discoveries in that branch of research for many years. She has, by subjecting bacteria to ultra-violet rays, succeeded in creating a new species of bacteria from a species already known. The experiment was made with the anthrax bacillus, which from a rod shape was transformed into a spherical coccus."

Thus another contention of Professor Béchamp's meets with modern substantiation. And more than this, the statement that he saw microzymian evolution bring about the formation of primitive organisms is at the present day being confirmed by an acknowledged student of his, a Frenchman named Galippe.

The following account of his work has been kindly summarised for us by Mr. E. J. Sheppard, a cytologist who formerly carried out some researches in connection with the late Professor Minchin, and who himself is conversant with and subscribes to much of Béchamp's teaching.

NORMAL PARASITISM AND MICROBIOSIS

> "Galippe[2] describes experiments with fruits and animal tissues which confirm the existence of various parasites in the normal tissues of the vegetable and animal kingdom.

---

1. *Les Microzymas*, p.972 (appendix).
2. *Bulletin de l'Académie de Méd.*, Paris, July 1917, No. 29, pp.30-76.

But besides this more or less accidental normal parasitism, he says, there is another order of facts – more general, more constant, and dominating to a certain extent the life of the tissues – namely, the presence in the cell itself of living elements, elements indispensable to its functional activity.

He accepts Béchamp's term of *microzyma* for these, and calls the manifestations of the biological activity of these intracellular elements *microbiosis*.

These infinitesimal elements may survive the destruction of the cell, and they may acquire forms and biological properties that they previously did not possess. They may function in a kind of autonomous manner and may adapt themselves to the new conditions in which they find themselves, and continue their evolution. The normal parasitism and the microbiosis may continue their evolution either parallel to or independently of each other.

In his experiments with apples, etc., Galippe relates that he was able to induce the appearance of micro-organisms from the microbiosis while excluding those from normal parasitism. The methods by which he achieved this included mechanical trauma, contusions, etc, and he thus was able to trace certain manifestations of intracellular life and observe the appearance and evolution of certain living elements and cultivate them further.

These facts of general biology are applicable to all tissues, he says; to all cells, whatever their origin. The most striking example is in war wounds. The crushed tissues in the wounds favour the development of the phenomena due to microbiosis. The danger from leaving these contused tissues in the wounds is recognised now by all surgeons, and the surgical cleansing of all wounds is now routine practice.

What they do not know – and what Galippe devotes the fifty pages of his monograph to prove – is that on account of the normal parasitism and the microbiosis, the part played by the crushed tissues and the more extravasated blood is at the same time more important and more decisive. They may give birth directly, without foreign collaboration, to infectious elements, so that an absolutely aseptic projectile is capable of infecting a wound solely by its mechanical action in starting the abnormal evolution of the living intracellular elements already present.

The research was undertaken in Landouzy's laboratory, and the data presented corroborate the lessons already learned from clinical observation."

In the *Vaccination Inquirer* for December 1st, 1920, Mr. Alexander Paul summarises from the reports of the French Academy of Science the results of other observations by M. V. Galippe of living microzymas and their modification into bacilli. Mr. Paul quotes the latter as follows:

> "Now, the microzymas form an integral part of the cell and cannot confer on the tissues a septic character which they do not themselves possess when they belong to a healthy organism. In spite of some failures, due without doubt to accidental causes, the brilliant results obtained in surgery by the process of grafting are an irrefutable proof of this. The grafts are not dead in the absolute sense of the word since they contain living elements capable of evolution *in situ*, or in the midst of appropriate cultures, as demonstrated by our experiments. Neither glycerine, alcohol, nor time destroy the microzymas of the tissues. These different agents can only diminish or suspend their activity. They are endowed with perennial life."[1]

Mr. Paul refers to another communication by M. Galippe to the Academy of Science entitled *Living Micro-organisms in Paper: Their Resistance to the Action of Heat and of Time*.[2] In this the writer discusses cultivable elements found in all paper, even in ancient Chinese manuscripts and Egyptian papyrus, which have yielded micro-organisms endowed with movement.

Mr. Paul subsequently quotes Galippe's summary of his research on flowers:

> "Reviewing this long series of experiments, the facts that we have set forth show that *the living part of the protoplasm is constituted of microzymas*."[3]

Finally, Mr. Paul refers to Galippe's discovery of microzymas in amber, and himself comments:

> "How sad to think that M. Béchamp, after his valiant struggles till a ripe old age against Pasteur and his school – whom he accused of perverting his discoveries and building upon them a false microbian hypothesis – should have gone to the grave without enjoying the satisfaction of hearing that later research has established his position, and seeing the too long tabooed name *microzyma* reinstated in the records of the Academy of Science!"

1. *Comptes Rendus*, September, 1919.
2. *Comptes Rendus*, November 3, 1919.
3. *Comptes Rendus*, February 9, 1920.

Béchamp's findings have certainly been borne out by Dr. J. A. Goodfellow, who writes in his booklet *Hands Off Our Milk*:

> "I have recently been investigating the bacteria found in the clay strata beneath the coal measures. Talk about Rip Van Winkle and his century of slumber! These germs have been asleep, according to the computations of our geologists, for at least 250 million years, but when I transferred some of them to a suitable liquid medium, they woke up and got busy with as much vigour as if they had only been indulging in forty winks!"[1]

Many who seem never to have heard of Béchamp appear to be working slowly and laboriously towards his views. We may quote, for example, a passage from page 64 of *Health, Disease and Integration*, an interesting and advanced work by H. P. Newsholme, Medical Officer of Health for the City of Birmingham:

> "Thus we again reach a position in which, while not negating the role played by an extraneous virus in producing *encephalitis lethargica*, we nevertheless find reason for not rejecting the possibility that a purely natural enzyme or 'virus', produced by the individual and not by any bacteria harboured by him or introduced from outside, may on occasion be the cause of particular cases of a syndrome indistinguishable from that arising from extraneous infection."

In conclusion we may say that not only have we evidence of modern confirmation of Béchamp's views, but indications are many that his explanation of cellular and micro-organic life will receive a warm welcome from disinterested, unprejudiced inquirers. For instance, we may quote from a work published in 1918, entitled *Philosophy of Natural Therapeutics*[2], by Dr Henry Lindlahr:

> "Until a few weeks ago, I was not aware of the fact that a French scientist, Antoine Béchamp, as far back as the middle of the last century, had given a rational, scientific explanation of the origin, growth and life activities of germs and of the normal living cells of vegetable, animal and human bodies. This information came to me first in a pamphlet entitled *Life's Primal Architects*, by E. Douglas Hume.[3]

---

1. Printed and published by Wilfred Edmunds Ltd, Chesterfield.
2. Since the death of Henry Lindlahr, all references to Béchamp have been eliminated from later editions of the *Philosophy of Natural Therapeutics*.
3. Chapter 10 of the first edition of *Philosophy of Natural Therapeutics* is, for the most part, a reprint of portions of *Life's Primal Architects*.

According to the teachings of Béchamp, cells and germs are associations of microzymas. The physical characteristics and vital activities of cells and germs depend upon the soil in which their microzymas feed, grow and multiply. Thus microzymas, growing in the soil of procreative germ plasm, develop into the normal, permanent, specialised cells of the living vegetable, animal or human organism. The same microzymas feeding on morbid materials and systemic poisons in these living bodies develop into bacteria and parasites.

How wonderfully the discovery of microzymas confirms the claims of Nature Cure philosophy, according to which bacteria and parasites cannot cause and instigate inflammatory and other disease processes unless they find their own peculiar morbid soil in which to feed, grow and multiply!

Knowledge of the researches and teachings of Béchamp came to me but recently, after the manuscript of this volume had been practically completed. It was most gratifying to discover at the last moment this missing link which corroborates so wonderfully my own experience and teachings.

What a wonderful correspondence this theory of the origin of cell life bears to the latest scientific opinions concerning the constitution of the atom! As all elements of matter and their atoms are made up of electrons vibrating in the primordial ether, so all cells and germs are made up of the microzymas. As the electrons, according to their numbers in the atom and their modes of vibration, produce upon our sensory organs the effects of various elements of matter, so the microzymas, according to the medium or soil in which they live, develop into various cells and germs, exhibiting distinctive structure and vital activities.

Modern biology teaches us that all permanent, specialised cells present in the complicated adult body are actually contained in the original procreative cell which results from the union of the male spermatazoon and the female ovum.

Science, however, has failed to explain this seeming miracle – how it is possible that all the permanent cells of the large adult body can be present from the beginning in the minute procreative cell and in the rudimentary body of the foetus. Béchamp's theory of microzymas provides the rational and scientific explanation.

If these microzymas are as minute in comparison to the cell as the electrons are in comparison to the atom, and the atom in comparison to the visible particles of matter, then the mystery of the genesis of the complex human body from the procreative cell, as well as the mysteries of heredity in its various phases, are open to explanation. If the microzymas are the spores, or seeds, of cells, it is possible to conceive that these infinitesimal, minute living organisms may bear the impression of the species and of racial and family characteristics and tendencies, finally to reappear in the cells, organs and nervous system of the adult body."

Just as Dr. Lindlahr has accepted Béchamp's microzymian doctrine as the explanation of pathogenic and other mysteries, so we cannot but anticipate a similar acceptance on the part of other workers, and considerable advance, as an ever-widening circle makes acquaintance with Béchamp's epoch-making discoveries.

A deeply interesting tribute to his teaching by Lord Geddes may be found in a reprint of speeches in the House of Lords on February 2nd, 1944, on a motion standing in the name of Lord Teviot, asking whether the Royal Commission appointed to investigate the birth rate and trends of population would cover, in its terms of reference, the condition of the soil in relation to the health of man, animal and plant:

"Lord Portsmouth moved the motion in the absence through illness of Lord Teviot. Lord Glentanar and Lord Hankey supported the motion, as did Lord Geddes. Lord Geddes referred to the controversy regarding the food required and the use of chemical fertilisers. He said it goes back for nearly a century and has been made a very difficult controversy to follow by the dominance for so many years of the German school of biology.

'The German school – Virchow, Schwann, Liebig – laid the emphasis upon the cell out of which, in their millions, our bodies are created, and they regarded food for the cell as all that was required. Apart from that, and really obliterated and eclipsed by the German school, very likely as a result of the Franco-Prussian War and the prestige the Germans got through that war, there was a French school, of which Professor Béchamp was the leader, working at Montpellier in the 'fifties of last century. This school had a quite different idea about the structure of the body and the vitality and vigour of the body, and I think it was a great pity that, as a result of the Franco-Prussian War and various things that followed it in the

1870s, a great deal of the work of Professor Béchamp was entirely ignored and overlooked.'

Lord Geddes then described the great contribution Professor Béchamp made, a contribution his lordship had been familiar with for over thirty years, to the whole idea of life, namely, that the cell is *not* the fundamental unit of life, but that there is a much smaller, more minute unit of life, which he called, in his later reports to the Academy of Science, the *microzymas*, but which in his earlier reports he always referred to as the 'little bodies'.

Lord Geddes showed how these little living bodies have the power of organising life, and suggested that as they are not present in artificial chemical manures, the German school – which we have in this country largely followed in biology for many years – overlooked something of great importance; something which may be necessary for our human bodies, if they are to maintain their full vitality by receiving in their food a continuous supply of the little living bodies.

Lord Geddes emphasised that there is a real divergence of opinion between two schools which have existed for a long time, one of which has become dominant and out of whose practice and beliefs the whole of the chemical industry has arisen and has been able to show results of the most remarkable kind in boosting production in the plant's growth and those portions of the food that are required as fuels. But he suggested that the composters had got hold of the real source of vitality. The little bodies could be seen in drops of blood under a microscope, and during the course of that week he had examined a great many and had seen most extraordinary differences between people fed in different ways and in different states of health.

He proposed that the research that was needed was investigation of the question: *Is the supply of these little living bodies in the food essential to the continued vitality of human beings, or is it not?*

He thought there was the possibility – many think the extreme probability – that the presence of these little living bodies in the food is essential to health.

He went on to describe how these little bodies are found in the most antique remnants of life, and how they can start organisation in a sugar solution that is sterile and dead; and concluded by saying that the problem could best be answered with a combination of research by the Agricultural Research Council, and of observation carefully conducted and carefully checked by way of studies of groups of people fed on different diets."

We repeat the prophecy of the *Moniteur Scientifique* that time will do justice to Béchamp's work and make it known in its entirety. And with this end in view, we would advise all students to go direct to the writings of this brilliant Frenchman who, even in that epoch of intellectual giants, is an outstanding genius of the nineteenth century!

PART 3

THE CULT OF THE MICROBE

15.
The Origin of 'Preventive Medicine'

It was at the beginning of 1873 that Pasteur was elected by a majority of one vote to a place among the Free Associates of the Academy of Medicine. His ambition had indeed spurred him to open 'a new era in medical physiology and pathology', but it would seem to have been unfortunate for the world that instead of putting forward the fuller teaching of Béchamp he fell back upon the cruder ideas now widely known as the 'germ theory' of disease. He even used his influence with the Academy of Science to anathematise the very word *microzyma*; so much so that M. Fremy, even though a friend of Béchamp, declared that he dared not even utter the word any more.[1]

As a name was, however, required for airborne micro-organisms, Pasteur accepted the term *microbe* suggested by the surgeon Sédillot, a former Director of the Army Medical School at Strasbourg. The criticism might be made that this term is an etymological solecism; the Greeks used the word *macrobiorus* to denote races of long-lived people, and now a name concocted from Greek words for short-lived was conferred upon micro-organisms whose parent-stem, the *microzyma*, Béchamp had described as being 'physiologically imperishable'. Man, who so seldom lasts a century, might better be called a 'microbe', and the microzyma a 'macrobe'!

It was not until 1873 that Sédillot put forward his suggestion; but before this Pasteur had been busy promoting micro-organisms as the cause of varying troubles, and in 1874 he was gratified by an appreciative letter from Lister. The latter wrote that the Pasteurian germ theory of putrefaction had furnished him

> "with the principle upon which alone the antiseptic system can be carried out."[2]

However, let us turn to the verdict of time, which – according to Pasteur's own dictum – must pronounce judgment on a scientist. Before the last Royal Commission on Vivisection, which sat from 1906 to 1908, Sir Henry Morris, President of the Royal College of Surgeons,

---

1. *The Blood*, A. Béchamp, p.43, note.
2. *The Life of Pasteur*, René Vallery-Radot, p.238.

wishing to put the best case possible for Pasteur, was forced, all the same, to acknowledge:

"In consequence of further researches and experience, some modification of the technique first introduced by Lord Lister occurred, and the evolution of the aseptic method resulted."[1]

Dr. Wilson points out in his Reservation Memorandum of the Royal Commission that

"...the basis of aseptic surgery, which in essence is clean surgery, was explained – as stated in the report and in reply to a question by Sir William Collins – by Semmelweiss before 1850, who attributed the blood poisoning which devastated his wards in a Viennese hospital to putrid infection, and strongly urged cleanliness as a means of preventing it."[2]

Dr. Wilson shows how Lord Lister brought about the application of this advice as to cleanliness considerably before his ideas were moulded by Pasteur. This latter influence, this Pasteurian theory

"...that the *causa causans* of septicism in wounds rested on micro-organisms in the air *was an altogether mistaken theory.*"[3]

It was on this 'mistaken theory', this 'principle', provided for him by Pasteur, that Lord Lister based his use of carbolic spray, of which, before the Medical Congress in Berlin in 1891, he made this recantation:

"I feel ashamed that I should ever have recommended it for the purpose of destroying the microbes in the air."

Thus pronounces the verdict of time against the theories of Pasteur; while as regards the teaching of Béchamp, what do we find? Dr. Wilson continues:

"The real source of all the mischief was the unclean or putrefying matter which might be conveyed by hands, dressings, or other means, to freshly made wounds."

Such contamination is exactly explained by the microzymian doctrine, which teaches that this putrefying matter with its morbid microzymas can affect the normal conditions of the inherent microzymas of the body with which it comes into contact.

Thus the verdict of time corroborates Béchamp.

---

1. *Final Report of the Royal Commission on Vivisection*, p.23.
2. p.89.
3. p.90.

Pasteur declared danger to arise from atmospheric microbes. He talked of 'invaded patients', and triumphantly chalked upon a blackboard the chain-like organism that he claimed to be the germ of puerperal fever.

Béchamp maintained that in free air even morbid microzymas and bacteria soon lose their morbidity, and that inherent organisms are the starting points of septic and other troubles.

What was Lord Lister's final judgment, after having abandoned the method into which he was misled by Pasteur? Here are his own words, as quoted by Dr. George Wilson:

> "The floating particles of the air may be disregarded in our surgical work, and, if so, we may dispense with antiseptic washing and irrigation, provided always that we can trust ourselves and our assistants to avoid the introduction into the wound of septic defilement from other than atmospheric sources."[1]

Comment is unnecessary.

But in the 1870s, the specific airborne germ theory had the charm of novelty, and its crude simplicity attracted the unscientific, although many scientists opposed it sturdily. Pasteur, however, continued upon a triumphal career of pronouncements of disease germs, and was assisted by the conclusions of Dr. Koch and other workers.

Anthrax, to which we have already alluded, offered him a convenient field for his quest of the microbe, and a little later his attention was turned to an organism first noticed by a surgeon named Moritz, and afterwards claimed by Toussaint to be responsible for chicken cholera.

This so-called microbe Pasteur cultivated assiduously, as he had already cultivated the *bacillus anthracis*. He also inaugurated the fashion for what may be called the study of artificial disease conditions; that is to say, instead of giving attention to Nature's experiments in naturally diseased subjects, human and animal, the mania was aroused for inducing sickness by poisonous injections, a practice Pasteur started about this time and which his followers have so persistently copied that some have even deliberately performed iniquitous and unethical experiments upon men, women and children.

There can also be no question that since his day, bird and animal victims of every species have died and suffered in the millions all over the world in laboratories, and that had Pasteur never lived, our 'little

---

1. See Dr. G. Wilson's *Reservation Memorandum of the Royal Commission on Vivisection*, p.90.

brothers and sisters', to quote St. Francis of Assisi, would have been spared incalculable agonies.

His admirers will, of course, retort that his experiments were undertaken with a direct view to alleviate suffering and, in the first instance, animal sicknesses, particularly splenic fever. But it must strike anyone as a topsy-turvy method to start the cure of natural diseases by the production of artificial; and the principle of vicarious suffering can surely only hold good ethically by voluntary self-sacrifice. But we are not here so much concerning ourselves with the ethics of Pasteur's procedure as with the practical outcome, so let us turn our attention to the unfortunate hens that were numbered among his early victims.

Pasteur tested his cultures of the so-called chicken cholera microbe on poultry, and killed birds with systematic regularity. It came about, however, that a few were accidentally inoculated with a stale culture, and these merely sickened and went on to recover. This did not, however, save them from further experiments, and these 'used' hens were now given a fresh dose of new culture. Again they proved resistant. This immunity was promptly ascribed to the previous dosage of stale culture. Pasteur then started to inject attenuated doses into hens, and claimed that this protected them from death when afterwards inoculated with fresh virus. His biographer asks:

> "Was not this fact worthy of being placed by the side with that great fact of vaccine over which Pasteur had so often pondered and meditated?"[1]

His meditations, however, show nothing of the caution his biographer is so anxious to ascribe to him. Vallery-Radot says:

> "Original researches, new and bold ideas, appealed to Pasteur. But his cautious mind prevented his boldness from leading him into errors, surprises or hasty conclusions. 'That is possible,' he would say, 'but we must look more deeply into the subject.'"[2]

However, bold ideas had apparently only to have been made familiar over time for caution to forsake Pasteur. A true disposition of scientific doubt would have prompted him to establish the truth of the success or failure of Jennerian vaccination before accommodating accidents or theories to account for it. As a matter of fact, Koch, in 1883,[3] would not admit that the chicken cholera prophylaxis had the value that was

---

1. *The Life of Pasteur*, by René Vallery-Radot, p.300.

2. *ibid*, p.33.

3. *Medical Press and Circular*, January 17, 1883.
   (Quoted in *Rabies and Hydrophobia* by Surg. General A. C. Gordon.)

claimed for it; while Kitt in 1886[1] declared that ordinary precautions (cleanliness, isolation of infected birds, etc.), were preferable. In regard to the particular accident of the stale culture, which was made the foundation stone for the whole system of inoculation; it is evident that, like most people, Pasteur had accepted vaccination without personal investigation, and so, like many others, showed himself possessed of a simple credulity that is the antithesis to scientific cautiousness.

This criticism is the more justified because at this date in France, as in England, the subject of vaccination had become controversial.

In 1863 Ricord, a famous French physician, was already delivering a warning against the transmission of syphilis by the practice. By 1867, the Academy had received evidence of the truth of this contention; and in 1870 Dr. A. Caron of Paris declared that he had long since refused to vaccinate at any price.

We should relate what happened when Dr. Charles Creighton was asked to write an article on vaccination for the *Encyclopaedia Britannica*. He complied, but being a scientist in deed as well as in name, felt it incumbent first to study the subject. As a consequence, the article had to be condemnatory, for investigation proved vaccination to be 'a grotesque superstition' in the opinion of the greatest of modern epidemiologists.

Pasteur, on the contrary, incautiously accepting the popular view, had a credulous belief in the success of vaccination, and made his hens' behaviour account theoretically for a practice that he seems never to have investigated historically. It is true that he paused to notice a discrepancy between Jenner's vaccination and the theory founded upon it. According to Pasteur, a previous injection of a stale culture safeguarded against a later injection of fresh virus; but how could two such dissimilar disease conditions as cowpox and smallpox be a protection the one from the other? His response:

> "From the point of view of physiological experimentation, the identity of the variola virus with the vaccine virus has never been demonstrated."[2]

We are not engaged upon an anti-vaccination treatise, but as Jennerian vaccination – whether in its original form of cowpox, or its modernised guise of smallpox matter, passed (usually) through a heifer – is the foundation of Pasteurian inoculation, the two subjects are linked

---

1. Deutsche Zeitschrift fur Tiermedizin, December 20, 1886.
   (Quoted in Sternberg's *Textbook of Bacteriology*.)
2. *The Life of Pasteur*, René Vallery-Radot, p.308.

together, and with the demolition of the first follows logically the downfall of the second. The whole theory is rooted in a belief in the immunity conferred by a non-fatal attack of a disease. The idea arises from the habit of regarding a disease as an entity, a definite thing, instead of a disordered condition due to complex causes; the germ theory of disease, in particular, being the unconscious offspring of the ancient Eastern faith in specific demons, each possessed of his own special weapon of malignity. Thus the smallpox inoculation introduced into England from Turkey by Lady Mary Wortley Montague in the eighteenth century and its Jennerian substitute of cowpox inoculation were based on the ancient Indian rite of subjecting people to an artificially induced attack of smallpox to propitiate Sheetula-Mati, the goddess of that torment.

Believers in the doctrine of immunity may correctly retort that seeming superstitions are often founded upon the observations of experience. Be that as it may, what remains for the lover of accuracy is to examine each superstitious belief upon its own merits and test the facts of life in regard to it. The assertion that because many people have had a one and only attack of any specific complaint, an auto-protection has thus been afforded them is surely no more scientific than the old Indian belief in the assuaging of the wrath of a malignant goddess.

As Professor Alfred Russel Wallace says:

> "Very few people suffer from any special accident twice – a shipwreck, or railway or coach accident, or a house fire – yet one of these accidents does not confer immunity against it happening a second time. The taking for granted that second attacks of smallpox, or of any other zymotic disease, are of that degree of rarity as to prove some immunity or protection, indicates the incapacity for dealing with what is a purely statistical question."[1]

Yet so imbued is medical orthodoxy with the immunity theory that we recall a doctor[2] laying down the law on this subject even though his own daughter had recently died of a *third* attack of scarlet fever!

As Herbert Spencer has shown in his *Principles of Psychology*,[3] there is in the genesis of nerves a great likelihood of the development of

---

1. *The Wonderful Century*, by Alfred Russel Wallace, Ch. 18, p.296. In recent editions of this book, Ch. 18 is omitted owing to its former publication as a separate pamphlet.
2. Dr. Alfred Salter.
3. Vol. 1, p.579.

habit. All of us know how easy it is to catch colds, and that complaints such as influenza are apt to be repeated. A trifling trouble such as a cold sore may often be observed to reappear time after time in the same spot.

If we wish to theorise, it might seem probable that when the system undergoes such a thorough upheaval as that brought about by serious disorders like smallpox, the chance of recurrence is markedly less than in more trifling disturbances, such as colds and influenza. We should remember that what we call disease is often nature's method for ridding us of poisons; and, to take a homely example from household life, while a thorough house-cleaning takes place usually once a year, the dusting of rooms is of frequent occurrence. Such a theory is, however, palpably opposed to belief in immunity through artificially induced disorders, and, moreover, plausible though it may seem, it is contradicted by statistical evidence.

The testimony of Professor Adolf Vogt, who from 1877 to 1894 was Professor of Hygiene and of Sanitary Statistics in the University of Berne, Switzerland, is quoted by Professor Alfred Russel Wallace in Chapter 18 of *The Wonderful Century*.

Using the statistical data available to him at the time, Vogt supplied a mathematical demonstration that a person who had undergone smallpox once was 63% more liable to suffer from it again in a subsequent epidemic than a person who had never had the disease. Vogt concluded:

> "All this justifies our insisting that the theory that immunity can be confered by a previous attack of smallpox – whether the natural disease or the disease produced artificially – *must be relegated to the realm of fiction.*"

Certainly, if no auto-prophylaxy is induced by natural disorders, no claim can surely be made for auto-prophylaxy from artificially provoked disturbances.

In regard to vaccination against smallpox, experience can be our guide, since we have a whole century's history to consider with regard to its efficacy. We are faced by outstanding facts, from among which we may quote an illustrative example provided by Professor Wallace in Chapter 18 of *The Wonderful Century*.

In it he shows how free vaccination was offered in 1840, made compulsory in 1853, and in 1867 the order was given to prosecute evaders; and so stringent was the application of the regulations that few children escaped vaccination. Thus the following table provides a striking illustration of the inefficacy of vaccination in regard to smallpox mortality:

Date	Deaths from Smallpox (England and Wales)
1857–59	14,244
1863–65	20,059
1870–72	44,840

Between	Increase % of population	Increase % of smallpox deaths
1st & 2nd epidemic:	7	40.8
2nd & 3rd epidemic:	9	123.0

These figures show that while the population went up only 7% and 9% in the years covered, smallpox mortality increased at the rate of 40.8% and 123% – and this in face of an ever increasing number of vaccinations!

Now let us turn to some military testimony, since in all countries the armed forces are the most thoroughly vaccinated members of the community.

In January 1899, Chief Surgeon Lippencott of the U.S. Army, writing from Manila, said:

> "The entire Command has been vaccinated at least four times since the appearance of the disease (smallpox)."

In the following March, he wrote again to state that all danger was over. However, in the reports of the Surgeon-General of the U.S.A. Army are to be found the following figures of smallpox cases and deaths:

Year	Cases	Deaths	Fatality rate (%)
1899	267	78	29.21
1900	246	113	45.93
1901	85	37	43.53
1902	63	12	19.05

During the same period, the smallpox fatality rate among the far less vaccinated general population of the United States did not exceed 3%!

To turn back to *The Wonderful Century*,[1] Professor Wallace provides a comparison between the British Army and Navy and the unvaccinated

1. Chapter 18, pp.284-5.

inhabitants of Leicester during a period when the fighting forces on land and sea, at home and abroad, were stated to have been 'completely revaccinated'. Leicester is taken as an example because of the unvaccinated condition of almost all its inhabitants since the smallpox outbreak of 1871–2. Before this, 95% of the children born were vaccinated, and the huge attack and death rates during the epidemic were sufficient to prove the futility of vaccination. The authorities were, therefore, led to try improved sanitation and isolation as preventives, and have been rewarded not only with comparative freedom from smallpox, but also with the best health rate of all the industrial towns of Great Britain.

Professor Wallace writes as follows:

> "The average annual smallpox death rate of this town (Leicester) for the 22 years 1873–94 inclusive is thirteen per million (see 4th Report, p.440); but in order to compare with our Army and Navy we must add one-ninth for the mortality at ages 15–45 as compared with total mortality, according to the table at p.155 of the *Final Report*, bringing it to 14.4 per million, when the comparison will stand as follows:
>
> Smallpox death rate per million, 1873–94
> Army 37.0
> Navy 36.8
> Leicester (ages 15-45) 14.4
>
> It is thus demonstrated that all the statements by which the public has been reassured as to the almost complete immunity of the revaccinated Army and Navy are absolutely false. There is no immunity. They have no protection. When exposed to infection, they suffer not just as much as other populations, but even more. In the nineteen years 1878–1896 inclusive, unvaccinated Leicester had so few smallpox deaths that the Registrar-General represents the average by the decimal 0.01 per thousand population, equal to ten per million, while for the twelve years 1878–1889 there was less than one death per annum! Here we have *real* immunity, *real* protection; and it is obtained by attending to sanitation and isolation, coupled with the almost total neglect of vaccination. Neither the Army nor Navy can show any such results as this."

And the lessons of the past continue up to the present in Leicester, where for the 26 years ending 1931, there have been only two deaths from smallpox.

Similarly, the experience of Germany and of Japan shows us that with much vaccination there is also much smallpox, while the Philippine Islands provide us with the most striking example on record.

Since the taking over of the islands by the USA, every attention has been paid to the perfecting of sanitation. But not content with this, their Public Health Service has undertaken the thorough and systematic vaccination of the population, adding thereto a considerable amount of serum inoculation.

For the result, let us turn to an American paper, published in Minneapolis, *The Masonic Observer* of the 14th January, 1922:

> "The Philippines have experienced three smallpox epidemics since the United States first took over the Islands, the first in 1905–6, the second in 1907–8, and the third and worst, the recent epidemic of 1918–1919.
>
> Before 1905 (with no systematic general vaccination) the case mortality was about 10%. In the 1905–6 epidemic, with vaccination well started, the case mortality ranged from 25% to 50% in different parts of the Islands. During the epidemic of 1918–19, with the Philippines supposedly almost universally immunised against smallpox by vaccination, the case mortality averaged over 65%.
>
> These figures can be verified by reference to the *Report of the Philippine Health Service* for 1919, p.78. These figures are accompanied by the statement that "the mortality is hardly explainable". To anyone but a Philippine Medical Health Commissioner, it is plainly the result of vaccination.
>
> Not only has smallpox become more deadly in the Philippines, but, in addition:
>
> > 'The statistics of the Philippine Health Service show that there has been a steady increase in recent years in cases of preventable diseases, especially typhoid, malaria and tuberculosis.'
>
> (Quoted from the 1921 *Report of the Special Mission on Investigation to the Philippine Islands*, of which General Leonard Wood was head.)"

Going more into detail in an earlier issue (10th December, 1921), *The Masonic Observer* writes:

> "The highest percentage of mortality, 65.3%, was in Manila, the most thoroughly vaccinated place in the Philippines; the lowest percentage of mortality, 11.4%, was in Mindanao, where, owing to the religious beliefs of the inhabitants, vaccination had not been practised as much as in most other

parts of the islands.

To the everlasting shame of the misnamed 'Health' Service, vaccination has been forced on Mindanao since 1918, despite this proof that their people were safer without it, and, as a result, smallpox mortality increased to above 25% in 1920.

In view of the fact that sanitary engineers had probably done more in Manila to clean up the city and make it healthy than in any other part of the islands there is every reason to believe that excessive vaccination actually brought on the smallpox epidemic, in spite of the sanitary measures taken to promote health."

Again, from the issue of the 17th December, 1921:

"Think of it – less than 11 million population in the Philippines and 107,981 cases of smallpox with the awful toll of 59,741 deaths in 1918 and 1919. Bear in mind that, in all human probability, the inhabitants of the Philippines are as thoroughly vaccinated and revaccinated as any people in the world.

Systematic vaccination started in the Philippines in 1905 and has continued ever since. It is certain that over ten million vaccinations for smallpox were performed in the Philippines from 1905 to 1917, and very probable that the vaccinations numbered even as many as fifteen million during that time. This can be verified by reference to reports of the Philippine Health Service."

Turning to those reports, we find evidence that the facts must have been even worse. In letters to the Secretary of Public Instruction, Dr. V. de Jesus (the Director of Health) states that in 1918 and 1919 there were in the Philippines 112,549 cases of smallpox with 60,855 deaths. The Chief of the Division of Sanitation in the Provinces gives yet higher figures for the year 1919, increasing the total for the two years to 145,317 cases and 63,434 deaths.

So the facts pronounce firmly against Jenner and Pasteur. Yet, basing his theories upon a practice already discredited by those who had given it close and impartial scientific study, Pasteur proceeded to inaugurate a system of preventive medicine focused on what he proclaimed to be the ravages of airborne microbes. The attenuated doses which, according to his theory, were to prevent natural diseases did due honour to Edward Jenner by being called *vaccines*.

Pasteur's son-in-law tells us:

> "Midst his researches on a vaccine for chicken cholera, the etiology of splenic fever was unceasingly preoccupying Pasteur."[1]

Although a vaccine for the former complaint was the first he professed to discover, it was in regard to splenic fever that a great stir was occasioned; for Pasteur was called upon in various instances to test his method of vaccination.

We will, therefore, include in the next chapter a study of his methods against anthrax, which form the starting point of the subsequent mania for inoculation which has proved so financially profitable to the manufacturers of vaccines and sera and has so disastrously polluted the advance of science with the pecuniary considerations of commercial interests.

---

1. *The Life of Pasteur*, p.303.

16.
The International Medical Congress and some Pasteurian Fiascos

It was in the year 1877 that Pasteur took up the subject of anthrax, and, as usual, pushing himself to the front, he promoted far and wide his method of cultivating the rod-like organisms, or *bacteridia*. These he claimed to have proved to be the sole cause of the complaint, which he proposed impressively to rename the disease of the bacteridia.

He asserted that the blood of an anthracised animal contains no other organisms but the bacteridia, which he considered to be exclusively aerobic. He argued that they, therefore, take no part in putrefaction, which, according to him, is always due to anaerobic micro-organisms of the order of vibrios, and that consequently, anthracised blood of itself is imputrescible. In the corpse, on the contrary, he believed that anthracised blood quickly becomes putrescent, since, according to him, every corpse provides a home for vibrios which enter from without into the intestinal canal, always fuel of vibrios of all kinds, and so soon as the normal life does not hinder them they bring about a prompt disintegration.

This was the teaching upon which Pasteur was to build up his prophylaxis against anthrax, and so, for his prophylactic, he put forward a mixture of 'aerobic germs' – namely, the bacteridia – with 'anaerobic germs' of putrefaction. He maintained that a result would be obtained that should neutralise the virulence of the *bacillus anthracis*, and thus if injected into animals would protect them from infection.

It was while Pasteur was putting forward such views that he fell foul of another member of the Academy of Medicine; Dr. Colin, who asked how anthrax could be due to the bacteridia when it was sometimes found in a virulent stage, and yet without the presence of these micro-organisms. He claimed the floor on 12th March, 1878, to criticise the printed report of the former session.[1] He said:

> "M. Pasteur, at the previous session, had formulated two propositions, which are not to be found in the Bulletin. The first is that the bacteridia of anthrax do not develop in the

1. *Bulletin de l'Académie de Médicine*, 2e Vol. 7, p.220-235.

blood of healthy animals; the second is that the bacteridia will not supply germs to the organism. I replied that these two allegations seemed to me open to dispute, but all criticism of them becomes pointless, owing to their suppression from the printed record. Other statements of Pasteur have also been suppressed from the record, for example:

'It would take a man his lifetime to examine a drop of anthracised blood,'

and also that

'The search for a bacteridium in a drop of blood is as difficult as that for a cell of a ferment in a litre of beer yeast.'

These suppressions, and some additions of which I need not speak, are absolutely a matter of indifference to me, although they make me appear as having spoken 'in the air' and without object. But what is *not* indifferent to me is that M. Pasteur represents me in the Bulletin as saying something I did *not* say – inserting as mine a mode of experimentation and of reasoning that is not mine at all. It is against this that I protest."

Pasteur gave a confused reply, which did not answer Dr. Colin's accusation – which, be it noted, did not concern the natural correction by an author of the report of his observations, but a direct alteration of the records. In the absence of any proper explanation and apology from M. Pasteur, we can quite understand Dr. Colin saying:

"...henceforth I will have no discussion with M. Pasteur."[1]

The glowing panegyrics that now surround the memory of Pasteur considerably obscure the disfavour in which his methods were held by many of his contemporaries.

Pasteur lost no time in pushing his views on anthrax and kindred subjects, and on the 30th April, 1878, read before the Academy of Science a memoir bearing his own name and those of Messrs. Joubert and Chamberland. It was entitled *The Theory of Germs and Their Application to Medicine and Surgery*, and was the first trumpet blast of the germ theory of disease.

Pasteur seized this opportunity to advertise widely that he had discovered the fact that 'ferments are living beings'. It goes without saying that not one word of acknowledgment was made to Béchamp for his illumination of the subject. The memoir began by asserting that

---

1. *Bulletin de l'Académie de Médecine*, 2e Vol. 7, p.261.

this discovery was a result of Pasteur's communication in 1857-8 on fermentation; that the germs of micro-organisms abound everywhere; that the theory of spontaneous generation was thus shown to be a chimera, and that wine, beer, vinegar, blood, urine and all the liquids of the body undergo none of their ordinary changes in contact with pure air.

We have already seen:

Firstly, that with regard to fermentation in general and vinous fermentation in particular, and also in regard to silkworm diseases, *it is impossible to deny that Pasteur plagiarised Béchamp.*

Secondly, we have seen that Pasteur's experiments were insufficient to defeat the theory of spontaneous generation, and that they never satisfied Sponteparists such as Pouchet, Le Bon and Bastian. Béchamp's experiments and explanations alone seem to account for phenomena that without them can only be explained by heterogenesis.

Thirdly, notwithstanding the assertions of this memoir of triple authorship, both the liquids and solids of animal and vegetable bodies do undergo changes because, Béchamp explained, of the infinitesimal living organisms they contain, to which he gave the illuminating name of *microzyma*.

Even Pasteur hinted at belief in this when he claimed that:

> "every being, every organ, every cell that lives or continues its life without the help of the oxygen of the air… *must possess the character of a ferment.*"

His own self-styled 'famous experiment' on meat actually bore witness to such changes, although he denied them.

The authors of the memoir went on to describe how, in their judgment, an infinitesimal quantity of their last-produced culture was capable of producing anthrax with all its symptoms. On sowing their septic product (vibrios obtained from the carcass of an animal that had died of septicaemia), the authors found that their first efforts failed. Their cultures were not barren, but the organisms obtained were not the septic vibrios, but had the common form of chaplets of small spherical grains, exceedingly minute and not virulent.

Similar observations had already been made by Professor Béchamp, who, with his collaborators, had demonstrated the connection between a disturbed state of body and the disturbed state of its indwelling particles, which, upon an unfavourable alteration in their surroundings, are hampered in their normal multiplication as healthy microzymas and are consequently prone to develop into organisms of varied shape, known as bacteria. Upon an improvement in their environment, the bacteria, according to Béchamp's view, may through a process of devolution return to their microzymian state, but much smaller and more numerous than they were originally.

It is regrettable that expositions by Béchamp should have been set aside, especially as Pasteur and his friends could only account for the phenomena described in the memoir by concluding that they had introduced an unobserved impurity at the same time as the septic vibrio. They also stated that each micro-organism of a particular form and shape was a disease-causing agent; thus, according to them, the septic vibrio produced septicaemia, and the rod-shaped bacterium, usually associated with anthrax and since known as the *bacillus anthracis*, was the direct originator of that torment of animals.

They made, in addition, the dogmatic claim that their 'proof' was not open to dispute, although in their theory confusion reigned until the German, Dr. Robert Koch, came to their rescue and formulated a set of rules for the recognition of supposed disease germs. According to him, these must be:

1. Found in every case of the disease.

2. Never found apart from the disease.

3. Capable of culture outside the body.

4. Capable of producing by injection the same disease as that undergone by the body from which they were taken.

Here we see the basic theory of the airborne disease germ doctrine contradicted by the last postulate; for if to invoke disease, organisms require to be *taken from bodies*, either directly or else intermediately through cultures, what evidence is adduced of the responsibility of invaders *from the atmosphere*?

As Béchamp showed:

> "In all the experiments of recent years, it has been the microzyma proper to an animal and not a germ of the air that has been found to be the seat of the virulence. No one has ever been able to produce with germs obtained from the atmosphere *any* of the so-called parasitic diseases. Whenever, by inoculation, a typical known malady has been reproduced, it has been necessary to go and take the supposed parasite from a sick animal; thus to inoculate tuberculosis, the tubercle has to be taken from a subject already affected."[1]

---

1. *Les Microzymas*, p.819.

It is noteworthy that neither Pasteur nor any of his successors have ever induced a complaint by the inoculation of airborne bacteria, but only by injections from bodily sources. Furthermore, the verdict of time is pronouncing firmly against the microbian rules, and even medical orthodoxy has reluctantly had to acknowledge that

"Koch's postulates are rarely, if ever, complied with."[1]

But Pasteur, as we have seen, had never shown any interest in speculative theories, which were so all-engrossing in themselves to a student of nature such as Béchamp; that is to say, Pasteur's mind always turned quickly to the business side of any proposition. He recognised the possibility of great profit, and dreamed of a means of arresting, or professing to arrest, the ravages of anthrax among sheep and cattle. Using his classification of aerobic and anaerobic micro-organisms, he proposed by a mixture of the two sorts to neutralise the virulence of the bacteridium.

We have already seen how he regarded the accidental administration of some stale culture to hens as a guide to his subsequent proceedings, and it was for chicken cholera that he first endeavoured to procure what he called a 'vaccine'.

Professor Toussaint, of the Toulouse Veterinary School, worked on 'vaccination' against anthrax, which Pasteur subsequently took up, and announced himself satisfied that he had discovered a real preventive.

In May 1881, Pasteur was invited to put his vaccine to the test at a farm near Melun, and in June he wrote home triumphantly that complete success had resulted. By this was meant that sheep that had been first inoculated with his preparation did not succumb to a subsequent dosage of poison. The test was artificial; no real success could be proved unless it was found that natural infection was powerless against inoculated animals.

This objection was put forward, and in July, some experiments were undertaken that were supposed to satisfy it. The power of the vaccine was to be tested by a subsequent injection of blood taken from a sheep that had actually died of anthrax. But here again it is obvious that the procedure was distinct from natural infection, especially as certain sheep remained impervious to the complaint although feeding on ground supposed to be pervaded by bacteria from the buried carcases of diseased sheep. However, success seemed sufficient for a commercial asset to be made of the supposed prophylactic. It does not take much

---

1. *The Lancet,* March 20, 1909.

observation to note that pecuniary profits obstruct unbiased criticism, and thus real investigation was checked from the first by Pasteur's alliance of science with commercialism.

In the midst of his experiments a break came. An International Medical Congress took place in London in August 1881, and the French Republic sent Pasteur as its representative.

His son-in-law tells us[1] of the outburst of cheering that arose as he approached the platform after entering St. James's Hall; while quietly seated in his place amidst the great assembly, unnoticed for the most part, was the real discoverer of the fermentative role of micro-organisms of the air and of the internal tissues; the real elucidator of the mysteries of silkworm diseases and vinous fermentation; the founder of views considered to be new even today by cytologists.

Béchamp watched the triumph of his rival in silence. In a foreign assembly he would have been the last to cast any stigma upon a compatriot, and it never entered his head that Pasteur would go out of his way to attack him in the presence of strangers.

But unhappily, ambition was to trump common decency.

The incident took place at a sectional meeting at which Professor Bastian put forward his view of the development of micro-organisms in internal tissues, his opinion differing from Béchamp's in that, instead of acknowledging living granulations (the microzymas) as parent units, it involved the spontaneous generation of organic from inorganic matter.

Pasteur, called upon to answer, went off on a tangent to the subject, and to refute Bastian, described a cruel experiment which in itself contradicts his apologists' attempts to whitewash his callousness towards animal suffering. *The Times* of the 8th August, 1881, quotes his words as follows:

> "If Dr. Bastian took the limb of a living animal, healthy or ill, provided the illness was not *microbienne*, bruised the tissues of it and reduced it to a most unhealthy condition, without, however, breaking the skin, and taking care to exclude microbes from the intestinal canal, he would never find in it the smallest microscopic organisms. Had Dr. Bastian forgotten his (Pasteur's) experiment of 1863 by which he had shown that the blood and urine of a living animal introduced into glass vases could not putrefy, although exposed to free contact with the air, and with air, moreover, which was constantly renewed, provided only the air was free of germs?

1. *The Life of Pasteur*, René Vallery-Radot, p.329.

In the study of microscopic organisms, there was an ever-present source of error in the introduction of foreign germs, in spite of the precautions that might be taken against them. When the observer saw first one organism and afterwards a different one, he was prone to conclude that the first organisms had undergone a change. Yet this might be a pure illusion....

The transformation of a *bacillus anthracis* into a *micrococcus* did not exist."

Alas for Pasteur and the verdict of time upon a scientist! That same newspaper, *The Times*, which quoted his glib assertion, many years later, on the 8th April, 1914, related the contradictory testimony of a worker at the Pasteur Institute:

"Mme. Henri's discovery marks a step in the evolution of the science of bacteriology. Briefly stated, what has been accomplished is the transformation of a well-known bacillus of definite shape and possessing definite toxic properties into another type of micro-organism apparently possessed of properties of a kind entirely different from those of the original anthrax bacillus."

Or, as the *Daily News* of the same date put it:

"The experiment was made with the anthrax bacillus, which from a rod shape was transformed into a spherical coccus."

So much for Pasteur's assertion that

"...the transformation of a *bacillus anthracis* into a *micrococcus* does not exist."

As to the newness of 'Mme. Henri's discovery': Professor Béchamp could have explained it at the Medical Congress in the year 1881, when he was already familiar with the transformation of bacilli, both as regards form and function.

The Times said:

"This discovery (Mme. Henri's), is regarded as important and possibly marking a step towards finding some protoplasmic form of the origin of life."

This form would appear to be the minute granulations of cells of which Professor Minchin was to speak a year later before the British Association for the Advancement of Science, and which had already been investigated by Béchamp since the 1860s. We can imagine the trial it was to him to listen to assertions made by Pasteur upon matters that he could so easily have refuted. But, as he tells us in the preface to *Les Microzymas* –

"I let him talk, because I was to speak after him."[1]

This was when Pasteur, most unfairly, suddenly included his compatriot in his strictures against Sponteparists, speaking as though Béchamp were a believer in heterogenesis, instead of the real destroyer of the belief in spontaneous generation through his microzymian explanation of the presence of micro-organisms within internal organs and tissues.

The Times thus quotes Pasteur:

"The same error was made in this respect by Dr. Bastian in England and Professor Béchamp in France. The latter was wholly mistaken, for instance, in his theory as to the existence of microzymas in chalk."

The Times, kind to the fashionable demagogue, leaves Pasteur's criticism at this; but what fired Béchamp's indignation was, as he tells us in the preface to *Les Microzymas*, Pasteur's subsequent unpardonable accusation of plagiarism:

"If there was anything exact in Béchamp's viewpoint, he had conceived it in assimilating his (Pasteur's) labours and. modifying his ideas according to the other's."

Such a barefaced reversal of facts was too much for long-suffering Professor Béchamp. He sprang from his seat and faced his traducer, indignantly demanding proofs and promising that he himself would supply proof to establish the exact opposite.

Pasteur's behaviour cannot, we think, be condoned by even his most enthusiastic admirer. Confronted by his victim, he simply turned on his heel and quitted the assembly, defrauding Béchamp of any opportunity for a proper public vindication of himself and his discoveries.

As *The Times* has quoted the latter's speech, we can see for ourselves the contrast of the Professor's magnanimous and dignified treatment of Pasteur.

---

1. p.7.

"Professor Béchamp of Lille, likewise speaking in French, affirmed that the microzymas in chalk *did* exist, and that if Pasteur had not obtained such results, it was because his experiments were badly conducted.

On other points also, Béchamp contested Pasteur's views. He held that the cause of disease and of death lay in the animal itself. The so-called 'molecular granulations' of histologists were living organised things, endowed with chemical gravity, and having the same functions as the similar granulations which existed in the air and in chalk under the name of *microzymas*; they were the primitive agents of the organisation and the chemical activity of living organisms – though, strange to say, these *microzymas*, while morphologically identical, performed different functions in different organic centres and tissues, e.g. the *microzymas* of the pancreas compared with those of the liver. He could not admit that they entered the tissues from the air.

Pasteur denied their existence there because it conflicted with his theories. For his own part, however, he was convinced that tissues did show bacteria of different shapes and sizes where no penetration of germs from the air could have occurred. In Pasteur's experiment with blood and urine, these liquids really underwent a change, and, far from disproving the existence of *microzymas* in them, served to confirm it."

Pasteur was spared the difficulty of replying, since he had already withdrawn after his uncalled-for attack upon the fellow countryman to whose researches he owed such a vast debt. Possibly it was this very fact that envenomed him against Béchamp. We are reminded of the story of the man who, upon being told that a neighbour detested him, asked 'Why should he? I have never done him a good turn'.

Lionised by the elite among whom he found himself, Pasteur felt secure in his triumph. At one of the great general meetings, at the request of the President, Sir James Paget, he gave a lecture on his method of vaccination against chicken cholera and anthrax, for which he naturally claimed unmitigated success, while he took the opportunity to extol Edward Jenner, relegating himself and his own works to what was certainly very suitable company.

Delighting almost childishly in the flatteries that had been showered upon him, announcing his triumph in private letters, Pasteur returned to France, where a fresh honour soon overjoyed him; his election to the French Academy. He had grown so accustomed to riding down like a juggernaut any contradictions or dissent that dared to show itself that it was very galling to him when, about this time, his triumphal progress met with obstructions from abroad.

His biographer tells us that 'the sharpest attacks came from Germany'.[1] Dr. Koch and others disputed Pasteur's conclusions and dared to doubt the efficacy of his prophylactic against anthrax.

At home, too, there were annoyances. At the Academy of Medicine, voices were raised against the germ theory of disease, and in particular M. Peter ridiculed Pasteur's all-conquering microbe. It was easy for him to do this, as in March 1882 the reputation of the vaccine for anthrax had met with a disastrous downfall.

It had come about in this way; in Italy it had been thought worth while for a commission composed of members of the University of Turin to perform experiments such as Pasteur had described, and thus test his prophylactic. As a result, to quote René Vallery-Radot,

> "all the sheep, vaccinated and unvaccinated, had succumbed subsequently to the inoculation of the blood of a sheep that had died of charbon."[2]

No failure could have been more complete.

Pasteur wrote for particulars and was informed that the sheep which had been used for the experiment had died of anthrax on the 22nd March, 1882, and that the following day its blood had been inoculated into other sheep, every one of which died as a consequence.

According to Pasteur's theories this should not have happened, for in a communication on the subject to the Academy of Medicine on the 17th July, 1877, he had maintained that blood from the heart would not be virulent, even though taken from an animal already putrid and virulent in many extensive parts of its body. Pasteur tried to wriggle out of the dilemma by denying that this applied to an animal that had been dead for twenty-four hours. He claimed that the catastrophe was due to a mistake on the part of the Turin professors, who had inoculated blood that had been septic, as well as tainted by anthrax.

The eminent Italians, men of excellent standing, were naturally very indignant at his accusation that they did not know how to recognise septicaemia and that a man – who was, by the way, neither a doctor nor a veterinary surgeon – should consider himself able from Paris to diagnose conditions in an animal on which he had never set eyes.

---

1. *The Life of Pasteur*, René Vallery-Radot, p.357.
2. *ibid*, pp.367-8.

For a year a battle royal waged hotly between the Turin Veterinary School and Pasteur, who, finally, in the spring of 1883, wrote and offered to go to Turin and personally repeat the experiment in which the professors had failed so thoroughly and show that the blood of an anthracised carcass would be also septic on the second day after death.

But Pasteur was now dealing with men of the race of Machiavelli. These Italians at once saw how easy it would be to make such an experiment appear to succeed by some trickery. They were determined to safeguard its repetition under exactly similar conditions to their own disastrous trial. They therefore replied to Pasteur that, as a condition of the acceptance of his offer, he should first give some precision to his proposed experiments by informing them:

1. What, in his opinion, would be the microscopic characters presented by the blood of a sheep, taken directly from the heart, when it is at the time septic and anthracised?

2. What, in his opinion, would be the genus and course of disease, and what would be the macroscopic and microscopic changes that should be expected to be found in sheep and in horned cattle made ill and even killed by the inoculation of this blood? Such experiments, in the opinion of the professors, would be necessary to complete those proposed by Pasteur.

Pasteur was not dealing with fools. He was asked to set down in writing definite descriptive statements, which would be tested against hard facts and run the grave risk of being found wanting. This reasonable test of his views, which any scientist should have welcomed, was to him a trap into which he had no intention of walking. The only chance of escape lay in throwing the onus on the Italians, and in a communication to the Academy of Science[1] he actually dared to say:

> "The Commission of Turin then does not accept my offer to go to them!"[2]

He was careful to keep from the Academy the letter he had received in which his suggestion was by no means declined, but merely made accessory to preliminary and clear statements in regard to the proposed experimentation. What Pasteur, however, did not hesitate to do was to accuse the Commission of erroneous statements and quotations. His biographer is careful to avoid telling us that he was promptly challenged

---

1. *Comptes Rendus* 96, p.1457.
2. *ibid*, p.1459.

to point these out.

He did so by quoting an extract the Commission had taken from his own statement of the 17th July, 1877, in which he had said:

> "The blood from the heart will not be at all virulent, although it be taken from an animal already putrid *and virulent*, in several *extensive* parts of the body."

To this he made retort:

> "I have never written anything of the sort with regard to an animal that has been dead twenty-four hours."

He went on to quote his own version of what he had said, concluding with:

> "The blood will not be at all virulent, although it be taken from an animal already putrid in several parts of its body."

The Commissioners, having the text of his Communication of 1877 before them, were able to reply that Pasteur, in quoting himself, had omitted the words *and virulent* after *putrid* and *extensive* before *parts*, thus manipulating his own statement.

They published this communication of Pasteur's together with their own criticism in a pamphlet entitled *Of the Scientific Dogmatism of the Illustrious Professor Pasteur*, which was published on the 10th June and translated into French in August 1883, and bore the signatures of Vallada, Bassi, Brusasco, Longo, Demarchi and Venuta – all men of high character and reputation.

In this document, it was pointed out that Pasteur seemed to have forgotten that the putrid decomposition of bodies might vary in rapidity according to the temperature of March, a month notably changeable in its climatic relation to time and place. The professors now explained that they had regarded Pasteur's offer as a trick and that, not being the fools he had taken them for, they had decided that they must know what he understood by the term *septicaemia*, and that the experiments should be made fully and under the conditions and in the way that they had followed in their own experiment of March 1882.

With cutting irony the Commission rejoiced with their illustrious opponent for having at last admitted that the inoculation of blood at once anthracised and septic could, according to the relations of the two taints in the blood doubly infected, produce sometimes pure anthrax, sometimes pure septicaemia, and sometimes anthrax and septicaemia combined. By this admission he destroyed his own dogma of the non-development of the bacillus of anthrax when it is associated with other organisms, aerobic or anaerobic.

The Commission further congratulated themselves on having convinced Pasteur that he could not at Paris diagnose the complaint of an animal that had died at Turin, and they were glad that they had caused him to review his dogmas through the researches of his assistant, Roux, and to recognise as erroneous the following principle laid down in his communication of July 1877:

> "The bacteria of anthrax may be profusely introduced into an animal without giving it anthrax. It will be sufficient if the bacteridia suspended in the liquid have at the same time the common bacteria associated with them."

The Commission pointed out that Pasteur's assertion that the blood of an anthracised carcass would be septic after 24 hours was as much as to describe septicaemia as a necessary consequence of the progress of putrefaction, reasoning they considered narrow and inconsistent with facts. They compared various statements of Pasteur's taken from his communication of July 1877 and from his memoir of 1878 on *The Theory of Germs and Their Application to Medicine and Surgery*. He had stated:

> "The blood of an anthracised animal contains no other organisms than the bacteridia, but the bacteridia are exclusively aerobic. They therefore take no part in the putrefaction; thus the anthracised blood is not capable of putrefaction by itself. But in the carcass things happen differently. The anthracised blood enters rapidly into putrefaction, because all corpses give a home to vibrios coming from without, that is to say, in the present case, from the intestinal canal, which is always filled up with all kinds of vibrios.
>
> The septic vibrio is none other than one of the vibrios of putrefaction."

After asking himself whether septicaemia or putrefaction in a living subject is a special disease, he answers:

> "No! So many vibrios, so many different septicaemias, benign or malignant."

Yet in his memoir on the germ theory, he asserts:

> "We have only met one single vibrio in septicaemia, properly so-called, which the media in which they are cultivated cause

to change in appearance, as regards facility of propagation and of virulence."

After many other quotations, the Commission summed up that it was clearly to be deduced that, according to the illustrious Pasteur, the blood of anthracised carcasses must be necessarily and fatally septic in 24 hours or less, because it contains the vibrios of putrefaction.

They sarcastically referred to his admission of septicaemias benign and malignant:

> "but it seems that the vibrios of the benign septicaemias reside in Paris only and that in Italy they do not exist, because he has declared positively that the unfortunate animals which died as a result of our former experiment on the 23rd March were killed by septicaemia, which having succeeded in killing must, without doubt, belong to the category of the malignant.
>
> Notwithstanding the competence of the illustrious M. Pasteur in such an argument, we venture to differ from him, and, to show that our opinion is correct, we will say in a few words that some of our experiments have proved that even in Turin there are vibrios of benign septicaemia, that is to say, of septicaemia that is not fatal; and they have further proved that the blood of sheep and horned cattle suffering from anthrax, the blood of the latter not anthracised, the juice of the flesh a prey to putrefaction, containing septic vibrios in the sense understood by Pasteur, may sometimes produce neither pure anthrax nor pure septicaemia, nor anthrax and septicaemia combined...
>
> And that such negative result may be obtained even when the blood contains millions of the vibrios that Pasteur regards as septic, and when these are in very active movement."

The pamphlet then describes the Commission's experiment in full detail, showing how lowered conditions of temperature, etc., must have retarded putrefaction and that, according to Pasteur's own dogmas, it was

> "certain that there were neither vibrios of putrefaction nor other evidence of septicaemia in the blood inoculated into our animals, vaccinated or non-vaccinated. But suppose that there had been the vibrios of septicaemia and that neither we nor other competent persons had perceived them, what then ought to have happened according to the dogmas proclaimed by Pasteur in 1877?

Either the little droplet or two, spread out in a thin layer upon the wound of each animal and exposed to the action of air, would become harmless as a septic agent of infection, because the vibrios, thronging the septic fluid in the form of moving threads, were destroyed and disappeared on contact with the air, since it was said that air seems to burn the vibrios. (But in this case the *bacillus anthracis* ought to be able to develop easily, as, being aerobic, it would not have to struggle, on contact with the air, with anaerobic vibrios.)

Or, alternatively, the vibrios are *not* destroyed on contact with the air... and in this second case, there would necessarily develop in the inoculated animals a malady that in its course, duration, symptoms and lesions would exhibit characteristics of septicaemia and septicaemia only. But in such a case, lesions of septicaemia and not of anthrax should be found in the carcass.

Even admitted as a hypothesis that the blood of the anthracised sheep which we employed on the 23rd March had also been septic, but that we in our crass ignorance and incapacity were unable to perceive it, nevertheless it could not have produced in the animal, inoculated in the way that we have described, anything but pure anthrax.

This result, which before the new experiments of Roux was passionately contested by Pasteur because he thought it improbable, is today admitted to be possible, because it does not find itself any more in contradiction with the new dogma, reformed in accordance with the new results of experiments of the month of May 1883, which he has communicated to the Academy of Science in Paris."

The pamphlet winds up by showing that the quotations of the Commission had been accurately given, and that it was Pasteur who had suppressed certain words to modify his original assertion. Moreover, although he had asked the Commission to correct the faults in the French translation of their Italian Report, he actually published this in the *Revue Scientifique* without paying the slightest attention to the all too numerous corrections of mistakes that put a totally different construction upon the original signification.

Perhaps it is not a surprise that while the Turin controversy was raging, his son-in-law should put on record[1] that Pasteur

"was tired of incessant and barren struggles."

------

1. *Life of Pasteur*, p.369.

The Italian professors, however, did not consider their time to have been wasted. On the contrary, they declared themselves satisfied,

> "because we have attained our proposed end; the research and demonstration of truth and the refutation of error."

It is only to be regretted that this attitude of scientific doubt should have given way to the simple credulity, the unquestioning faith, of modern medical orthodoxy towards almost any dogma enunciated by the followers of Pasteur.

It did not require much perspicacity to realise that if Pasteurian treatment could secure any appearance of success, the pecuniary advantages would be considerable. Thus Pasteur inaugurated the era that was to see the prostitution of science to commercialism. Bacteriological institutes for experimentation upon living animals and for the production and sale of vaccines and sera came into being all over the world, modelled upon the one opened in 1888 in Paris.

Odessa was one of the places provided early on with such an institution; but its experience with the anti-anthrax vaccine was calamitous.[1]

The vaccine was sent to Kachowka in Southern Russia, where it was administered, according to Pasteur's description, to 4,564 sheep, of which number 3,696 were very soon dead.

The first vaccinations were performed in August 1888 by Dr. Bardach, commencing on the 8th. 1,582 mother sheep were divided into two flocks. One lot was vaccinated before 11a.m., of which one sheep died within 24 hours and seven others within 36 hours of the operation.

The second lot was vaccinated on the evening of the 10th August. The first to die succumbed during the night of the 9th–10th August. The greatest mortality occurred on the 10th and 11th. Of the 1,582 sheep vaccinated, 1,075 died from the effects – 68%.

Another trial took place at a farm belonging to a man called Spendrianow. The first flock consisted of 1,478 sheep of one, two and three years of age. The other flock consisted of 1,058 sheep, some older than those in the first lot and some younger. The sheep were vaccinated on the 10th August, between 7 and 11a.m.

The next day, at 1p.m., the first death took place; the following day the mortality was at its highest and it diminished from August 13th. Altogether, out of 4,564 animals vaccinated, 3,696 died – 81%.

---

1. See introductory letter from Professor Peter (pp.8-9) to *Études sur la Rage*, Dr. Lutaud.

Thus the Turin disaster is shown to have been by no means an isolated example, and, in answer to Pasteur's supposed benefactions, these unfortunate animals, had they been given a voice in the matter, would certainly have prayed to be delivered from such a friend.

Moreover, Vallery-Radot, in his biography of Pasteur, tells us nothing of the private owners in France and elsewhere whom Pasteur had to compensate for animals killed by his vaccine.[1]

A special Commission in Hungary recommended that the Government of that country prohibit its use; Koch and Muller in Germany pronounced against it; the English Board of Agriculture declined to recommend it; while finally, before the last Royal Commission on Vivisection, its protagonists could not do any better than damn the modern 'modified' edition with faint praise.

Alas for Pasteur and his pronouncement that 'the only sovereign judge must be history!'

---

1. *Études sur la Rage*, Dr. Lutaud, p.419.

17.
Hydrophobia

To the average person of the present day, the mention of the name Pasteur immediately conjures up the thought of a horrible malady – *hydrophobia*. To the many who have only a superficial understanding of his connection with fermentation, silkworm troubles and anti-anthrax inoculation, he is nevertheless famous as the saviour of humanity from the ravages of mad dogs!

The pity is that since Pasteur's day there should have been so much fear mongering on the subject, for hydrophobia is a complaint of the nerves and, consequently, fear is its primary factor. Various instances have been recorded of cases unquestionably brought on by suggestion.

For example, two young Frenchmen were bitten at Havre by the same dog in January 1853. One died from the effects within a month, but before this the other young man had sailed for America, where he lived for fifteen years in total ignorance of the death of his former companion. In September 1868, he returned to France and learned of the tragedy, and then himself developed symptoms; within three weeks he was dead of hydrophobia![1]

Again, a patient who had first threatened to bite his medical attendant, after being told that the correct symptom in a human being was actually the use of the fists, struck out all round him like a boxer and indulged up to the time of his death in this quite novel form of paroxysms.[2]

The avoidance of fear is, therefore, of fundamental importance after a dog bite, and the very slight risk of serious disease is confirmed by the thousands of innocuous bites received by veterinary surgeons and others who constantly handle animals. Occasionally there may be a victim to a bite in the same way that deaths have been known to occur after pin-pricks and stings of insects, while scratches and wounds sometimes bring about tetanus – of which complaint hydrophobia appears to be a variety.

---

1. *Études sur la Rage*, Dr. Lutaud, p.262.
2. *ibid*, p.269.

According to Sir Victor Horsley's evidence before the Lords' Committee on Rabies, the probability of hydrophobia after dog bite among the untreated has been variously calculated to be from 5% to 15%. A French researcher named Bouley has stated that of 100 persons bitten by rabid animals and entirely untreated in any way whatever, not more than five would develop symptoms of hydrophobia.

Thus, happily, the victim of a supposed mad dog stands a very good chance of escaping any trouble, if he can only be left alone. To begin with, it has to be remembered that there is considerable doubt of there being any such specific disease as rabies, and a 'mad dog', in the popular sense, may possibly be relegated to the same category as the 'witch' of the Middle Ages! The neglected lives of the pariah dogs of the East are sufficient to account for many finally suffering from the paroxysms and other symptoms that go by the name of rabies; and when we contemplate the chained existences of numbers of dogs in Europe our only wonder is that more do not develop madness.

It may safely be said that a healthy, happy life is the best safeguard against trouble. For an animal to be in a savage state or to foam at the mouth is no real indication of rabies. For instance, in *A System of Surgery*, we read:

> "Some idea may be gained of the frequency of mistakes of diagnosis in connection with canine rabies by the statement of Faber, who says that of 892 dogs brought into the Veterinary Institute of Vienna under suspicion of rabies, *only 31 proved to be really affected*."[1]

During a scare in England, according to the *Field* of the 19th April, 1919, Mr. Robert Vicary, a well-known kennel owner, believed that

> "many of the experts called in to diagnose the supposed cases of rabies were quite wrong in their reports."

It seems likely that many animals were merely suffering from dietary problems due to wartime conditions; as wrong feeding has been known to produce symptoms like those of so-called rabies, as evidenced in the scare in the Klondyke in 1896, an account of which has been given in the *Journal of Zoophily*, by Arnold George.[2]

It is clear that more fear than intelligence is shown in regard to rabies, particularly as animals suspected of it are almost invariably put to death summarily, instead of being kept alive under kind and careful

---

1. T. Holmes and J. Hulke, p.329 (note).
2. See also article *Rabies and Hydrophobia*, L. Loat, in the *Bombay Humanitarian*, April 1920.

observation. Moreover, once they are dead, the complaint cannot be traced by a post-mortem examination. The test applied is the one introduced by Pasteur, and this brings us to his commencement of work on the subject.

It was in the year 1880 that two mad dogs were presented to him for investigation by an army veterinary surgeon named Bourrel. Then began the series of observations, very cruel for the most part, that resulted in the proud announcement to the Academy of Science at Paris of a process that would, so Pasteur maintained, infallibly prevent rabies from developing in persons who had undergone the misfortune to have been bitten by rabid animals.

The date of this communication (26th October, 1885) was 'memorable in the history of medicine and glorious for French science', according to the enthusiastic praise of the chairman of the Academy, M. Bouley. The day was also memorable for the inauguration of a system of intolerance – the antithesis of all that is scientific – which has, sadly, continued with regard to the fetish worship of Pasteurian orthodoxy.

On this eventful date this intolerance was carried to the length of refusing to hear a word from M. Jules Guérin, Dr. Colin and others who dared to offer any criticism of Pasteur's conclusions. The great man had spoken. He dared to claim infallibility – *'I call my method perfect.'* It was demanded that others either offer praise or else hold their peace.

Yet how much there was to criticise! The very inoculation test for proving madness was quite uncertain. This test, introduced by Pasteur, involved taking some matter – saliva, blood, part of the brain or spinal cord, usually the cerebral-spinal fluid – from the suspected animal and injecting it into a living rabbit.

It is obvious common sense, apart from Béchamp's illuminating explanation[1], that matter from one creature introduced into another is likely to be injurious. Vulpian, a French doctor and physiologist and a supporter of Pasteur, himself found that the saliva of healthy human beings killed off rabbits as quickly as the saliva of a child who had died of hydrophobia.

The condition of a rabbit after inoculation proves nothing except the strength or weakness of its powers of resistance; and yet the paralysation of the hindquarters of a rabbit is made the test of rabies in the dog from which it received the injection. True that nowadays rabid dogs are said to have *negri* bodies in the nerve-cells, or their

---

1. *Les Microzymas*, p. 690.

branches, and these are claimed to be not causal, but diagnostic agents; but considering the contradictions and mistakes in regard to bacteria and disease, we may well question a diagnosis that depends upon these *negri* bodies, especially as it does not seem to have been proved that they are always absent in other diseases.

So much for the test: now as to the prophylactic – what changes Pasteur made from the start in his nostrum!

In 1884, at a Medical Congress at Copenhagen, he announced that by weakening the virus from dogs (supposedly mad) by transmission through monkeys and by fortifying it again through rabbits, he had obtained something protective to dogs and which would eradicate rabies from the world. Considering that nothing then was, or now is, known of the cause of rabies, if regarded as a specific malady, as it was in Pasteur's opinion, surely such a boast savours very much of the 'cure-alls' of quackery.

Pasteur himself had to admit that he had not succeeded in rendering 'refractory' more than 15 or 16 out of 20 dogs. Afterwards he abandoned the monkey as a transmission agent, having originally chosen it, he said, because of its physical resemblance to man. In a pamphlet *Hydrophobia and Pasteur*, by Vincent Richards, the author asks:

> "Does the result that 15 or 16 out of the 20 dogs inoculated remained unaffected in any way warrant the assumption that the method adopted by Pasteur was protective?"[1]

On the 26th October, 1885, Pasteur described his later method of treatment, which was to take the spinal cords of rabbits that had received injections of virus, keep these for varying lengths of time, then beat them up, each with twice its own weight of sterilised bouillon; finally, commencing with the weakest, inoculate the patient for ten days successively. Moreover, he triumphantly pointed to a successful case, that of Joseph Meister, a little Alsatian boy, nine years old, who had been badly bitten by a dog on the preceding 4th July, 1885, and two days later was taken to Pasteur for treatment.

This being the crucial case upon which Pasteur inaugurated his claim to success, let us now review it.

The worst of the many severe bites received by the child were cauterised the same day with carbolic acid. At 8 p.m. on July 6th Pasteur, by means of a Pravaz syringe, inoculated the boy with some drops of his broth of spinal cords, taken from rabbits that had died of the paralytic

---

1. Leaflet published by Thacker, Spink & Co., Calcutta (1886).

complaint induced by injections into the brains of these poor little animals. The actual operation was probably undertaken by Dr. Grancher, who was present on the occasion. For the following ten days, Joseph Meister was regularly inoculated, receiving in all about a dozen injections of the spinal cord broth.

Now, in considering this case, we must ask what proof Pasteur had of either the madness of the dog or the probability of hydrophobia ensuing in the victim?

The rabid state of the animal was inferred by its savagery and the fact that a post-mortem examination disclosed 'hay, straw and pieces of wood' in the stomach.[1] The presence of the latter would seem far more likely to indicate that the dog had been ravenous, probably starving, a condition that in itself would have accounted for its savage behaviour. As to the boy, the number and severity of the bites he had received caused the doctors Vulpian and Grancher, who were called in, to decide that he was almost inevitably exposed to contract hydrophobia in consequence.

Why? As we have seen, there was no real proof of rabies in the dog that had attacked him. But, for argument's sake, granting that the animal had been mad, it must be remembered that the wounds had been cauterised. Though opinions differ as regards cauterisation, many authorities seem strongly in favour, and reference may be made to Youatt's cauterisation of upwards of four hundred persons, including such application five times on himself, without hydrophobia developing in so much as a single case.[2]

Dr. Cunningham, of Chicago, reported as cauterising 120 persons annually, has averaged the mortality as about three in that number. Pasteur himself once wrote to a doctor near Paris as follows:

> "Sir, the cauterisations that you have carried out ought to reassure you fully as to the consequences of the bite. Attempt no other treatment: it is useless."[3]

Apart from cauterisation, the chance of hydrophobia developing in a person bitten even by a so-called genuinely mad dog has been seen to be small; and, moreover, as incubation has been known to extend to twelve months, often to two years, or more, the danger for Joseph Meister had obviously not been ended when, after little more than three months, Pasteur dared to acclaim him as a brand snatched from

---

1. *The Life of Pasteur*, René Vallery-Radot, p.414.
2. Referred to in *Rabies and Hydrophobia*, Thomas M. Dolan.
3. *Études sur la Rage*, Dr. Lutaud, p.23.

the burning, so to speak, by his spinal-cord dosage. Finally, other people, including the dog's owner, Max Vone, who had been bitten by the same dog as Meister and on the same day, and who were neither cauterised nor treated by Pasteur, continued in good health.

Thus we see that this first much-vaunted case of Pasteurian success has no more to be said for it, when examined carefully, than that Joseph Meister, as far as his history is known, does not appear to have come off better or worse through Pasteur's treatment than several others who went without it.

But all were not so fortunate as young Joseph. Another child, Mathieu Vidau, inoculated by Pasteur and supposedly cured, died seven months after treatment.[1]

To excuse the death of again another child, Louise Pelletier, failure was attributed to the bites being on the head and too much time having elapsed after the bite before the inoculation; yet Pasteur had previously claimed that his treatment would be successful if commenced at any time before hydrophobia set in, even after a year or more. Contradictions seem to have been of no account when needed as excuses, so much so that an American, Dr. Dulles of Philadelphia, has said that on placing Pasteur's statements side by side, the acceptance of almost any one demands the obliteration of others!

Dr. Charles Bell Taylor, in the *National Review* of July 1890, gave a list of cases in which Pasteur's patients had died, while the dogs that had bitten them remained healthy.

A notable failure was that of a French postman named Pierre Rascol who, along with another man, was attacked by a dog supposed to be mad. He was not actually bitten, for the dog's teeth did not penetrate his clothing; but his companion received severe bites. The latter refused to go to the Pasteur Institute, and remained in perfect health; but unfortunate Rascol was forced by the postal authorities to undergo the treatment, which he did from the 9th to the 14th March. On the following 12th April, severe symptoms set in, with pain at the points of inoculation – not at the place of a bite, for remember that he had never been bitten. On the 14th April, he died of paralytic hydrophobia, the new disease brought into the world by Pasteur.[2]

Little wonder that Professor Michel Peter complained:

"Pasteur does not cure hydrophobia: he gives it!"

---

1. *Études sur la Rage*, Dr. Lutaud, pp.245-6 and following.
2. *ibid*, Dr. Lutaud, p.277-8. For a similar case regarding a Frenchman named Née, see the same work, p.345.

Already, in his own day, there were many unbelievers in his method. To these, in the *London Lancet* of the 15th May, 1886, the following caution was addressed by Dr. G. H. Brandt, evidently a sincere believer in the words and works of Pasteur:

> "To the unbelievers, M. Pasteur says: 'Wait! Time will reveal many facts connected with this question, and it is only by continual experience and constant observations carried on for a considerable time on hundreds of cases that we shall be able to arrive at positive and definite results.'"

Many years have gone by since these words were written, and we find ourselves now in a position to study the experience and observations for which earlier critics were told to be patient.

The claim for Pasteur's success is based upon the assertion that he reduced the death rate for hydrophobia from 16% to 1%. But a Colonel Tillard has shown in a pamphlet called *Pasteur and Rabies*[1] that the 16% theory of death rate before Pasteur brought in his supposed preventive must be ridiculously wrong. As the yearly average number of deaths for France up to then had not been more than 30, the number of the bitten, according to the 16% estimate, says Colonel Tillard, should have been less than 200; but Pasteur, on the contrary, had 1,778[2] patients during the year 1887, which meant, according to this calculation, that over 250 would have died had they not gone to him. This is nothing short of an absurdity in view of the fact that the highest total of deaths ever recorded for any year was 66!

If we turn from France to other countries, we find that in Zurich, for instance, of 233 persons bitten by rabid animals in a period of 42 years:

> "only four died, two of whom were bitten in parts where preventive measures could not be adopted."[3]

In addition,

> "Wendt of Breslau treated 106 persons bitten by mad animals between the years 1810 and 1823. Of these, *two died*."[4]

During an epidemic of rabies in Stockholm in 1824, 106 bitten persons presented themselves at the Royal Hospital, of whom only one contracted hydrophobia.[5]

---

1. Published by the British Union for the Abolition of Vivisection, London.
2. This is the number given in the article on Hydrophobia in Allbutt's *System of Medicine*, Prof. G. Sims Woodhead.
3. *Rabies and Hydrophobia*, Thomas M. Dolan, p.155.
4. *ibid*, pp.155–56.
5. *ibid*, p.156.

Many more instances might be enumerated; for example, the gunpowder treatment formerly carried out in the island of Haiti, where, though dog bites were common, hydrophobia was practically unknown.[1]

Such results of pre-Pasteurian treatment surpass the best boasts of Pasteur and upset the truth of the 16% to 1% reduction in mortality. Even were the latter claim correct, it would merely be brought about by the huge multiplication of cases, a method of manipulation continually found in statistics, and which, as Dr. Boucher of Paris points out,[2] does not prevent deaths from hydrophobia increasing even as the percentage decreases!

As to this increase, the facts speak only too painfully; before Pasteur's treatment the average number of deaths per annum from hydrophobia in France was 30; after his treatment the yearly average number increased to 45.

The late Professor Carlo Ruata gave the annual average mortality from hydrophobia in Italy as being 65 before the Pasteur treatment, and complained of its increase to 85 after the installation of nine anti-rabic institutes. We cannot therefore wonder at the criticism that he published in the *Corriere della Sera*:

> "The numerous 'cures' that are boasted of in our nine anti-rabic institutions (in Italy) are cures of bitten persons in whom the rabies would never have developed, even if they had not been subjected to the anti-rabic inoculations; and the small number of failures represent precisely the number of those in whom the rabies has taken, and who, for that reason, die after the inoculation, as they would have died without it.
>
> This is the mildest judgment that can be passed on the work of our nine anti-rabic institutes, even if we might not unreasonably ask if some of the inoculated persons were not killed by the inoculations themselves."

As a comment on this, we can add that the National Anti-Vivisection Society has collected a list of 1,220 deaths after Pasteurian treatment between 1885 and 1901, and that the British Union for the Abolition of Vivisection is making a further list, which amounts already to nearly 2,000, and that *every one of these deaths* after treatment has been taken from the official returns of Pasteur Institutes.

In regard to the statistical returns of these institutes, we will quote

---

1. *Rabies and Hydrophobia*, Thomas M. Dolan, pp.188–89.
2. *Anti-Rabic Inoculations: Their Deadly Effects*, Dr. H. Boucher.
   Published by The Animal Defence and Anti-Vivisection Society, London.

Dr. George Wilson's summary in his Reservation Memorandum of the Royal Commission on Vivisection:

> "Pasteur carefully screened his statistics, after some untoward deaths had occurred during treatment or immediately after, by ruling that all deaths should be excluded from the statistical returns which occurred either during treatment or within fifteen days of the last injection.
>
> It is in accordance with this most extraordinary rule that the percentage of deaths in all Pasteur Institutes works out at such a low figure. Thus, in the Report on the Kasauli Institute for 1910, Major Harvey commences his comments on the statistics of the year as follows:
>
> > 'In this year, 2,073 persons, bitten or licked by rabid or suspected rabid animals, were treated,'
>
> ...yielding a percentage of failures of 0.19. This percentage Major Harvey explains in these words:
>
> > 'There were 26 deaths from hydrophobia. Of these, 14 died during the treatment, eight within 15 days of completion of treatment, and four later than 15 days after completion of treatment. Only the last four are counted as failures of the treatment according to Pasteur's definition of a failure, and it is on this number that the percentage failure rate is calculated.' "

This screening of statistics prevents the inclusion of the death of the late King Alexander of Greece among the list of Pasteurian failures. The announcement was made, after a monkey had bitten the King, that expert advice had been summoned from Paris. Had the King lived, no doubt a paean of victory would have proclaimed his rescue through Pasteurian methods. As the King instead, unhappily, grew worse, a discreet silence was, for the most part, observed as to his treatment. The truth, however, we learn in a bulletin received by the Greek Legation in London and reported in the *Daily Mail*:

> "*Athens, Saturday*. The King passed a critical night. His fever attained 105.6 deg. Fahr., and was preceded by severe shivering and accompanied by a fit of delirium, which lasted one hour and a half. This morning he was again vaccinated. His heart has weakened. His breathing is irregular."[1]

As the King thus died during the course of treatment, we must apparently not only blame the monkey rather than the vaccination for

---

1. *Daily Mail*, 18th October, 1920.

his death, but must also not even count the latter as a failure of Pasteurian treatment.

Another more recent case cannot be thus excluded from this category. The *Daily Mail* of the 14th January, 1921, reports:

> "A rare case of hydrophobia was revealed in Paris yesterday when Mme. Gisseler, a Dutch woman, died as the result of having been bitten by a mad dog eight months ago. After the bite Mme. Gisseler was immediately treated at the Pasteur Institute and altogether received 25 injections of serum."

The excuse then follows that 'such cases of death after treatment are extremely rare'; this announcement loses its force when we consider that many deaths, like that of the late King of Greece, are excluded by an arbitrary time limit from being considered as failures.

Apart from the so-called 'accidents' of treatment and apart also from deaths after treatment (from whatever cause), an additional argument against Pasteur's method is its introduction of a new disease – *paralytic hydrophobia*, entirely different from the many forms of pseudo-rabies. That this complaint is often wrongly attributed to other causes – syphilis, alcoholism, or even influenza – and in other cases glossed over altogether, is disclosed in a report entitled *Paralysis of Anti-Rabies Treatment*, by Dr. P. Remlinger, Director of the Pasteur Institute, Morocco, to the International Rabies Conference held at the Pasteur Institute, Paris, April, 1927.[1] He writes:

> "We were impressed with the discrepancy between the number of observations published by directors of institutes and the number of cases orally acknowledged by them to have occurred. Such occurrences were commonly kept secret, as if they were a reflection on the Pasteur method or a reflection on the doctor who applied it. Such a policy appeared to us to be clumsy, and the reverse of scientific."

And again (p.85):

> "We have come to the conclusion that certain institutes conceal their cases. On various occasions we have found in medical literature observations concerning paralysis of treatment, and we have afterwards failed to find in the report and statistics of the institutes concerned any mention of these unfortunate cases."

---

1. Publications of the League of Nations. 111. Health. 1927. 111. 14.

As far back as the 1st January, 1920, Pasteurian statistics were criticised *in The Times* by no less an authority than the eminent statistician Professor Karl Pearson, well known as the Galton Professor of Eugenics and Director of the Laboratory for National Eugenics at the London University. Questioning the boast of Pasteur's 'conquest of hydrophobia', he wrote:

> "Full statistical data for the Pasteur treatment both in Europe and Asia are not available. What data are published permit no prudent statistical judgment.
>
> If the Indian Government is in possession of information on this point, why is it withheld? If it does *not* possess it, why does it not obtain it and issue it? Is there any cause for dissatisfaction with the results obtained, and have any changes been made in the treatment on the basis of such dissatisfaction with the results obtained, and have any changes been made in the treatment on the basis of such dissatisfaction or for any other reason?
>
> These are the questions for which answers should be demanded in the House of Commons. No Government is to be blamed for adopting a course recommended by its scientific advisers. But it sins not only against science and humanity, but against the world as well, if it does not provide the material it must possess for a judgment of the success or failure of its efforts.
>
> Given our present state of knowledge, I venture to assert that it is not wise to speak yet of the 'conquest of rabies'."

Such is the expert statistical commentary that after all these years answers Pasteur's request to await the verdict of time and experience.

Even the information obtainable from the Pasteur Institutes can hardly be encouraging to believers in Pasteur's treatment. For instance, if we turn to the reports of the Pasteur Institute at Kasauli in India, we find a big increase from ten deaths from hydrophobia in 1900 to 72 deaths in 1915. Against this we can scarcely set the corresponding increase in cases, because so many of the latter cannot be described as genuine; it is frankly acknowledged in the Sixteenth Annual Report[1] that many of the Europeans have undergone no risk whatever.

We can well believe this when we recall the example of Lord and Lady Minto, who went through the course of inoculations merely because their pet dog had been bitten by another dog supposed to have been mad! A large proportion of the Indians can run no risk either,

---

1. p.21.

except from the treatment, seeing that the patients, according to the report's own showing, have not all been bitten, but many merely 'scratched', or 'licked', and not all by rabid, but many by merely 'suspected' animals. Moreover, these animals included human beings, cows, calves, pigs, deer, donkeys, elephants and many other species! Between the years 1912 and 1916, there were 114 patients who had been bitten by horses and 80 who had been the victims of human bites! Thus we see that in a considerable number of so-called 'cures' there is no pretension to the patients ever having run any risk from actual mad-dog bites.

In an interesting note, this Sixteenth Annual Report[1] recommends

"the use of atropine[2] in cases which have developed symptoms of rabies."

It goes on to say:

"The use of this drug was suggested to us by Major F. Norman White, to whom we acknowledge our thanks. Its effect is to relieve throat spasm, and if it is given at suitable intervals, this distressing symptom can be entirely obliterated, with the result that the patient is able to eat and drink.

Apart from this beneficent effect, there is always in the background the hope that in certain cases throat spasm (which is the proximate cause of death) might be held in check until the phase of recovery had set in... *Clearly the most hopeful cases would be those of the untreated,* in which the incubation period was naturally a long one..."

So here we find Pasteurian workers themselves acknowledging a possible cure which has no connection with Pasteur and further, on their own admission, that it is quite possibly more profitable without the addition of his treatment.

For that matter, hydrophobia has never been a complaint without a remedy, even after the paroxysms have set in. Pilocarpine, a drug which induces profuse sweating, has been known to cure cases; while, on a similar principle, Dr. Buisson of Paris, author of a treatise entitled *Hydrophobia, Preventive and Curative Measures,* cured himself of an attack by the use of a vapour bath and inaugurated a remedial system, named after himself, which has been most successful.[3]

---

1. p.35.
2. "We have found that 1/100th grain of the sulphate, injected subcutaneously every four hours, is usually sufficient to obliterate spasm." *Kasauli 16th Annual Report,* p.36.
3. For cases of cures, see *On Rabies and Hydrophobia,* Surgeon-General Thornton.

It is, to say the least of it, remarkable that definite curative measures should be overlooked and set aside for a mere preventive which cannot set forward a single tangible proof of ever having saved anyone, while, on the other hand, as we have seen, there is undeniable evidence that it has created a new complaint, i.e. paralytic hydrophobia.

For such a situation there must be some explanation, and perhaps the Indian paper *The Pioneer*, on the 12th March, 1919, unconsciously provided it:

> "The Central Research Institute[2] at Kasauli has developed its vaccine production to an almost incredible extent. The yearly average before the war was 18,500 cubic centimetres; during the war it rose to over 2.5 million cubic centimetres, and included anti-typhoid, cholera, pneumonia and influenza vaccines. From a monetary point of view alone, the value of the Kasauli vaccines for the period of the war was about half a million sterling."

Pasteur's inoculations for hydrophobia form part of a vast money-making system, in which the beneficiaries have no wish that any item should be discredited. The Kasauli returns are only a fraction of the monetary gains accruing in Europe, Asia and America.

A few years back we were told by Professor Ray Lankester that the Lister Institute in London made £15,800 a year from the sale of vaccines and sera – a sum that seems likely to have increased largely.

Thus we find science dominated by commercialism. Were it not for pecuniary advantages, there seems little doubt that the broth emulsions of spinal cords would have gone the same way as an older less nauseous panacea – 'the hair of the dog that bit you'!

From the earliest records of history, the prevalent mania seems to have been for 'frightfulness' in medicinal remedies; but the witches' cauldron itself never surpassed the toxic concoctions inaugurated by Pasteur in what has truly proved to be – sadly – 'a new era in medicine'.

It is the era of the injection into the blood of matter of varying degrees of offensiveness, the era in which animal experimentation, vastly increased, has led to experiments on human beings, and the credulous and uninformed are everywhere at the mercy of the syringe – all because of the insatiable hunger of the pharmaceutical corporations for profit and domination of the health 'industry'!

---

1. A separate institution from the Pasteur Institute.

18.
A Few Examples of the Cult in Theory and in Practice

What a striking contrast there was between Louis Pasteur, the worn, paralysed man, aged before his time, and the magnificence of the Institute founded in his honour and named after him, which was opened on the 14th November, 1888, at Paris!

The ambitious chemist had achieved his goal – fame and fortune. He was now installed as the idol of medical orthodoxy.

The reason for the general public's acclamation of his views has been succinctly explained by Béchamp in the preface to *La Théorie du Microzyma*. Here he writes:

> "The general public, however intelligent, are struck only by that which it takes little trouble to understand. They have been told that the interior of the body is something more or less like the contents of a vessel filled with wine, and that this interior is not injured – that we do not become ill, except when germs, originally created morbid, penetrate into it from without, and then become microbes.
>
> The public do not know whether this is true; they do not even know what a microbe is, but they take it on the word of the master; they believe it because it is simple and easy to understand; they believe and they repeat that the microbe makes us ill without inquiring further, because they have not the leisure – nor, perhaps, the capacity – to probe to the depths that which they are asked to believe."

On the other hand, experts have been educated from the start to consider micro-organic life from the Pasteurian standpoint, and to accept these theories as though they were axioms. Thus it is perhaps understandable that it is only from an unbiased vantage ground that the contradictions of the germ theory of disease can be correctly understood to be ridiculous. Its rules – the postulates of Dr. Robert Koch – state, *inter alia*, that a causative disease germ should be present in every case of a disease, and never found apart from it.

What are the facts?

One of the original props of Pasteurian orthodoxy, the Klebs Loeffler bacillus, arraigned as the culprit behind diphtheria, was, by Loeffler himself, found to be absent in 25% of the cases; while, on the other hand, it is constantly revealed in the throats of healthy subjects – since, as Béchamp explained long ago – a bacterial evolution of microzymas is not necessarily noxious.

The followers of Pasteur, however, have their method of overcoming the theoretic difficulty; namely, the carrier theory, by which healthy people are accused of propagating certain 'germs' which they then supposedly disseminate. This accusation has been brought against those who have never in their entire lives suffered from the complaints that they are accused of distributing; while, in one noted case, that of a certain cook, Mrs. Roberts of Wrexham, whose microscopic inhabitants were said to have dealt out intestinal trouble, it was found that she had never seen, much less even touched, the pork pies described as the delivery medium of her murderous microbes.[1]

In their *Manual of Infectious Diseases*, Goodall and Washbourn state:

> "Enteric fever differs from other infectious diseases in not spreading directly from individual to individual. There is thus little danger in visiting patients suffering from the disease."[2]

Yet while actual victims of the fever are pronounced innocuous, no hesitation is shown in accusing healthy persons, some of whom have never undergone the complaint, of being promoters and disseminators of it.

The carrier theory is also constantly invoked in connection with diphtheria. Years ago, we read[3] of the throats of 700 schoolchildren at Alperton in Middlesex being examined, with the result that 200 were accused of being diphtheria carriers and were accordingly placed in isolation.

One telling weakness of the theory is that we never seem to hear of the isolation of prominent bacteriologists, who obviously should set the example in undergoing microscopic and chemical tests and the subsequent quarantine, which is, apparently, only advocated for other people!

But, as the editor of *The Lancet*[4] has confined, without the carrier theory, Koch's postulates could not even pretend to be fulfilled.

---

1. Some 20 cases of an illness called *para-enteritis*, with four deaths, were ascribed to the consumption of these pork pies, which Mrs. Roberts was accused of having infected.
2. First ed., p.293.
3. *The Evening News*, 4th June, 1920.
4. March 20, 1909.

Take, for instance, Koch's fourth postulate, which defines the causative germ as producing in an animal the same disease with which it was originally associated. But we are told in the same article in *The Lancet*[1] how the pneumococcus of pneumonia introduced into the lung of a rabbit brings about not pneumonia, but instead general septicaemia. According to Béchamp's theory of the differences between the microzymas of varying species, this result is understandable and presents no mystery; but it is the undoing of Koch's fourth postulate.

In Sternberg's *Text Book of Bacteriology*[2] we find:

> "The demonstration made by Ogston, Rosenbach, Passet and others, that micrococci are constantly present in the pus of acute diseases, led to the inference that there can be no pus formation in the absence of microorganisms of this class. But it is now well established by the experiments of Crawitz, de Bary, Steinhaus, Scheurlen, Kaufmann and others that the inference was a mistaken one, and that certain chemical substances introduced beneath the skin give rise to pus formation quite independently of bacteria."

On the other hand, Dr. Robb[3] has shown that under the most rigid antiseptic treatment, micro-organisms are constantly found attached to sutures when removed from wounds made by the surgeon, and that a skin abscess is frequently associated with the presence of the most common of these micro-organisms, e.g. *staphylococcus albus*.

Thus, on the one hand, we are given evidence that pus formation may be independent of bacteria, while on the other the utmost precautions against micro-organisms will not prevent their presence.

From the viewpoint of Pasteur, this is a contradiction not easily accounted for by his theory of invasion. (We are told by his son-in-law[4] that it was his habit to speak of an 'invaded' patient.) Yet we have just been informed, on the one hand, of pus without any so-called microbes, and, on the other, of microbes when every precaution has been taken against them. This is very confusing, according to Pasteur's teaching.

On the contrary, the matter is easily explained when we consider Béchamp's teachings. According to his doctrine, which, in keeping with a prudent approach to scientific investigation, he put forward as a probable hypothesis – instead of asserting it to be a proved fact,

---

1. *The Lancet,* March 20, 1909.
2. p.371 (1901 edition).
3. *Aseptic Surgical Technique*, Hunter Robb.
4. *The Life of Pasteur*, p.291.

'incapable of question' – it seems possible to understand the malignant influence of certain chemical substances upon the normal microzymas of the body, and the pus formation that might be the consequence. In the other example, where micro-organisms are seen, in spite of antiseptic precautions against external invasion, we are shown the apparent accuracy of Béchamp's view that the medium having become unsuited to normal microzymas, they themselves develop into bacteria, thus proving the latter to be the *consequence*, instead of the *origin*, of the disease condition.

Another remarkable theory that has had to be invoked in support of the general germ theory is that of Metchnikoff's phagocytosis, or the assumption that the leucocytes – the white corpuscles of the blood – are in effect its scavengers which destroy undesirable intruders. A favourite description of them has been that of the police of the body, notwithstanding the salient fact that the more of them there are the less the body seems safeguarded, while it gains in security with the diminution of this hypothetical 'police force'.

Béchamp taught that the leucocytes are living, but he disagreed with Metchnikoff's theory. He wrote in *Les Grands Problémes Médicaux*:

> "The leucocytes are even held to be so much alive that they are represented as pursuing the microbes to swallow and devour them. The droll thing is that this is believed!"

But without phagocytosis, what would become of the whole doctrine of invasion and resistance and all the other popular theories?

One likely reason for the popularity of the germ theory of disease has been the explanation that it has been supposed to provide for the problem of infection. It is so easy to conjure up arrays of malignant microbes passing from one diseased subject to another. Such an idea has become prevalent, even among men of science.

For instance, we find that before the Royal Commission on Vivisection, Dr. C. J. Martin of the Lister Institute is reported to have stated:

> "His (Pasteur's) experience on this subject (fermentation) led him to the great generalisation that infectious diseases might themselves be interpreted as particular fermentations and as due to specific micro-organisms. By a series of masterly experiments on animals. he established the truth of his hypothesis in the case of anthrax, chicken cholera and swine erysipelas. These results of Pasteur's may be regarded as the foundation of the whole modern study of contagious diseases

in both man and animals; and their extension by Pasteur and his pupils, and by bacteriologists and pathologists all over the civilised world, has led to the discovery of the causes of most of the infectious diseases to which man is liable."[1]

We have already compared Béchamp's and Pasteur's work on fermentation, and in regard to Pasteur's 'masterly experiments on animals' we have seen something of 'the truth of his hypothesis' in the case, for instance, of anthrax.

Finally, in respect of the most infectious diseases, such as scarlet fever, measles and smallpox, no specific micro-organisms are found in association, though that does not stop Pasteur's followers from claiming that they are there all the same, but are ultra-microscopic, even if this is hardly in accord with the 'cautiousness' advocated by Pasteur.

As Professor Béchamp once said:

"If virulent germs were normal in the atmosphere, how numerous would be the occasions for their penetration independently by way of the lungs and intestinal mucus! There would not be a wound, however slight, the prick even of a pin, that would not be the occasion for infecting us with smallpox, typhus, syphilis, gonorrhoea."

In regard to this, we will quote a passage from Mr. Alexander Paul's summary of the preface to *La Théorie du Microzyma*. Mr. Paul writes:

"M. Béchamp argues that if the simple or evolved microzymas, which may be found in certain humours of the body, came from the air and penetrated so easily the cells of the human body, there is one humour, in ceaseless contact with the air we breathe, in which we should find them always the same in all animals. This is the saliva of the mouth.

It is found, however, that the properties of human saliva and that of other animals are different. M. Béchamp says that the epithelial cells, the microzymas, and the bacteria of the tongue of man may have a certain chemical action unique to themselves, and altogether different from those of the tongue of the cow, the pig, the horse or the dog.

Now, if the germs of the air do not operate to modify the function of a humour which is so unceasingly, so largely, and so directly in contact with the common air, it is difficult to understand how they operate to modify the functions of the

---

1. *Final Report of the Royal Commission on Vivisection*, p.29.

inner tissues and humours, protected as they are by so many barriers."[1]

Were it not that the art of thinking is so rarely practised, reflections such as these should have established long ago something to be at fault with the Pasteurian notion of the germ theory. And, even in cases where the germ hunter seems sure of his microbe, in a little while dire confusion is apt to overtake his certainty. Never, for instance, did there seem to be a better bolstered case than Sir David Bruce's arraignment of the *micrococcus melitensis* in goat's milk as the cause of Malta fever.

Yet when Dr. Walter R. Hadwen of Gloucester took up the defence,[2] he proved the supposed offending germs to be innocent after all. The decline of the fever in the Navy was found to have had nothing to do with abstinence from goat's milk, but to have been gradual and to have coincided with the dredging of the harbour at Malta. Neither was the sudden drop in the Army disease rate to be accounted for by avoidance of the milk, for it had already taken place before that beverage was banned, when the troops were mostly removed from the insanitary St. Elmo barracks to new quarters at a higher altitude. To these measures the improvement in our sailors' and soldiers' health was clearly traced by Dr. Hadwen's investigations, and the main effect of the *micrococcus melitensis* was to gain a knighthood for its false accuser, while, incidentally, it occasioned a great deal of discontent among the Maltese population connected with the milk industry.

Dr. Agius of Malta, who at the time went into the matter very thoroughly, found that bad sanitation was invariably the cause of outbreaks of fever in private houses, which were sometimes the quarters of British officers. On one occasion, it was only after a floor had been taken up that the real cause of the trouble was discovered.

Yet upon a theory so constantly at fault when thoroughly examined there has been erected an entire system of inoculation. Or, perhaps, the facts may be stated conversely. Had it not been for the sale of sera and vaccines, nowadays grown to such vast proportions, Pasteur's germ theory of disease might before this have collapsed into well-deserved obscurity. It can hardly be denied that he committed an offence in dragging medical science down to a commercial level.

Moreover, he has besmirched the name of science by associating it with cruelty. In this also, he was merely an imitator. He was the friend of men like Claude Bernard, who, in the words of Professor Metchnikoff,

---

1. *The Vaccination Inquirer*, February, 1909, p.178.
2. *The Contemporary Review*, August and November, 1909.

"feel no scruples in opening bodies and submitting the animals to the most cruel sufferings."[1]

But, atrocious as is their torment, victims of the knife were and are few in number compared with the millions of animals that suffer in pathological laboratories, sometimes undergoing tests as fantastic and misleading as they are cruel, since they can never furnish real evidence of disease under natural conditions.

As examples might be mentioned birds and rats kept in cramped cages, slowly devoured by fleas, so that some 'scientist' can deduce whether the fleas convey sleeping sickness, without regard to the fact that the inevitable bad health of creatures thus tormented cannot with certainty guarantee anything other than the callousness of their tormentors.

Or, again, the test of milk by its injection into guinea pigs, which, kept in covered tins, would by the mere fact of such unhealthy captivity be made liable to tuberculosis. Yet for this the ratepayer dips into his pocket, while for all he can tell, the milk he consumes may have come from a consumptive cow wading through a filthy farmyard and milked by a diseased individual into a dirty utensil.

Hygienists in some part avert such conditions, leaving Pasteurians to torment their guinea pigs. The amount of harm that has ensued from the diversion of attention from real to false factors in the causation of ill health is probably incalculable. An example in this connection, with regard to plague in India, is the amount of time and money wasted over fleas and rats that might be expended upon the insanitary huts standing on filth-trodden soil, which Dr. Charles Creighton, in a treatise on the subject,[2] has clearly shown to be breeding grounds of the pestilence.

To return to the subject of milk, admirers of Pasteur may point in pride to the preservative method named after him; but even here the praise is so faint as to be damning.

If we turn to the *Journal of the Royal Society of Arts* for September 19, 1919, we find an article entitled *Problems of Food and our Economic Policy*, by Professor Henry E. Armstrong. Here we are told that:

> "the great reformer of recent times has been the chemist Pasteur – the extent to which he has influenced our doings is astounding."

---

1. *Les Annales*, Paris, April, 1908.
2. *Plague in India*, Charles Creighton, M.D.

Professor Armstrong then shows how, thanks to Pasteur,

"wines were sterilised and the *Grand Vin*, the result of a fortuitous concourse of organisms, became a great rarity; the quality of wines was reduced to a low general average, though of course much was saved from the sewer. Beer suffered a like fate, though on the whole the changes were much to the public advantage.

But the real harm was done when milk was tampered with... Dilution became a general practice; the public suffered from occasional dishonest tradesmen, and was in some instances deprived of the advantages up till then derived from dealing with the majority of purveyors who were honest. The blow was made all the heavier by the introduction of new engineering techniques for the separation of the cream. Then Pasteur's teaching became operative once more; aided this time by Koch – milk was not only diluted, but also sterilised. Some lives may have been saved, *but the step has undoubtedly been productive of untold misery*.

Not a few of us have long held, on general grounds, that a material produced as milk is cannot be heated above blood-heat without diminishing its dietary value. Recent observations show indeed that the anti-scorbutic advitant, which is none too abundant a constituent, is affected, although apparently the fat-soluble anti-rachitic and water-soluble anti-neuritic factors are not destroyed; but difficulties have been encountered in localities where the milk supply has been systematically sterilised, and it may well be that it suffers in quality in ways not yet elucidated.

The inquiries thus far held into the effect of sterilising are in no way satisfactory and are open to criticism on account of their incompleteness and unscientific character. The risks from typhoid and other similar infections are now slight, and the main object of sterilising milk is to secure the destruction of the organism which is held to be responsible for tubercular disease. But it may well be that in destroying some one or other mysterious constituent of the advitant class, the food value is so lowered that effects are produced which render the system specially sensitive to tubercular infection; such infection seems always to be with us, apart from milk. Moreover, when milk is sterilised, the lactic organism is destroyed and it becomes a particularly favourable nidus for the growth of putrefactive organisms: it is therefore a potent cause of infantile diarrhoea."

Thus the verdict of time and unbiased criticism continue to pronounce judgment on the works of Pasteur. But if the mere consumption of impoverished food can be believed to be so injurious to the consumer, what must be the effect of the deluge of sera and vaccines introduced directly into the bloodstream?

In spite of the modern medical mania for inoculations, a remarkable ignorance on the subject prevails among those most ready to submit to inoculation. Many cannot even distinguish between a serum and a vaccine.

Serum, the colourless part of the blood, is usually, for use in inoculation, taken from the blood of a horse into which diseased matters have previously been injected. The strength of this serum is generally tested upon guinea-pigs, that is to say, by their recovery or death from the sickness created by its injection into their bodies. Animal suffering comes into play in this connection from start to finish, while, as regards the human race, considering the danger of the introduction of the serum of one species into that of another, it is, perhaps, fortunate that serum therapy, although originally acclaimed as the panacea for all ills, has yielded in popularity to vaccine therapy.

The latter, needless to say, has no connection with cows. Under Pasteur's tutelage, precision in nomenclature was as much lost as precision in theories. The name 'vaccine' is now applied to micro-organisms and their surrounding medium abstracted from a sick body, the organisms being left to multiply in a suitable nutritive substance, known as a 'culture', afterwards being usually killed by heat and prepared in various ways, according to the prevalent fashion. The nostrum is finally sold as a cure, or, more often, a preventive against the disease with which the micro-organisms were originally associated. In this case animals are spared a part in the preparation, though, owing to their use as test subjects, suffering is for them by no means prevented.

We are here reminded of the homeopathic law of cure; that 'like cures like', though what a contrast is presented to Hahnemann's scientific precision in allowing for individual idiosyncrasies. Whereas he applied his drugs by way of Nature's laboratory – the stomach – the Pasteurian system, on the contrary, introduces substances directly into the blood, regardless of Nature's precaution, i.e. the efficient coverings with which she has protected this lifestream against all external intrusions.

It has indeed become the fashion for humanity to consider itself wiser than – choose which name you will – Nature or Providence.

We are well aware of the array of statistics with which Pasteurians confront the critics of the system of inoculation. In reply we would say that statistics are worthless in proving results without full investigation and thorough allowance for the specific conditions from which they are derived.

For instance, it is easy to parade a fall in the diphtheria fatality rate since the introduction of anti-toxin. Yet that fall does not confirm the merits of the serum if it is seen merely to be the result of a case rate inflated by a bacteriological – as opposed to a clinical – diagnosis and the inclusion as diphtheria of cases which in the past would have been considered to be merely sore throat, tonsillitis, laryngitis, etc.

This altered diagnosis in itself prevents proper comparison between past and present case rates. But if, with an inflated case rate, there is an increase, instead of a decrease, in the *death rate*, such an increase is surely highly significant. For instance, we find that, for the fifteen years subsequent to the introduction of anti-toxin, the number of deaths in England and Wales from diphtheria became 20% greater than they had been for the fifteen years prior to the serum treatment.[1]

Though the Metropolitan Asylums Board's report of cases may seem to show at first sight – by a decreased death rate – that advantage accrues from the use of the anti-toxin, their detailed particulars show the opposite to be the case. Whereas for the years 1895 to 1907 there were 63,249 cases of diphtheria treated with anti-toxin (of which 8,917 died, giving a fatality rate of 14.09%), there were for the same years 11,716 cases *not* treated with anti-toxin, of which only 703 died, giving a fatality-rate of 6%. Footnotes to the tables show that of the latter cases, 55 were moribund when admitted and 12 died of diseases other than diphtheria, so that the fatality rate should in reality be *under* 6%.

It is to be regretted that the cases treated with and without anti-toxin are no longer listed separately in the Metropolitan Asylums Board's Reports, and since 1930 the Board itself has ceased to exist. From those cases that have been particularised, there seems to be no denying that improved methods of nursing and medical treatment, which should reduce deaths, accomplish this to a lesser degree when anti-toxin is administered.

The following table supplies proof of this view with regard to infantile diseases. We see here the remarkable decrease in measles,

1. This calculation is based on the years 1880–94 as the pre-anti-toxin period. Were the comparison made from 1879–93, the increase would amount to 33.88%. The Registrar-General gives small support to the allegation that many of the earlier croup deaths should have been classified as diphtheria.

scarlet fever, and whooping cough – complaints not subject to treatment by inoculation; while diphtheria, with its specific anti-toxin, shows an increase of 102 per million. The contrast is striking.

Annual mortality per million at ages 1 to 5 years
in 1911–14 and 1916 (both sexes)[1]

	Death rate 1911-14	1916	Increase (+) or decrease (–) between 1911-14 and 1916
Measles	2,643	1,225	–1,388
Scarlet Fever	369	227	–142
Whooping Cough	1,202	1,050	–152
Diphtheria	**769**	**871**	**+102**

The claim for immediate injection and the advantage of a first-day inoculation as compared with a second day, and so forth, may surely be dismissed for the following reasons. Before clinical symptoms are manifest, it is impossible to tell whether the trouble would ever be serious, if indeed the diphtheria be genuine; and if, on the one hand, it be asserted that the prompt administration of anti-toxin has prevented dangerous illness, it is as easy to assert, on the other, that through anti-toxin a mere mild sore throat has been aggravated into severe sickness, sometimes complicated by heart trouble and paralysis. The one method of argument is no more inexact and unscientific than the other.

Also, one may ask; why, if diphtheria anti-toxin is such a reliable remedy, should it have been found necessary to introduce the Schick system of preliminary test and subsequent immunisation? The supposedly susceptible children should run small risk if provided with an infallible cure. If, in answer to this, it is argued that the immunisation is for the prevention of diphtheria for all time, it may be retorted that statistics show no improvement upon natural immunity; while, moreover, in many cases the preventive has proved far more dangerous than the disease.

---

1. Part of Table 34 on p.xiv of Registrar-General's Report for 1916 (England and Wales).

Cases of illness and death that have followed
the 'Schick' inoculation against diphtheria
A list of Immunisation Disasters, 1919–1941.

Year	Place	Injured	Died
1919	Texas, U.S.A.	60	10
1924	Bridgewater, U.S.A.	25	–
1924	Concord, U.S.A.	20	–
1924	Baden, Austria	?	6
1927	Russia	2	12
1927	China	37	5
1928	Bundaberg, Australia	5	12
1930	Colombia, S. America	32	16
1932	Charolles, France	171	1
1933	Chiavari, Italy	29	1
1933	Venice and Rovigo	?	10
1935	San Francisco	3	2
1936	France	75	1
1937	Waterford, Ireland	23	1
1938	Waterside, Canada	11	1
1941	Freiburg, Switzerland	4	11
	Totals	497	89

Over and above these mass disasters, there are too many tragic cases of injury and death following inoculation for space to be allotted to more than a few of them in this volume.

John Gordon Baker, aged 7 years, of Saxholm Way, Bassett, died five days after his second inoculation against diphtheria.

Dennis Hillier, aged 11, a healthy boy from London, excelled in games. He died two months after his second inoculation.

William Martin Graham, aged 4 years, of Bownem, Wigton, died in the Birmingham Children's Hospital two days after being inoculated with alum-precipitated toxoid.

Rosemary Jane Webb, Ernest Eales, Joan Hudgeon and many more swell the lists of young victims who might be alive, but for Pasteurian medical methods.

Neither has freedom from diphtheria resulted as a reward of the grave risks taken. During the four years 1941-44, the Ministry of Health and the Department of Health for Scotland reported almost 23,000 cases of diphtheria in immunised children, of which more than 180 proved fatal.

With regard to the decline of diphtheria in Great Britain during 1943 and 1944, we are reminded that 58 British physicians who signed a statement in 1938 against compulsory immunisation in Guernsey were able to point to the virtual disappearance of diphtheria in Sweden without any immunisation.

On the other hand, if we turn to Germany we find that, after Dr. Frick's order in April 1940 for the compulsory mass-immunisation of children, this country in 1945 had come to be regarded as the storm-centre of diphtheria in Europe. From some 40,000 cases, there had been an increase to 250,000 cases.

An article in the March 1944 edition of a publication called *Pour la Famille* documents the rise in cases of diphtheria after compulsory immunisation. For instance, the increase in Paris was as much as 30%; and in Lyons the number of diphtheria cases rose from 162 in 1942 to 239 in 1943. In Hungary, where immunisation has been compulsory since 1938, the rise in cases was 35% in two years. In the canton of Geneva, where immunisation has been enforced since 1938, the number of cases trebled between 1941 to 1943.

A startling tragedy of Pasteurian preventive methods was the murder of innocents at Lubeck, during the early summer of 1930, from B.C.G., or the Calmette Tuberculosis Vaccine, a culture administered by mouth to newborn infants.

The Health Department of the city made an emotional appeal to parents to allow immunisation of their children, whether likely to grow up in a tubercular environment or otherwise. Of the 253 babies subjected to the Calmette treatment, 69 died of it and 130 were made seriously ill. In view of such a calamity it is not surprising that the Reich Health Office decided that such prophylactics were not to be recommended, and the Reich Health Council

> "...considers an extension and tightening up of the existing regulations for the production, issue and employment of vaccines of all kinds to be desirable."[1]

Finally, we have to remember what wonderful statistical boasts have been demolished when genuine epidemics have made their appearance. For some considerable time one of the trump cards, so to speak, of the Research (i.e. vivisection) Defence Society was the anti-meningitis

---

1. *The Times*, 15th December, 1930.

serum of Dr. Flexner and Dr. Jobling of the Rockefeller Institute, New York. Remarkable statistics were produced without explanation. The serum, first tried in the spring of 1907, was acclaimed as bringing about a 'complete revolution'. Yet what use was this wonderful cure when a terrible outbreak of meningitis in New York, with a death roll of 745 for the single month of July 1916, transformed the American capital into a city of mourning?

Flexner's marvellous serum was so useless that we find it barely gained a mention, and its discoverer confessed that 'there exists at present no specific or curative treatment'.

It transpired, further, that this complaint, known also as spotted fever, is, at any rate according to bacteriological diagnosis, fast losing its limitation to childhood. Outbreaks of it are said to have been frequent among young men in military training camps. It has followed so suspiciously in the wake of anti-typhoid and other inoculations that, instead of such measures having provided safeguards for health, it would seem far more probable that they can be directly implicated in causing sickness.

And now this brings us to a few lessons that we may be able to derive from the inoculation experiments that were practised upon our fighting men during the course of two World Wars.

19.
Some Lessons from World War I and a Few Reflections on World War II

It is constantly asserted that the comparative freedom from epidemic disease of the armies fighting on the western front during World War I is a demonstration of the value of 'preventive' inoculations.

We, on the contrary, believe that a study of the subject proves such a conclusion to be based upon only superficial observation. It has to be remembered that every sanitary and hygienic precaution possible was attended to on the western front.

And here we may pause to notice that World War I was not without accompanying epidemics, providing an interesting illustration of the substitution theory of disease conditions, to which we have already alluded.[1]

Throughout history we find that plagues have followed in the wake of war, with a systematic diminution in intensity according to the establishment of sanitary and hygienic conditions among the population. Thus the black death of the Middle Ages was, in later times, replaced by smallpox, which, in our own day, has found its substitute in mysterious outbreaks of influenza.

In reference to World War I, we read as follows:

> "The war ended with the outbreak of the influenza epidemic of 1918-19 (just as that of 1870-71 ended with pandemic smallpox) – an epidemic which, without including South America, China, Japan and great tracts of Asia and Africa, is estimated to have claimed eight million lives."[2]

Thus it can be suggested that the war involved the inevitable aftermath of disease, whose far-reaching ravages may perhaps be explained by the distribution of campaigns in widely diversified areas.

To return to the subject of inoculation; its success as a preventive of disease can only be tested under conditions where sanitary and hygienic measures fail, and as, wherever these were wanting, whether in East Africa, Gallipoli, Palestine or Mesopotamia, disease conditions ran riot,

---

1. See Chapter 13.
2. *Report of Chief Medical Officer to the Ministry of Health on Influenza*, p.46

we confess that we fail to see where the success of inoculation has been demonstrated.

Nevertheless, the press is inundated with medical arguments such as the following statement by Lieutenant-Colonel S. Copeman, Officer-in-Charge of the R.A.M. College, which appeared in *The Times* for the 15th February, 1917:

> "As to typhoid fever, contrasting admissions to hospital and deaths in the South African campaign and in France for the first two years of the war, there had been a marvellous effect of prophylactic inoculation in the prevention of attack, and to an even greater extent in the saving of life. A similar result had followed the later introduction of inoculation in the French Army, which suffered heavily from typhoid fever in the early months of the war."

No better criticism of the above can be found than that of Mr. E. McCormick in the *Vaccination Inquirer* for March 1917:

> "The implication here is that conditions during the South African and European wars were similar, apart from the time at which inoculation was introduced during the campaigns.
>
> Now, nobody denies that sanitary conditions are a governing factor, or at least an important one, in the prevalence of typhoid. It is well known that sanitary conditions were deplorable in South Africa, whereas in France they have been, in Sir Frederick Treves' words, without parallel in the history of war.
>
> What are we to think of medical logic which (in its special pleading for inoculation) continues to ignore this vital factor?
>
> When we remember further that the two campaigns are not even fully differentiated in respect to inoculation, but that 400,000 doses of Sir Almroth Wright's poison were sent to South Africa for the Army, and that in the first part of the campaign in France inoculation was hardly practised at all amongst British troops, the grotesque inadequacy of Lieutenant-Colonel Copeman's line of argument is apparent.
>
> That his accuracy on points of fact is on a par with his logic is demonstrated by his suggestion that the introduction of inoculation was later in the French Army than in ours, whereas the fact is that it was not only introduced earlier, but was made compulsory by law in 1913, whereas ours is still nominally optional. The admission that the French Army suffered heavily from typhoid in the early months of the war is therefore worth noting."

Where we *can* make something of a comparison is in respect to the Japanese troops, who, in the Russo-Japanese war, inaugurated the sanitary and hygienic measures that have since been followed in the European war, where they were rigorously carried out on the western front. As regards inoculation, the conditions are diametrically opposite. At the time of the Russo-Japanese war, it was stated that:

> "no prophylactic inoculations are being practised in the Army with regard to enteric fever. Professor Kitasato has advised them, but the Army medical authorities refuse to allow them until they are better satisfied as to the results of Wright's prophylactic treatment."[1]

Yet among those uninoculated troops, the cases of enteric numbered only one-sixth of those that occurred among the partly inoculated British troops in the Boer War. The Japanese cases were almost entirely in the First Army, in which sanitary and hygienic regulations were less adhered to; whereas in the Second and Third Armies, enteric was almost eliminated, although these armies were uninoculated. This Japanese experience surely supports the argument that sanitary and hygienic precautions, not inoculation, were the cause of the good health rate on the western front.

Foremost among safeguards for the health of the troops was, undoubtedly, the care exercised in regard to the water supply. On occasional houses in the outskirts of Lille and along the Menin Road, German notices still remain[2] to indicate where good drinking water may be obtained. Such was the Teutonic attention to details.

The history of water purification for our own troops has been described by Captain J. Stanley Arthur, in a paper read before the Institution of Mechanical Engineers on November 19th, 1920, and published in *The Engineer* of November 26th and December 3rd, 1920. Here we are told how:

> "bleaching powder, or chloride of lime, was first used to sterilise drinking water in 1897 at Maidstone, where an epidemic of typhoid was raging. Its use was attended with very successful results, typhoid being rapidly stamped out."

---

1. *The Russo-Japanese War Medical and Sanitary Reports*, p.360. See also *Anti-typhoid Vaccines*, by L. Loat, published by The National Anti-Vaccination League, London. See also *Anti-Typhoid Inoculation*, by M. Beddow Bayly.
2. August, 1922.

Further, we read that:

"chlorine in the gaseous condition, although used in America to a small extent for some time, has only come into general use during the last few years. The amount of chlorine, either as a gas or from bleaching powder, required to sterilise water is quite small.

At the outbreak of the war, the only method of water purification – other than that involving the use of tablets of acid sodium sulphite – that could be carried out in the field was embodied in the water cart.

Attempts were made to devise a simple method by which the amount of bleaching powder required to sterilise a given amount of water could be determined in the field. The first suggestion was made by Professor Sims Woodhead, and the actual technique, involving the fitting up of a case containing the necessary apparatus and chemicals with instructions for carrying out the test, were worked out at the Royal Army Medical College under the direction of Sir William Horrocks.

With this test case, known in the Army as 'the Case Water Testing Sterilisation,' and the water cart as the starting point, the whole of the water purification scheme of the Army has been built up. That the methods adopted have been successful is seen from the fact that throughout the war, there has been no epidemic of any waterborne disease."

Captain Arthur goes on to speak of advances in the water cart technology and also of work done in America for the administration of chlorine gas to water for sterilisation purposes. The two types of chlorinators constructed by Messrs Wallace and Tiernan of New York have proved most satisfactory, and their direct feed type was 'adopted throughout the water purification plants in use in the British Army.'

The article also deals with stationary and portable plants and the whole process of purification. Captain Arthur also mentions the difficulty of supplying sterilised water to the troops in the East in the early days of the war; but shows that now

"a supply of sterilised water can be maintained under almost any possible conditions, by use of one or the other of the various types of water purification plants mentioned,"

and he tells of the new plants ordered for use in the East. To this system of water purification he gives all the credit for the Army's good health rate.

That this is the case is evident from the contrasting rates of sickness on all those fronts deprived of similar advantages. With a contaminated water supply, inoculation proved to be useless as a preventative of disease. And if inoculation, unnecessary under safeguarded conditions, is useless when such conditions fail, of what use is it at all?

Lack of utility, however, is not the only, or the most serious, criticism to be levelled against the practice: the teachings of World War I point to inoculation being directly harmful.

In a pamphlet entitled *Microbes and the War*,[1] by Dr. Walter Hadwen, we find a quotation from Professor Ernest Glyn:

> "Sickness (in the South African campaign) was responsible for the loss of 86,000 men by death and invaliding (in nearly three years); yet the total number of officers and men, including native Indian troops, leaving the Gallipoli Peninsula on account of sickness from April 25 to October 20 may be stated as 3,200 officers and 75,000 other ranks! The total has since been increased to 96,000."
>
> In short, the toll of disease and death in these modern days of serums and vaccines, with all their 'protecting' influences against microbes, was, in proportion to the period and the respective number of troops employed, nearly six times greater in the last six months of the Gallipoli disaster than in the whole three years of the Boer War."

The following official figures for the losses in the Gallipoli Expedition speak for themselves:

Killed	25,270
Wounded	75,191
Missing	12,451
Sick	96,684

Taking into consideration the shot and shell from which there was no escape in that inferno of fighting, this enormous number – 96,684 victims of disease – is nothing short of amazing. The sick far outnumber those killed and even the number wounded; and we should remember that of this great number of invalids, almost every man had been inoculated. The nomenclature applied to their complaints is a minor matter in face of the fact that the application of Pasteurian methods on a vast scale happened at the same time as an epidemic of the illness. Indeed, so high was the rate of sickness among the soldiers of Gallipoli that the inference must be made that inoculation contributed to it by poisoning the systems and lowering the vitality of the fighting men.

---

1. Published by the British Union for the Abolition of Vivisection, London.

In spite of this damning evidence, bacteriological diagnosis has done its utmost to demonstrate the success of inoculation by giving every name except typhoid to intestinal troubles, which, in previous wars, would have been thus classified. The process of bacteriological diagnosis has been illuminatingly divulged by Lieutenant-Colonel C. J. Martin and Major W. G. Upjohn, Pathologists of No. 3 General Hospital, A.I.F.[1] The exceedingly doubtful agglutinin reaction was the method adopted, and, with a candour as delightful as it was unconscious, these gentlemen confessed that in patients 'previously inoculated' the development of typhoid agglutinins was regarded 'with suspicion'. They went on to say that they

> "...only diagnosed typhoid when the typhoid bacillus was isolated or when, the case being clinically typhoid, no paratyphoids could be detected."

The *Vaccination Inquirer*, in criticising the report, remarks:

> "Thus the mere presence of paratyphoids in addition to the true typhoid was sufficient to take it out of the typhoid class, unless the patient was uninoculated; in which case, of course, the typhoid is as true as can be. We always maintained that typhoid in the inoculated would be regarded 'with suspicion' by the medicos, and here with charming naiveté we have the process disclosed by which the inoculated officially escape, and the uninoculated 'get it in the neck'."[2]

This method of diagnosis well explains the statement of one invalided soldier:

> "First they said I had typhoid, and then they said I had paratyphoid, and then they said I had dysentery; *but it feels the same all the time!*"

To the devout Pasteurian, an illness has little connection with symptoms or feelings: its reality consists in the form of a micro-organism seen through a microscope.

As the late Mr. Stephen Paget, Secretary of the Research (i.e. vivisection) Defence Society, wrote to the *Daily Mail* of April 16, 1920:

> "The symptoms of paratyphoid have a general likeness to typhoid, but the germs are different."

This viewpoint of disease conditions leads to the extraordinary obsession that, provided a specific nomenclature be avoided, inoculation

---

1. *The British Medical Journal*, 2nd September, 1916.
2. November, 1916.

has gained a triumph, no matter how great the sickness rate, or even death rate, may be. That this criticism is justified may be seen from the same article in the *Daily Mail* by Mr. Paget:

> "See, in the light of these facts, the infamy of the suggestion that the protective treatment failed at Gallipoli. It gives me pleasure to nail that lie to the counter."

The 'facts' that provide this 'light' are given in a quotation from Dr. Charles Searle, of Cambridge, who has stated:

> "Before Gallipoli we only inoculated for typhoid, and the result was that out of 100,000 cases of sickness, there were only 425 cases of typhoid and 8,103 of paratyphoid. We were under the most appalling conditions: we were on half a pint of water a day; we drank from any pool of muddy water, any filthy stuff so long as it was moist. There is nothing more terrible than thirst; we had no relief, we lived in the trenches. *Every man was sick, and we had something like 50,000 cases of dysentery*; but we had only a very small proportion indeed of typhoid."

Dr. Searle continues by giving some figures for Egypt and Palestine in regard to typhoid and paratyphoid, incidentally interjecting that

> "there was any amount of dysentery in Palestine."

All we can say is that the official figures for these countries have been repeatedly asked for in Parliament, and that they have not yet been provided. But to return to Gallipoli, Colonel Martin and Major Upjohn have described the kind of bacteriological diagnosis that brings about the naming of diseases, while Dr. Searle himself bears witness that 'every man was sick' and provides figures to show that nearly 60,000 were down with intestinal complaints. Granted that the conditions were 'appalling': we are not denying it, though they might possibly have been less bad if it were not for the extravagant assurances of the value of preventive inoculation, which inclined those in command to take less precautions about a pure water supply.

What we *are* debating is whether our troops would not have withstood those conditions very differently had they been free from the pollution of Pasteurian interference. This obsession of viewing disease from the standpoint of micro-organisms, regardless, too, of their possible variability, seems to ignore the obvious fact that in serious illness mere nomenclature can be of no solace to the patient; neither would it console a mourner to be assured that dysentery rather than typhoid had been responsible for the death of his or her friend or relative.

Of what value is artificial immunity from a particular complaint if a similar complaint is its substitute? The matter must be judged upon general health and the disease rate, and when again we learn from General Smuts, in regard to the East African campaign, that 'disease has wrought havoc', we are once more provided with proof of the failure of Pasteurian methods in World War I.

Another paean of medical victory that has been sung, even from the pulpit of St. Paul's,[1] is that of the success of inoculation against tetanus. The prophylactic use of anti-toxin is claimed to have modified the complaint.

What, however, are the proofs of this claim?

When we consider the commencement of the war, we find that Sir David Bruce had stated[2] that the ratio of tetanus in September 1914 was 16 per 1,000; in October it was 32 per 1,000; and in November only 2 per 1,000. Sir David states that there were:

> "...several factors at work in September and October 1914 to raise the ratio,"

and says that

> "the most important factor was the prophylactic injection of tetanus anti-toxin. This was not carried out during the first two months of the war,"

Although this assertion is modified by his disclosure that

> "the amount of serum sent out to France in the first five months was: August 1914 – 600 doses; September – 12,000; October – 44,000; November – 112,000; December – 120,000."

He refers to a letter from Sir William Leishman, who

> "feels sure that the drop in the incidence of tetanus in November 1914 was due to the use of the prophylactic dose, and does not think any large complicating factor comes in."

To those who recall the insufficiency of ambulances and medical appliances in the early days of the Great War, an immense complicating factor is self-evident, and this Sir David Bruce himself acknowledges when he describes:

---

1. by Dean Inge.
2. *The British Medical Journal*, January 27th, 1917, p.118.

"...the difficulty of collecting the wounded on account of their numbers and the movement of the troops, and finally the difficulty of giving the thorough surgical treatment to their wounds which is so essential in the fight against tetanus."

In passing judgment upon all preventive treatment there is naturally always an initial difficulty as to whether any given complaint has really been prevented, or whether it would not have appeared in any case. In tetanus this difficulty is augmented by the fact that the anti-tetanic injection, following customary Pasteurian procedure, as in hydrophobia, has brought about the creation of a new disease. *The Lancet* for the 23rd October, 1915, refers to Dr. Montais' observations, as set forth in the *Annales de L'Institut Pasteur*:

"Dr. Montais has collected from French sources alone no less than 21 cases of purely local tetanus, without trismus, as well as a number of similar cases in which trismus and other general symptoms later intervened. *All were in persons who had received a prophylactic injection of serum.* Although the form of tetanus which begins locally and is followed by trismus has long been known, pure local tetanus is a pathological novelty in man. *The condition, Dr. Montais claims, is entirely the creation of preventive serotherapy.*"

Again, *The Lancet* for January 27th, 1917,[1] contains an article on modified Tetanus by Captain H. Burrows, which begins as follows:

"There are two reasons why tetanus should be of interest.
Firstly, the disease still occurs among the wounded. During the months of July, August and September 1916, at the General Hospital, we had one case of tetanus in every 600 cases of gunshot wound. And this, of course, does not represent the full liability, for cases have occurred in patients who have been evacuated to England, and possibly at casualty clearing stations also.
Secondly, a large proportion of the cases which have been seen recently have been abnormal in character, inasmuch as the muscular spasms have not become general. They have remained localised to the muscles in the neighbourhood of the original wound.
In local or modified tetanus *we have a new form of disease*. The disease is new because its cause is new, for local tetanus is tetanus modified by the prophylactic use of anti-tetanic serum."

1. p.139.

We see the inference here that tetanic anti-toxin has mitigated what, without it, would have been definite cases of ordinary tetanus. So in a military medical manual entitled *Abnormal Forms of Tetanus*, by Courtois-Suffit and Giroux, edited by Surgeon-General Sir David Bruce and Frederick Golla, published in 1918, we find:

> "One fact alone tends to emerge, and that is the undoubted effect which anti-toxin given prophylactically has in modifying the disease."

But, of course, we want to know *how* and *why*.

Since this 'new disease', local tetanus, is, on the whole, a concomitant of serum treatment, what real ground is there for assuming that it is a mild and safer form of an otherwise virulent and fatal onslaught of tetanus? Can the discharged soldier with a limb contracted for life really take comfort that but for inoculatory measures he would have been a dead man? May he not equally lament that but for serum treatment he might have retained the full use of his body?

The weakness of serotherapy is readily apparent when dealing with the factor of time in regard to preventive measures. It has been stated by Sir William Leishman and Major A. B. Smallman that

> "it is, of course, well known that the earlier the preventive dose is taken after the receipt of the wound, the more likely it is to be of use"[1]

though with the usual prevarication that invariably safeguards all Pasteurian pretensions, they assert in the same breath:

> "At the same time, there is little positive information as to the effects of delay."

Be this as it may, they go on to describe the conditions that made delay inevitable:

> "It should be borne in mind that delay in giving the preventive inoculation is almost always caused by the impossibility of removing the injured man from the place where he was wounded, until such time as military conditions permitted. Such cases are therefore specially liable to gangrene, and to the more severe forms of septic trouble."

This confession turns the searchlight of common sense onto the question. The men who received early doses of serum were the men who were rescued soon after receiving their injuries, and whose wounds

---

1. *The Lancet*, January 27th, 1917, p.133.

gained prompt cleansing from filth, along with its untoward influence upon their muscular and nervous systems. The men who went without or received belated serum treatment were the men whose wounds were left to fester for hours, or even days, the unhappy victims abandoned in shell holes, or left exposed in no man's land to the hellfire of shell and bullet. Is it not self-evident that these, rather than others, should have fallen victims to tetanus – quite apart from any question of inoculation?

It appears that inoculation has introduced a new form of tetanus – one which vitiates statistical judgment of the death rate. We read, for example, in the same military medical manual, *Abnormal Forms of Tetanus*:

> "Inasmuch as the true local tetanus has practically no mortality, it may readily be seen how the introduction of such cases in statistics of tetanus has reduced the apparent mortality of the disease, and incidentally encouraged many observers to regard the reduction of mortality as a demonstration of the efficacy of some particular form of treatment."

Leaving the prophylactic and turning to the curative aspect of the anti-tetanic serum, even such orthodox critics as Sir William Leishman and Major Smallman have had to admit that

> "...there exist wide differences of view, both as to the usefulness of antitoxin at all, and, admitting its value, as to the system of its employment"[1]

while, in announcing a case mortality from tetanus of 78.2% in hospitals in France, they were forced to admit:

> "This, as far as it goes, does not disclose any considerable degree of improvement in the treatment employed."

The contradictions between the different routes of administration throw further light upon the experimental nature of the treatment. Leishman and Smallman say:

> "Taking the intravenous route first... We are in full agreement with the recommendation of the Tetanus Committee in their revised memorandum that this route should *not* be used; not only does it introduce a risk of anaphylactic shock, from which other methods are practically free, but it appears to us from our records that it has done little, if any, good in treatment.

---

1. *The Lancet*, January 27th, 1917, p.131.

As to the intrathecal route – the study of our own cases
has not impressed us favourably. The evidence is strongly
against its employment. The method appears to us to possess
some definite disadvantages and dangers. In at least one case,
death followed rapidly after a thecal dose, when the patient
was said to have been progressing favourably."

Here we have a specific example of the dangers that our soldiers
and sailors had to face from Pasteurian methods, in addition to the
risks they ran from the Germans; for, in spite of being dubbed
'dangerous', this intrathecal route was the one emphatically
recommended by the War Office Committee.[1] Its decision was,
apparently, based on Professor Sherrington's experiments on monkeys,
and so another instance is provided of the misleading results that
are obtained from the use of vivesectionist 'science'. As regards
clinical observation of the treatment, Sir David Bruce has supplied a
comical instance.[2]

Detailing case mortality, with the object of seeing whether 'the
intrathecal route had any advantage over the other methods of
injection',[3] he proved his highest mortality, 47.1%, to have been in 53
cases treated intrathecally with anti-tetanic serum on the day that the
tetanus symptoms appeared, and his next highest, 43.7%, in 96 cases
treated with the serum also on the same day that the disease set in.
The lowest mortality rate, 26%, was in 23 cases treated with serum,
but not intrathecally, on the day after the onset of the disease; while
the next lowest, 26.9%, was in 26 cases which received the anti-toxin
any time between three and twelve days after the appearance of tetanus.
Thus Sir David Bruce is driven to bewail:

"Last year (1915-1916) the difference was in favour of the
intrathecal route. Now the opposite is true. From these figures
it would appear that it is better to defer treatment until the
symptoms have been manifest for one or more days. *Quod
est absurdum*."

(We have no argument with such a commentary on Pasteurian
theories.) Meanwhile, leaving the doctors to theorise, let us take the
figures for tetanus that deal only with the wounded soldiers who
reached the hospitals in the United Kingdom.

1. *The British Medical Journal*, July 21st, 1917, p.89.
2. *The Lancet*, June 30th, 1917, p.986.
3. *ibid*, p.988.

Year	Cases	Deaths
1914	192	104
1915	134	75
1916	501	182
1917	353	68
1918	266	68

These numbers can surely only be few compared with the corresponding number in hospitals in the war zones and other quarters. Thus there appears to be no reality in the boast that tetanus was eradicated from the British Army by the use of inoculation. Indeed, it seems the other way about, as we see more clearly by a comparison with two former wars.

If we turn to *The Lancet* of 29th December, 1917, we find *An Analysis of Recent Tetanus Statistics* by F. Golla. In this, while trying to eulogise prophylactic treatment for a lengthening of the incubation period, Captain Golla has to make the following striking admissions in regard to the Franco-Prussian war – where inoculation was unknown – and World War I, during which the cult of inoculation was so widely practised. On page 968, referring to cases of tetanus, we read:

> "If, however, the first three week periods are compared, it will be found that during the first two weeks, the mortality in the 1916 cases is slightly below that of 1870 – i.e. 75.5% and 70%, as against 96.5% and 85.5% – whereas in the third week *the 1916 mortality is slightly above that of 1870.*
>
> This is precisely what we should expect given the hypothesis that the slight diminution of mortality is due to our improved methods of rendering first aid to the wounded and abstention from drastic operations. After the first two weeks, when the cases of exhaustion and post-operative shock become fewer, the mortality from both statistics becomes practically the same in the third week.
>
> On the hypothesis that the slight diminution of mortality is due to therapeutic serum treatment alone, there would appear to be no reason to account for serum treatment being less efficacious in the third week than in the two preceding weeks. It must at any rate be conceded that if the slight initial decrease of mortality is all that can be claimed for serum treatment, the result is not very encouraging."

Thus a graceful apology is made for a mortality that, in the third week period, actually outnumbers that of a war that took place half a century previously.

To move to more recent times, let us quote information supplied by Mr. Churchill in the House of Commons on July 6th, 1920. In reply to a question, he stated that there were only six cases of tetanus among the soldiers wounded or injured in action in the South African war; that is, an attack rate of .28 per thousand. Further, he stated that there were three deaths, or a death rate of 14 per thousand. There were no cases of tetanus among officers.

Asked to supply the same information in regard to the late war, Mr. Churchill, two days later, was not able to give any figures except as regards the western front, where he omitted to state the number of cases and deaths. The attack rate he gave as *approximately* 1.22 per thousand, and the death rate as *approximately* .49 per thousand. We have already seen that the fatality rate is reduced by the inclusion of local tetanus, which appears to have no mortality; but, even disregarding this convenient statistical factor, the attack and death rates remain greater than among the troops in South Africa, amongst whom 'preventive' inoculation against tetanus was entirely unknown!

To sum up, medical results throughout World War I did not equal in any measure the surgical. This is all the more remarkable in view of the modern improved methods of hygiene, the improved system of nursing and the grand self-sacrifice of most of the Army doctors and nurses. Pasteurian methods alone seem to account for the medical success falling short of the surgical.

As an example, we may cite the prevalence of sepsis. Even such an orthodox Pasteurian as Dr. Saleeby[1] has admitted that the war

> "raised new problems, including that of septic wounds, of a number and kind which reach serious military importance and which the previous experience of our surgeons has scarcely encountered."

The trouble was, of course, conveniently ascribed to a malignant organism inhabiting manured soil; but with the tiresome perversity with which Nature knocks over such implausible excuses, wounds received at sea – where there is no soil at all – proved to be as septic as wounds encountered on land.

Had our medicos followed Béchamp's teaching as the Frenchman, Galippe, has done, they would, like him, have understood the phenomena to be due to microbiosis, the part played by the crushed tissues and the extravasated blood, which, through their inherent

---

1. *The Daily Chronicle*, January 18th, 1917.

microzymas, may give birth, in themselves, according to Galippe, to infectious elements.[1] It seems reasonable to suppose that such trouble would be far more likely to arise in blood contaminated by Pasteurian nostrums than in the unpolluted blood of healthy subjects.

The *Vaccination Inquirer* sums up the matter succinctly:

> "It looks more than probable that the doctors have been at their ancient practice of sowing with one hand the disease which they pretend to cure with the other – of course in all stupidity and good faith."[2]

It is an unhappy fact that, apart from generalisations, the war provided concrete instances of the truth of this opinion. We will only refer to one example; the enforced inoculation of the Bedford Regiment on board the *Empress of Britain* on her voyage from South Africa to India in April 1917. Although the vessel was vermin-ridden and the water supply, for both drinking and washing purposes, quite inadequate, the inoculation of the men of the Bedford Regiment was insisted upon, in spite of advice to the contrary. The result was that ten died on board, five more after landing at Bombay; in addition, 50 men were laid low with serious illness. And no official inquiry has ever taken place in regard to this highly regrettable episode, such is the smoke screen that routinely shields even the most flagrant and destructive Pasteurian 'incidents'.

As regards World War II, the information currently available is insufficient for a comprehensive review of the outcome of medical methods. There are, however, some informative anecdotes and reports.

For instance, we find that Captain Walpole Lewin gives details in the *British Medical Journal* of July 1st, 1944, of a case in which an R.A.F. pilot developed tetanus and died five days after a penetrating head injury, although he had received active immunisation and the standard 3,000 units of A.T.S. one hour after the accident in his aeroplane. Captain Lewin accounts for this failure by inadequate surgical cleansing owing to the nature and situation of the wound, and continues to praise immunisation combined with prophylactic A.T.S. given at the time of wounding. He quotes examples to support his approval, but does not always provide full details, and has to admit contradictory results in certain instances. In any event, he rubs the gilt off his eulogy with this, his final sentence:

---

1. See Chapter 14.
2. March, 1917, p.36.

> "Proper surgical treatment and service, whenever possible, is an essential factor in the prevention of tetanus."

This would certainly seem a much more comfortable procedure than the *Neurological Complications of Serum and Vaccine Therapy* about which Major R. R. Hughes, a Medical Specialist, writes in *The Lancet* of the 7th October, 1944:

> "While neuritis can be caused by a variety of sera, it is most commonly precipitated by tetanus anti-toxin. Young (1932) states that of 50 cases, 21 followed administration of anti-tetanic serum, 12 anti-pneumococcal serum, 5 anti-meningococcal serum, 2 T.A.B. vaccine, 1 staphylococcal aureus vaccine, and 1 anti-tuberculous serum."

...and so forth and so on. He has more cases to add to this depressing narrative. What a mercy for our men that so many were able to be flown quickly to base to receive the 'surgical treatment and service' pronounced by Captain Lewin to be 'an essential factor in the prevention of tetanus'.

Another safeguard that we may be sure has been provided in World War II is the system of water purification for which first thanks are due to Professor Sims Woodhead. Details have been given of the success of this approach in the case of Italian troops during their shocking onslaught on the Abyssinians. Simple precautions must not be pushed out of sight because of the great monetary returns that can be derived from the use of inoculation.

This has not been without its unnecessary tragedies. For example, at a training centre at Neepawa, Manitoba, Reuben W. Carlier, an airman from Essex in England, died on 11th May, 1943, from a streptococcus infection 'introduced into the bloodstream at the time of inoculation,' according to the verdict of the jury as reported in the *Victoria Daily Times* of the 10th June, 1943. Other airmen were made ill by the injection, including ten whose serum sickness obliged them to be taken to hospital.

The terms 'serum sickness' and 'anaphylaxis' point to the dangers incurred by the stab of the syringe. Happily, most constitutions can endure fairly heavy doses of poison. Immediate discomfort and pain are in case after case glossed over, while malignant aftereffects, more likely to be suffered by those who do not react at the time of the operation, are usually too far removed for the realisation of any connection.

We may be certain that World War II has been fought not only against human enemies, but also against subhuman nuisances. In the case of such an unpleasant creation as the louse, it seems superfluous to act as counsel for the defence and insinuate that its share in outbreaks of typhus may possibly be overrated.

We may well rejoice in the discovery of such an effective insecticide as DDT and the earlier methods of louse control that are said to have been relatively effective among our troops before the introduction of mass immunisation during civilian epidemics of typhus in 1942 and 1943 in Egypt and North Africa. For the control of the Naples epidemic, after the landing in Italy of the Allied Forces, DDT is apparently given the credit. Two British soldiers went down with the complaint, and one died. So he certainly had no help from the anti-typhus vaccine with which he had been 'immunised' nine months previously (*Lancet*, 9th May, 1945).

No one can be particularly anxious to act as advocate for the noisy and voracious mosquito; nevertheless, there is danger in the shifting of responsibilities from human beings to insects. 'Kill the mosquito and you will kill malaria,' crowed Sir Ronald Ross.

As a reply comes the report of the Malaria Commission of the Health Organisation of the late League of Nations, in which, on page 13, it is stated that belief in the causation of malaria by anopheline mosquitoes has been a big obstacle to the control of malaria. According to the Annual Report of the Medical Council in 1933:

> "the total number of sufferers from malaria has increased rather than diminished."

In spite of incontrovertible evidence on all sides that the mysteries of malaria are profound, highly involved and still largely unfathomed, the childish accusation continues against an insect that, being fastidious about her meals, feasts for the most part on the healthy blood of those who never go down with malaria! So trying is the complaint that a welcome must be given to mepacrine *if* it has really worked the wonders ascribed to it during the campaign in Burma. But as it appears to be a suppressive drug, its aftereffects, whether for weal or woe, seem yet to have to be recorded.

In the United States, the authorities apparently feel at liberty to trumpet the success of the Medical Department of the American Army. On page 26 of *The Lancet* of July 7th, 1945, we find reference to a press conference on May 24th at which the United States Acting Secretary of War stated that 97 out of every 100 men who reach a hospital have their lives saved, as compared with 92 in the last war. During the past three years, the U.S. Army had less than one death from disease per 1,000 men per year, compared with 19 in the last war. Malaria had been reduced from hundreds of cases per 1,000 men per year to less than 50; and

> "the incidence of dysenteries, which once put entire regiments and armies out of action, has been less than 9% per annum."

It all sounds splendid! Until we read that

> "...the Army Medical Department during 1944 took care of 4,435,000 patients in hospitals – 2,315,000 in the United States and 2,120,000 overseas."

Do 4,435,000 hospital patients – more than half the number in arms – signify a glow of health irradiating the American fighting forces? We merely put the query.

One answer may well be that much of the sickness was deliberately induced by fatal procedures for which Louis Pasteur must bear the primary onus. For instance, in *Newsweek* of the 3rd August, 1942, reference is made to a statement by Secretary Stimson of 28,000 cases of jaundice in American soldiers' camps, with 68 deaths. It was acknowledged that a serum supposed to combat yellow fever was probably responsible for this victimisation and slaughter.

Newsweek, trying to whitewash this Virus 17D, comments:

> "Jaundice usually occurs when the liver gets out of kilter and discharges too much bile into the bloodstream. Could the many inoculations given soldiers to protect them from various diseases have overtaxed their livers ?"

You cannot tamper with the body without risking disaster. Yes, Louis Pasteur, the revelations of time, to which you yourself appealed, have proved you to be stupendous as a business man, but the *worst of meddlers in medical methods*. For there is a body of evidence that no monetary returns can obscure, no prevarication and prejudice blot out – the evidence of the facts, the danger signals of experience.

Though the careless may pass them by, to the observant they stand out in warning, like the ominous hand that startled the roysterers in ancient Babylon; and, happily, there are still Daniels in our midst with the gift of interpretation.

We shall consider this 'writing on the wall' in the next chapter.

20.
The Writing on the Wall

The whole subject of injecting into the body foreign matters associated with disease conditions must he considered broadly from every aspect. Perhaps no better opinion can be quoted than that of Herbert Spencer, for what applies to one injection must also have some application to all others. In the chapter on vaccination in his book *Facts and Comments*, the philosopher quotes the following remark of a distinguished biologist:

> "When once you interfere with the order of Nature, there is no knowing where the results will end."

Mr. Spencer continues:

> "Jenner and his disciples have assumed that when a vaccine has passed through a patient's system he is safe, or comparatively safe, against smallpox, and there the matter ends. I will say nothing for or against this assumption."

He does, however, say something in a footnote, and it is decidedly against the assumption. He proceeds:

> "I merely propose to show that there the matter does *not* end. The interference with the order of Nature has various sequences other than those counted upon and expected. Some have been made known.
>
> A Parliamentary Return issued in 1880 (No. 392) shows that comparing the five year periods 1847–51 and 1874–78, there was in the latter a lessening in the deaths from all causes of infants (under one year old) of 6,600 per million births per year; while the mortality caused by eight specified diseases, either directly communicable or exacerbated by the effects of vaccination, increased from 20,524 to 41,353 per million births per year – more than double. It seems that far more were killed by these other diseases than were saved from smallpox."

There is another footnote, which is worth quoting:

> "This was in the days of arm-to-arm vaccination, when medical men were certain that other diseases (syphilis, for instance) could not be communicated through the vaccine virus.

Anyone who looks into the transactions of the Epidemiological Society of some 30 years ago will find that they were suddenly convinced to the contrary by a dreadful case of wholesale syphilisation. In these days of calf lymph vaccination, such dangers are excluded; not that of bovine tuberculosis, however.

But I name the fact as showing what amount of faith is to be placed in medical opinion."

Once more, he continues:

"To the communication of diseases thus demonstrated must be added accompanying effects. It is held that the immunity produced by vaccination implies some change in the components of the body; this is a necessary assumption.

But now if the substances composing the body – solid or liquid or both – have been so modified as to leave them no longer susceptible to smallpox, is the modification otherwise inoperative? Can anyone dare to say it produces no further effect than that of shielding the patient from a particular disease?

You cannot change the constitution in relation to one invading agent, and leave it unchanged in regard to all other invading agents."

We may ask here: how much more must this be the case if disease conditions depend upon inherent organisms, rather than invading ones? Mr. Spencer then inquires:

"What must the change be? We have no means of measuring alterations in resisting power, and hence they commonly pass unremarked. There is, however, evidence of a general relative debility.

Measles is a more severe disease than it used to be, and deaths from it are numerous.

Influenza also yields proof. Sixty years ago, when only at long intervals an epidemic occurred, it seized but few, was not severe, and left no serious aftereffects; now it is permanently established, affects multitudes in extreme forms, and often leaves damaged constitutions. The disease is the same, but there is less ability to withstand it.

There are other significant facts. It is a well known biological truth that the organs of sense and the teeth arise out of the dermal layer of the embryo. Hence abnormalities affect all of them; for example blue-eyed cats are deaf and hairless dogs have imperfect teeth (*Origin of Species*, Chapter 1).

The same holds for constitutional abnormalities caused by disease.

Syphilis in its earlier stages is a skin disease. When it is inherited, the effects are malformation of teeth, and in later years, iritis (inflammation of the iris).

Kindred relations are also found with other skin diseases: for example scarlet fever is often accompanied by loosening of the teeth, and measles is often accompanied by disorders, sometimes temporary, sometimes permanent, of both eyes and ears.

May it not be thus with another skin disease – that which vaccination gives? If so, we have an explanation of the frightful degeneracy of teeth among young people in recent times; and we need not wonder at the prevalence of weak and defective eyes among them.

Be these suggestions true or not, one thing is certain; the assumption that vaccination changes the constitution in relation to smallpox and does not otherwise change it is sheer folly.

Is it changed for the better? If not, it must be changed for the worse."

He delivered this warning against only one form of injection. How much greater must be the danger in view of the myriad and frequent inoculations in fashion at the present day? We are reminded of an invalided Australian soldier in the medical ward of a London hospital who, upon being asked whether he believed in inoculation, replied:

"Well, hardly! I've been inoculated against half a dozen complaints, and I've had everything I've been inoculated against except cholera, and I dare say I'll be getting that next!"

Béchamp wrote long ago:

"All is danger in this kind of experimentation, for the reason that it is not anything inert that is acted upon, but that there is a modification, more or less injurious, of the microzymas of the inoculated."[1]

Many years after this statement, a remarkable confirmation has been provided by outbreaks of a disease of the central nervous system, commonly known as encephalitis, and which has so often

---

1. *Les Microzymas*, p.902.

followed vaccination that compulsory vaccination was suspended in Holland, and its abolition suggested by a medical congress in Sweden; while even in Germany its dangerous possibilities have been officially recognised.

The cases of post-vaccination encephalitis in England resulted in the appointment of two committees of investigation, whose reports, published in July 1928, dealt with 90 cases, 52 of which ended in death. In answer to a question in Parliament, on February 26th, 1932, the Minister of Health gave as the latest figures 197 cases, with 102 deaths.

As a consequence of this serious development the Ministry of Health, in August 1929, issued a new Vaccination Order reducing the vaccination marks from four to one, and, in the accompanying circular, referring to this danger, suggested that it was inexpedient to vaccinate for the first time adolescents or children of school age. Controversy continues as to the cause of the malady – Professor James McIntosh, of London University and the Middlesex Hospital, attributing it to the actual vaccine, while other investigators consider that the vaccine simply arouses some existent but hitherto latent trouble.

During the very period in which sanitation and hygiene have played a part unknown before in recorded history, a disappointing deterioration seems discernible in the human physique. The phenomenon of crowding into cities, the strain of the wear and tear of modern existence, and the breeding of the unfit are, no doubt, contributing causes – and we must include with these the introduction into bodies of poisons whose far-reaching effects are entirely beyond knowledge and control.

On the face of it, how futile it is to attempt to safeguard the individual against a disease like smallpox, which can only be eliminated in the general population by wholesale cleanliness, while gruesome dangers – such as cancer – are a hideous warning against playing with unknown quantities. We do not attempt to theorise upon the cause of malignant growths, but we certainly point to their alarming increase.

According to a statement put forward by the Cancer Research Fund, one man in twelve and one woman in eight over forty years of age are liable to this horrible torment. In regard to the useless, misdirected efforts made against it, F. McDonagh, in *The Nature of Disease Journal*, Vol. 1 (1932), writes that more than £4,000,000 had been wasted on cancer 'research'.

For the ten years 1922–31, there were over 180,000 experiments on animals. In many cases, a single one of these experiments involved the sacrifice of many creatures. The complete failure of these vivisectional cruelties is well demonstrated by the steady increase shown in the following statistics from the Registrar-General:

1891-1900	23,218 } Yearly Average		
1901-1910	30,914		
1912	37,323	1926	53,220
1913	38,939	1927	54,078
1914	39,517	1928	56,253
1915	39,847	1929	56,896
1916	40,630	1930	57,883
1917	41,158	1931	59,346
1918	41,227	1932	60,716
1919	42,144	1933	61,672
1920	42,687	1934	63,263
1921	46,022	1935	64,570
1922	46,903	1936	66,354
1923	48,668	1937	66,991
1924	50,389	1938	68,605
1925	51,939	1939	68,981

Deaths per year from cancer in England and Wales

1891-1900	758 } Yearly Average		
1901-1910	900		
1912	1,021	1926	1,362
1913	1,055	1927	1,376
1914	1,069	1928	1,425
1915	1,121	1929	1,437
1916	1,166	1930	1,454
1917	1,210	1931	1,484
1918	1,218	1932	1,510
1919	1,145	1933	1,526
1920	1,166	1934	1,563
1921	1,215	1935	1,587
1922	1,229	1936	1,625
1923	1,267	1937	1,633
1924	1,297	1938	1,665
1925	1,336	1939	1,672

Deaths each year from cancer, per million population

When such ominous danger signals flare into view after a century of vaccination, the thoughtful may well contemplate with alarm the risks of wholesale inoculation.

That medical orthodoxy should be blind to the dangers of Pasteur's techniques should not surprise the honest student of medical history. He has, for instance, only to remind himself how, in 1754, the Royal College of Physicians pronounced the inoculation of smallpox to be 'highly salutary,' and how in 1807 the same body, in reply to a question from the House of Commons, had changed its mind, and declared it to be 'mischievous'.

Fashions in medicine, like fashions in clothes, change from generation to generation, and it is as difficult for a medical man to break away from the one as it is for a society belle to free herself from the trammels of the other. Independence of income, as well as independence of intellect, is needed for a man to set aside dogma. If the desired goal is the attainment of worldly ambition, unquestioning adherence to orthodoxy is the price that must be paid. So long as the discovery of a 'microbe' may result in a medical knighthood and the discovery of a 'vaccine' in a comfortable income, no one need be surprised at the continuing popularity of the germ theory and its consequent system of inoculations.

The dangers of Pasteurism have never been revealed to the public in the light of Béchamp's doctrine that *the microzyma is at the beginning of all organisation, and that every organism may be reduced to the microzyma.*

If Béchamp is correct, the corporate life of a biological entity such as a human or an animal is composed of a united multiplicity of infinitesimal cytological and histological elements, each possessed of its own independent being. According to Béchamp, it is because every organism is reducible to the microzyma that life exists in the embryo before it develops organs. It is because there are in the microzyma permanent principles of reaction that we have at last realised some idea of life. It is because the microzymas are endowed with an individual independent life that there are in the different centres of the body differing microzymas, with varying functions.

This biological teaching explains the potency of the minutely small doses used in homeopathy; it explains the changes that must be involved in what Herbert Spencer called 'invading agents', a danger he immediately sensed, quite apart from such teaching as that provided by Béchamp, in whose *Les Microzymas* we find the following passage:

> "The most serious, even fatal, disorders may be provoked by
> the injection of living organisms into the blood; organisms
> which, existing in the organs proper to them, fulfil necessary
> and beneficial functions – chemical and physiological – but

injected into the blood, into a medium not intended for them, provoke redoubtable manifestations of the gravest morbid phenomena.

Microzymas, morphologically identical, may differ functionally, and those proper to one species or to one centre of activity cannot be introduced into an animal of another species, nor even into another centre of activity in the same animal, without serious danger."[1]

How much more dangerous is it, then, when the microzymas, artificially inoculated, are not only of a foreign species, but are in a morbid condition, even in the species from which they are taken?

Béchamp follows the passage quoted above with a description, based on experiments, of the microzymian capacity for changing function.

It would seem that Pasteurians, in their fear of parasites, have overlooked the effects of inherent elements, and have reduced their system of inoculation to one of raw experimentation. Already they appear to have commenced a retreat, albeit a partial one.

We refer, for instance, to the views of Dr. Besredka of the Pasteur Institute, which the *British Medical Journal* has described as 'subversive of the ideas hitherto held by bacteriologists'. *The Times* of the 28th August, 1920, sums up Besredka's teaching as follows:

"Here, then, was the idea that immunity or protection against dysentery is not an affair of the blood at all, but an affair of those special parts of the body in which the dysentery germs live and act. In short, that salvation is not by antidote, but by some local effect; 'the intestinal barrier becomes unbreakable,' whatever the nature of the barrier may be.

This, it will be seen, is a conception of an absolutely different kind from that to which we are accustomed. One result – for the work applies also to typhoid fever – is that *vaccination as now practised is unnecessary.*"

Thus, overboard goes the whole Pasteurian theory of immunity and with it the system of inoculation, for, according to Dr. Besredka:

"vaccination is only efficacious when the vaccine finally reaches the intestine or certain zones of it... The mode of vaccination to be preferred is the oral route."

The Times of the 31st August, 1920, further comments:

"These results turn attention positively from the seed to the soil; from germs to the men and animals who harbour them."

1. *Les Microzymas*, p.690.

And in so doing the advice is followed that was given so long ago by Professor Béchamp.

So much for the shufflings of those who have based their work on the teachings of Louis Pasteur; and we cannot but sympathise with the innocent among the public who blindly submit their bodies to the shifting fashions of Pasteurian treatment. The victimisation of animals has brought about its logical sequence – the victimisation of human beings.

For this we have to thank the imitator of Edward Jenner, the chemist Louis Pasteur, who, by a majority vote of one, gained his place among the Free Associates of the Academy of Medicine. Thus has the most jealous trade union in the world, that of orthodox medicine, been completely brought under the sway of a fraud and charlatan.

21.

Conclusion

On an autumn day in 1895, the daily life of Paris gave way to the pageantry of a state funeral. The President of the French Republic, Members of Parliament, Government officials and members of scientific societies thronged to the obsequies of their compatriot Pasteur, whose worldwide fame seemed to bring honour to all France. In death as in life, no scientist ever reaped so much glory.

Symbol of worldly prosperity, in the centre of the Pasteur Institute, is the costly chapel, resplendent with marble, porphyry and lapis lazuli, where the poor paralysed body has crumbled to dust beneath recorded boasts that can only read strangely indeed to those who have made a study of the old scientific records of the period. Here, for instance, on the walls of the chapel we find inscribed:

1857 – Fermentations
1862 – So-called spontaneous generation
1863 – Studies in wine
1865 – Diseases of silkworms
1871 – Studies in beer
1877 – Virulent microbic diseases
1880 – Vaccinating viruses
1885 – Prophylaxis of rabies

Let us briefly annotate these so-called 'triumphs'.

1857 – Fermentations

The *Encyclopaedia Britannica* tells us that Pasteur's 'theory of fermentation was materially modified…'

And this, as we have seen, was inevitably the consequence of his separating this chemical phenomenon from 'the acts of ordinary life', and in so doing proving that he did not understand Béchamp's explanation of fermentation as being the result of acts of assimilation and excretion.

1862 – So-called spontaneous generation

We have seen that Pasteur never satisfied the Sponteparists, and that his experiments sometimes contradicted his own conclusions.

1863 – Studies in wine

In dedicating his work to Napoleon III, Pasteur wrote:

> "Sire, if, as I hope, time consecrates the exactness of my work..."

Dr. Lutaud comments:

> "The hope has been misplaced. Time has *not* consecrated the exactness of this work. All who placed confidence in this process underwent heavy loss. Only the State persisted in heating the wines destined for the armies of land and sea. This rendered them so bad that the men preferred to drink water. It is high time that the apparatus for heating wines according to the Pasteur system should be put into the melting pot."[1]

1865 – Diseases of silkworms

We have seen how, in regard to these complaints, Béchamp provided Pasteur with the correct diagnosis, and that after the latter inaugurated his system of grainage, this 'salvation of sericulture' led to a drop in production, according to M. de Masquard, from 15,000,000 to 8,000,000 and, later on, to 2,000,000 kilograms.

1871 – Studies in beer

Dr. Lutaud[2] tells us that the boast that French breweries owe an incalculable debt to Pasteur is best answered by the facts that the latter's process was abandoned as impracticable, and that the brewing of beer in France is almost nil, most of the amount found there having been imported from Germany.

1877 – Virulent microbic diseases

We have seen how Pasteur opposed the microzymian doctrine after failing in an apparent attempt at plagiarism, and followed instead the ideas of Linné, Kircher and Raspail.

---

1. *Études sur la Rage et la Méthode Pasteur*, p.429.
2. *ibid*, pp.428-9.

1880 – Vaccinating Viruses

The Sanitary Commission of the Hungarian Government in 1881 included in a report this comment on the anti-anthrax inoculation:

> "The worst diseases – pneumonia, catarrhal fever, etc. – have exclusively struck down the animals subjected to injection. It follows from this that the Pasteur inoculation tends to accelerate the action of certain latent diseases, and to hasten the mortal issue of other grave affections."

As we have said, the Hungarian Government forbade the use of the inoculations.

1885 – Prophylaxis of Rabies

Dr. Lutaud reminds us how Professor Peter put pertinent questions to the Academy of Medicine on the 18th January, 1886, in the early days of Pasteur's so-called preventive treatment.

> "Has the annual mortality from hydrophobia in France been diminished by the anti-rabies medication?"[1]
> "No."
> "Does this mortality tend to augment with the intensive rabies methods?"
> "Yes."
> "Where then is the benefit?"

As we have seen, the benefit lies in the monetary returns to be gained by manufacturers of vaccines. Pasteurism has become a vested interest, and one unfortunately supported by that powerful trade union, the medical establishment.

Far be it from us to deny that Pasteur's place in the world of science was gained by genius – but it was a genius for business, and he was certainly not of the order of intellectuals who are above the temptation of money.

Although he professed reverence for religion, we find, on the authority of Dr. Lutaud,[2] that he secured the election to the Institute of the physiologist Paul Bert, who had been objected to as an atheist. Dr. Lutaud claims that he did not resile, as well, from bringing about this election at the expense of his old friend and benefactor Davaine. To complete matters, he also made a condition of it that Bert, a member

---

1. *Études sur la Rage et la Méthode Pasteur*, p.404.
2. *ibid*, p.409-10.

of the Budget Commission and influential with the Government, should obtain for him a pension of 25,000 francs.

We, who live in an age of advertisement and unceasing adulation of celebrity, can appreciate Pasteur's power in this direction. Ambition was his driving power, and even before any triumph had fallen his way, his mind was set firmly upon honour and glory.

Early in his married life, when, according to his biographers 'success did not come', Mme Pasteur wrote to her father-in-law:

> "Louis is rather too preoccupied with his experiments; you
> know that those he is undertaking this year will give us, if
> they succeed, a Newton or Galileo."[1]

The admiring wife was unaware of her testimony to her husband's self-interest; there is certainly no allusion to any excitement as to the secrets that Nature might unfold. The exaltation of the individual is made the pivot of hope. More than this, as we study his life we find, throughout, his cleverness in allowing others to sound his praises, while at the same time he himself gave vent to self-depreciation; he thus, apparently, clothed himself in a humility seemingly not quite sincere; we can take note of his indignation against those, like Béchamp, who in asserting their just claims in any way detracted from his own honour.

On no account would we deny his power in gaining affection. Parents, sisters, wife and children all appear to have lavished love upon him; while he also seems to have held the devotion of those who worked for and with him, and, on his side, to have been as good a friend to those as he was a bitter antagonist to all who differed from him.

The claim of a tender heart has been advanced by his admirers. In his biography we read:

> "He could assist without too much effort, writes M. Roux, at a
> simple operation such as a subcutaneous inoculation, and
> even then, if the animal screamed at all, Pasteur was
> immediately filled with compassion, and tried to comfort and
> encourage the victim in such a way which would have seemed
> ludicrous if it had not been touching."[2]

Such a comment certainly shows that M. Roux was himself too devoid of sensibility to be a fit judge of it.

He goes on to describe the first trephining of a dog for Pasteur's benefit, and concludes:

---

1. *The Life of Pasteur*, René Vallery-Radot, p.78.
2. *ibid*, p.318.

"Pasteur was infinitely grateful to this dog for having borne trephining so well, thus lessening his scruples regarding future trephining."

So the gradual hardening process went on until any original compunction was blunted, leaving Pasteur unimaginatively callous to the sufferings he caused. An example may be taken from the journal *L'Illustration*:[1]

"The inoculated dogs are shut in circular cages, provided with a solid, close network. It is one of these dogs, in the paroxysm of rabies, which Pasteur showed us, observing: 'He will die tomorrow.'
The animal looked at him, ready to bite. Pasteur having kicked the wires of the cage, the animal dashed at him. It bit the bars, which became red with bloody saliva. Then, with its jaws bleeding, it turned, tearing the straw of its litter, back into its kennel, which it had gnawed the preceding night. From time to time it uttered a piercing and plaintive cry."

This teasing, worrying kick at the bars of the cage of his piteous victim, a dog – that true friend of man, coerced to suffer torment in the service of this 'science' – is a fitting commentary upon the heart of Louis Pasteur. Tenderness may have been for him all right in its place, but it was quite out of place when it stood in the way of ambition.

Personal success dominated all other considerations, and the attainment of this was made easy by a forcefulness and tenacity nothing short of remarkable. Such traits are seen everywhere to be more cogent factors of worldly success than high intellectual ability. Of the latter, his childhood gave little evidence. His son-in-law honestly tells us:

"Those who would decorate the early years of Louis Pasteur with wonderful legends would be disappointed: when he attended the daily classes at the Arbois College he belonged merely to the category of good average pupils."[2]

His strongest force was his willpower, of which he wrote to his family:

"To *will* is a great thing, dear sisters, for action and work usually follow, and almost always work is accompanied by success."[3]

Here again, as ever, we find success the leading motive of his life. Had he not put personal ambition before love of science, it would seem

---

1. May 31st, 1884.
2. *The Life of Pasteur*, p.7.
3. *ibid*, p.15.

impossible for him to have opposed the fellow worker whose ideas, in numerous instances, he unquestionably pirated. Had his forcefulness and great business ability been harnessed to Béchamp's idealistic intellect and all-round knowledge, incredible advances might have been made in science, rather than years being wasted on unsatisfactory theories at the cost of vast animal suffering and a dangerous form of experimentation on human beings.

Time has, indeed, brought him triumph in the form of worldly acclamation. This is hardly surprising, for the way of popularity is through the wide gate, easy of entrance and undemanding. Pasteur, although during his life reviled and exposed by a few keen-sighted observers who saw through his pretences, was in general a popular man, and his cult of the microbe is a popular theory which the least scientific can easily understand: riches and prosperity attend upon it, as glory and renown attended upon him. Why should the ambitious imitate the self-immolation of the truthseeker Béchamp, who in his lonely apartment passed away almost unrecognised?

Truth, not self, was Béchamp's lodestar. Like Galileo, the simplest observation led him to his great discoveries, and, like Galileo, incessant persecutions, clerical and scientific, pursued him with unrelenting malignity. It was not through a lack of hatred among his opponents that he escaped the fate of Servetus, and his great work, *Les Microzymas*, an inclusion in the Roman *Index*.

Never had Truth a more zealous advocate than the man who, with Professor Estor, beheld with awestruck amazement the unfolding of Nature's secrets. With his extraordinary powers of labour, he amply justified Carlyle's definition of genius – 'the capacity for taking infinite pains'; while, also, he absolutely exemplified the reverse side of abnormal faculties, which may be described as the capacity for doing with infinite ease that over which others are required to take infinite pains. From his boyhood, ordinary studies were to him the lightest of labour, while for his incessant researches no toil was too insistent, no sacrifice too great.

Altogether he stood on an ethical plane elevated above much of his surroundings. He was surrounded by callous experimenters, men such as Claude Bernard, whose own daughters felt compelled to forsake him and undertake animal rescue work as atonement for their father's vivisectional atrocities.

Yet Professor Béchamp stands out in marked contrast, innocent of cruelty, convicted only of pity. In his own multifarious experiments we come upon no record of brutality, and, in reference to Magendie's work, he does not fail to voice sympathy for 'la pauvre béte,' Magendie's miserable victim.

The fact of Béchamp having delved so much deeper into knowledge than his callous contemporaries may well be an instance of the advantage of not blunting a scientific mind by familiarity with cruelty. His imagination possessed to the end the pristine sensitiveness essential to the discoverer, and, spurred and stimulated by his wonderful health and vitality, age itself had no power to dull his intellect.

It is no surprise that Pasteur's crude germ theory should have displaced Béchamp's deeper, more complex teaching, which was too demanding to become the immediate property of 'the man in the street'. Pasteur, who might have worked with Béchamp, on the contrary plagiarised and distorted his ideas.

It was Béchamp's fate to meet with neglect and disparagement. Pursued, on the one side, by the jealousy of his less gifted but more successful rival, and, on the other, by narrow-minded men with no understanding of how the Creator can best be known through the study of Creation, persecution and bitterness of spirit were the earthly rewards of his long life of toil.

Pasteur made a wise remark when he called upon the verdict of time to pass sentence on a scientist. As a matter of fact, Béchamp, with the assurance of genius, never lost hope in this final judgment. The *Moniteur Scientifique* tells us:

> "Those of his acquaintance who cared for him and were about him know that he never doubted that one day justice would be rendered him."

It is in this belief, and with this hope, that we have written down this story of a great plagiarism, and have tried to show the contrast between a successful world idol and an ignored genius to whom the world's scientists – most of them unaware of the fact – are indebted for much of their knowledge.

In closing, we hereby submit to the tribunal of public opinion the claims of Pierre Jacques Antoine Béchamp, embodied in this, a lost chapter of the history of biology.

THE END

CPSIA information can be obtained at www.ICGtesting.com
Printed in the USA
265827BV00002B/46/A